C000224740

ANIMAL HUSBANDRY

ANIMAL HUSBANDRY

REVISED BY

D.G.M. THOMAS

BSc, FIBiol
Principal
Aberystwyth College of Further Education

WITH CONTRIBUTIONS FROM

D.G. BEYNON
BEd, NDA
Agricultural Lecturer
Pembrokeshire Technical College

T.G.G. HERBERT
MRCVS
Part-Time Lecturer
Aberystwyth College of
Further Education

AND

J. LLOYD JONES
BSc, PostGrad Cert Ed
Head of Agricultural Department
Pembrokeshire Technical College

THIRD EDITION

BAILLIÈRE TINDALL
LONDON

Published by BAILLIÈRE TINDALL
1 St Anne's Road, Eastbourne
East Sussex BN21 3UN

© 1983 Baillière Tindall

All rights reserved. No part of this publication may be reproduced, stored
in a retrieval system or transmitted, in any form or by any means,
electronic, mechanical, photocopying or otherwise, without the prior
permission of Baillière Tindall, 1 St Anne's Road, Eastbourne,
East Sussex BN21 3UN

First published 1963
Second Edition 1971
Third Edition 1983

ISBN 0 7020 0973 3

Typeset by CCC, printed and bound in Great Britain by William Clowes
(Beccles) Limited, Beccles and London.

British Library Cataloguing in Publication Data

Thomas, D. G. M.
   Animal husbandry.—3rd ed.
   1. Livestock
   I. Title
   636.08′3 SF71.2

ISBN 0–7020–0973–3

Contents

Preface to the Third Edition

The third edition of this book continues to have as its main purpose the presentation in a simple and readable form of the basic biological and economic principles upon which husbandry practice is based. Thus it covers the fundamentals of breeding, feeding, disease control and management as they apply to the husbandry practices of milk, beef, sheep and pig production.

Since the appearance of the last edition quantitative estimating has become increasingly important in the farm business; the text therefore outlines many basic ways of using farm figures to formulate efficiency indicators. It is pertinent to point out that it is understanding the methods involved which is fundamental and not the figures themselves. The latter vary greatly from one farm situation to another but the basic methods of handling them do not.

This is apparent in two areas of development both covered in the new edition. Firstly, Kellner's Starch and Protein Equivalent method of food rationing ruminants has been replaced by the Metabolizable Energy method. Although the latter method is comparatively simple to use in a given practical situation, its theoretical basis and its resultant plethora of tables present problems of basic understanding and overall comprehension; we have attempted to describe the underlying principles as simply as possible and to collate in one visual 'image' the relationship of relevant tables to given rationing examples.

Secondly, 'Farm Business Management' as a method or technique of viewing the farm as a business has become accepted practice; such terms as analysis, planning, budgeting and controlling have become common in farming vocabulary. In writing this edition we thought it appropriate to consider feeding and management within the 'Framework' of the enterprise gross and net margin approach. Husbandry affects physical output and input with inevitable financial implications. Because prices constantly change, gross margins and other financial calculations rarely remain accurate; thus we have deliberately kept physical and price data separate so that the reader can update the figures himself according to prevailing prices. We also considered it appropriate to introduce the principles of partial budgeting for minor planning changes in the two chapters dealing with the feeding and management of dairy cows and heifers; such methods of budgeting are applicable to all other enterprises.

Some changes in authorship were necessary this time. It was regrettable that my former co-author Mr W. I. J. Davies was unable to undertake the extensive revision for this third edition. The task of researching developments and revising the text was too formidable for me alone. Mr T. G. G. Herbert, who collaborated on the second edition, was kind enough to revise section C on Health and Disease in Farm Livestock; the authenticity of the section has been retained because of his veterinary expertise. I was fortunate enough to enlist the support of my colleagues and friends of many years' standing, Mr John Lloyd Jones and Mr David Beynon, to assist me with the revision of sections A and B; their extensive teaching experience and practical sense have contributed greatly to the content, balance and depth of the difficult writing demanded with the breeding, feeding and management of livestock.

D. G. M. THOMAS   APRIL 1983

Acknowledgements

We are indebted to many people who have assisted with this extensive revision. We are grateful to Mr Brynmor Morgan MLC for offering suggestions for the re-writing of sheep breeding and feeding and to Mr Vivian Roberts, Head of the Farm Management Department, Welsh Agricultural College, for checking the budgets included in chapters 10 and 11. We wish to express our extreme gratitude to the following persons who have read and constructively commented on our drafts of the chapters mentioned: Mr Brinley Davies MLC – chapters 4 and 12, Mr H. V. Thomas and Mr Mike Potter MLC – chapters 6 and 14, and Mr Robin Gill, Vice-principal of the Welsh Agricultural College – chapters 3, 5, 8, 9, 10, 11 and 13.

In addition, for supplying us with materials for illustrations and tables we should like to acknowledge the following: Dr H. Thomas and his staff of the Cytology Department, Welsh Plant Breeding Station, for supplying photographs of cell division (Fig. 2.1), Mr Gwyn Williams, Senior Lecturer, Agricultural Department, Bangor University College, Dr Tony Kempster and Mr Joe Read of MLC, J. E. Newton and Dr R. J. Wil search Station, Derek H. C inson, Croston and Jor Breeding Research Organi and Publishers, the Meat mission, Ministry of Agricu Food, Milk Marketing Training Board, Nationa Council, Scottish Agricult tional Institute for Researcl College of Veterinary Surge Ltd, Fatstock Marketing Business Consultants Ltd.

We wish to thank our particular our editors Mr S. Cliff Morgan for their advic writing and for the present the new form.

We wish to thank Mr Jef drawing figures 4.2, 12.5 ai should like to thank the fo typing drafts and redrafts of a two year span of writing: F Keenan, Jean Middleton, El Terry and Llinos Williams.

1

Reproduction in Cattle, Sheep and Pigs

By reproduction is meant the ability of animals to produce young; male and female animals are required for this purpose.

CATTLE

Heat Period

This is a period during which a female animal may be served by a male animal and possibly conceive, i.e. bear a calf.

The first heat period, or oestrus, occurs in the heifer when she is about fifteen months old. The number of days between one heat and the next is normally around 21 days but it can vary from 16 to 25 days. The duration of heat is the number of hours the animal is fully on heat and standing to be mounted. For heifers in winter it can vary from 0.5 hour to 12 hours, and for older cows in summer up to 24 hours. Signs of heat are shown in Fig. 1.1.

Injections of prostaglandin can be used to control oestrus; two injections are given 11 days apart and the heifer is artificially inseminated 72 hours after the second injection. To ensure fertilization of the egg, natural service may be carried out 5 days after the insemination process. A pregnancy diagnosis is carried out approximately 6 weeks after service.

Service

Most farmers do not serve their heifers with a bull during the first heat period. Normally the animal is allowed to grow sufficiently large so that she may carry and deliver a calf without causing permanent injury to herself. Some breeds mature more quickly than others and consequently can receive their first service at a younger age. The recommended time of bulling heifers of different breeds is shown in Table 1.1.

When a heifer is served naturally with a bull

the semen (i.e. fluid and sperms) is passed from the testes along the vas deferens tubes to the penis, which deposits it at the upper end of the vagina (Fig. 1.2a). A fertile bull will produce about 5 cm³ of semen containing approximately 1000 million sperms.

Table 1.1

Breed	Usual age for service (months)	Approximate live weight at service (kg)
Jersey	12–15	230
Guernsey	15–18	270
Ayrshire		270
Red Poll	15–21	360
Welsh Black		360
Dairy Shorthorn	15–24	360
Friesian	15–24	380
South Devon		380
Hereford × Friesian	15–24	330

Fertilization

What happens to the semen after it has been deposited within the vagina or uterus of the cow?

The female reproductive system is adapted to produce eggs and to carry the young calf for the first 9.5 months of its development (Fig. 1.2b). Eggs are produced by a pair of small pimply-surfaced organs known as the *ovaries*. Two days after the onset of heat, an egg from one ovary is

(a) *Positive signs*

Standing to be mounted by another cow and does not move away.

Mounting another cow from *front*.

N.B. The cow that mounts may *not* be on heat; only if she in turn *stands*, is she on heat.

(b) *Minor signs of heat*

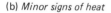

(i) Sniffing, especially of vulva and urine of other cows; both cows may come on heat.

(iii) Licking; both cows may come on heat.

(ii) Chin resting; both cows may come on heat.

(iv) Bunting; both cows may come on heat.

Fig. 1.1 Signs of heat (source: Agricultural Training Board).

released into the cup of the Fallopian tube embracing it. The sperms which have been deposited by the bull in the upper reaches of the vagina swim through the cervix into the *uterus* or calf bag. They continue their journey along the Fallopian tubes until they reach the egg which has been released from the ovary. Several sperms attack the egg until eventually one sperm head succeeds in entering the egg. The nucleus from the sperm joins with the nucleus of the ovum. The ovum is now *fertilized* (Fig. 1.3).

Artificial Insemination

The great majority of cattle are served artificially. A trained inseminator inserts a sterile tube containing the semen through the rounded muscle known as the cervix and deposits it within the uterus. Semen is obtained from bulls kept at cattle breeding centres.

The semen is collected from the bull by means of an artificial vagina. Because it contains millions of sperms, the semen can be diluted and divided into small lots. The number of lots made from each semen sample depends on the number and vitality of sperms.

Diluted semen is deep frozen and stored in liquid nitrogen at −192°C; special techniques have been developed to avoid killing the sperms during the process of freezing. It is stored either in the form of pellets or straws; when the inseminator arrives at the farm he takes it from

(a)

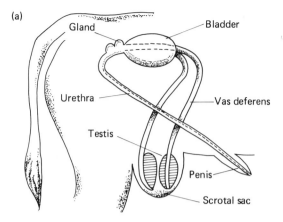

(b)

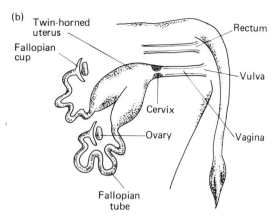

Fig. 1.2 Reproductive systems of cattle. (a) Male; (b) female.

the flask of liquid nitrogen, thaws it and inseminates the cow.

One good semen sample can be used to make 200–300 pellets or 400–600 straws. Deep frozen sperms can remain alive for many years and it is quite common for calves to be fathered by bulls who have been dead for a long time.

Pregnancy

The fertilized egg moves slowly down the Fallopian tube to the uterus. It attaches itself to the wall of the uterus. The egg divides repeatedly, first forming two cells, then four cells and continues dividing in this sequence (8, 16, 32, 64, etc.) until a small embryo of many millions of cells is formed.

The young embryo eventually becomes attached to the uterus by an umbilical cord (Fig. 1.4). This cord consists mainly of an artery and a vein. Soluble foodstuffs and oxygen are passed along the artery into the embryo; carbon dioxide, water and nitrogenous wastes are returned into the mother's blood system in the vein.

When the embryo is about 24 weeks of age it weighs about 0.45 kg (see Fig. 8.2, p. 94). The outline of a head, tail, legs and trunk can be distinguished at this stage. Although many important changes are occurring in the embryo during this period, the growth in size and weight

Stage	A single calf	Identical twin calves	Non-identical twin calves	
Sperms attacking egg			1st egg	2nd egg
One sperm head penetrating one egg				
Migration of male nucleus towards female nucleus				
Fertilization, i.e. fusing of two nuclei				
First division of fertilized egg				
Second division of fertilized egg				
Third division of fertilized egg				

Fig. 1.3 Stages in the formation of single and twin calves.

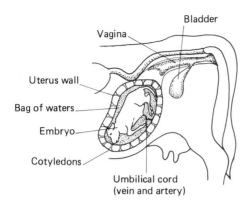

Fig. 1.4 Embryo within a cow's uterus.

of the embryo is limited. When the embryo is 32 weeks of age, its weight is only between 0.9 kg and 1.8 kg. Rapid increase in size and weight only occurs in the last 8 weeks of pregnancy. At birth the calf may weigh between 32 and 40 kg. The birth weight of a calf is approximately 7% of the body weight of the mature animal, e.g. a 450 kg Ayrshire produces a 32 kg calf, and a 570 kg Friesian produces a 40 kg calf. It is thus apparent that the embryo or foetus draws heavily on the mother's food supply during this period.

Twinning

Two kinds of twin calves can be born – identical and non-identical. Identical twins originate from the same fertilized egg (Fig. 1.3). After this egg has undergone its first division, the two cells formed separate instead of remaining joined together. Each of the two new cells divides in the normal way until a fully developed embryo is formed. Thus the nuclei in the body cells of both calves are identical with the nucleus of the fertilized egg from which they grew.

Non-identical twins are formed from two distinct and separately fertilized eggs (Fig. 1.3). Occasionally two eggs are released from the ovaries simultaneously; each egg is fertilized by one sperm. Each fertilized egg develops into an embryo. Thus the nuclei in the body cells of one calf are completely different from the nuclei in the body cells of the second calf.

Occasionally a female calf is born twin to a male calf. Such a female calf is sometimes infertile or sterile when it reaches maturity, i.e. it is not capable of breeding. Such a female calf is called a *freemartin*, and such a condition is caused as follows. Within the uterus, the twin embryos are supplied with a common source of blood from the mother cow through an umbilical cord. During its development the male embryo produces a male hormone from its simple testes. This liquid hormone is passed into the blood and eventually circulates around the body of the female. If sufficient hormone is produced it suppresses the complete development of the reproductive system in the female calf and renders her sterile in later life.

Signs of Pregnancy

Two days after an egg has been shed from an ovary a mass of fibre-like tissue is formed in the empty follicle. This is called a *yellow body* (see Fig. 1.8). This structure secretes a hormone called *progesterone*, which has two main effects:

1. It excites the uterus wall to flush with blood so that it is in a 'receptive' condition to receive the fertilized egg.
2. It prevents the cow from coming on heat.

If by accident the yellow body is removed or detached then the above effects disappear, the calf is aborted or born before its time, and the cow comes on heat again.

It is possible to tell whether an animal is in calf by looking for the following signs:

1. No heat periods occur.
2. The uterus of a heifer in its second month of pregnancy and of a cow in its third month of pregnancy is enlarged. Such an enlarged uterus can be felt through the wall of the rectum.
3. A thick and sticky mucus appears around the cervix.
4. A thick honey-like secretion is formed in the udder of the heifer when she is 5 months pregnant.

Care during Pregnancy

The rapidly growing foetus draws heavily on the food supply of the mother during the last 2–3 months of pregnancy. It is necessary to 'steam-up' the cow with extra food during this period so as to offset this heavy drain on the cow. Extra food, usually in the form of concentrates, is introduced into the daily ration of food fed to the mother cow, and gradually increased. These concentrates are sometimes fed to heifers in the parlour when the other cows are being milked. This helps the heifer to adapt herself to parlour routine by the time she comes into full milk production. Such a steaming-up ration also stimulates the cow to produce more milk after the calf has been born.

Since the calf is also drawing heavily on the mother's supply of minerals to build up its own bones, an ample supply of mineral-licks must be available to the cow during this period.

There is no better way of safeguarding the general health of the cow than by plenty of exercise. This keeps the mother fit and lean and reduces problems of difficult births due to over-fatness.

Care should be taken to prevent pregnant cows from causing injury to themselves and their calves by falling into open ditches and ponds or overcrowding in narrow gateways.

Udder Development

During this period of pregnancy in the heifer certain developmental changes also occur in the udder (Fig. 1.5). The young udder is mainly composed of fatty tissue and alveolar or secretory tissue. The amount of alveolar-tissue growth during later pregnancy does, to a large extent, determine the amount of milk given by the heifer after calving. When 5 months pregnant, a honey-like secretion is produced from the udder. Rapid growth of the alveolar tissue occurs from this period onwards, particularly during the last 2 months of pregnancy. Since protein encourages the growth of alveolar tissue and carbohydrates encourage the growth of fatty tissue, it is advantageous to feed a ration rich in protein during this period. Well-managed heifers are thus normally given a steaming-up ration of food which includes protein-rich concentrates some 6 weeks prior to calving.

Length of Pregnancy

The average pregnancy or gestation period is 280 days or 9 months and 10 days. It may vary between 240 and 321 days.

The onset of birth is determined by the interaction of two chemicals, i.e. progesterone and a second hormone produced from the pituitary gland situated at the base of the brain (see Fig. 7.17). This latter hormone stimulates the muscular wall of the uterus to contract in downward waves.

Towards the end of pregnancy the yellow body (see p. 7) shrivels up and dies so that eventually no progesterone is passed into the bloodstream. When this occurs the hormone from the pituitary gland exerts its full effect on the uterus without being inhibited by progesterone.

Calving

Unless a cow is calving in the open it is preferable for it to calve in a clean 'loose box' which has been well littered with clean straw. Most heifers and cows calve normally and no assistance is required.

The first stage in calving is the slackening of the ligaments at the base of the tail; this may occur days before the birth. Next the mucus plug of the cervix comes away, and is seen hanging from the vulva as translucent cords. The cow becomes generally uncomfortable and begins to strain. The 'water bag' should be seen at the vulva within about three hours of the onset of straining. This should not be punctured as its function is to dilate the cervix and vagina for the calf to be born. The bag bursts and the nose and feet of the calf will be presented at the vulva. The calf should not be pulled out at this stage and the birth should be left to proceed normally.

Some complications often occur.

(a) The head and fore-legs, or even just the fore-legs, may appear through the vulva, but the process does not proceed any further. An experienced stockman will be able to know how

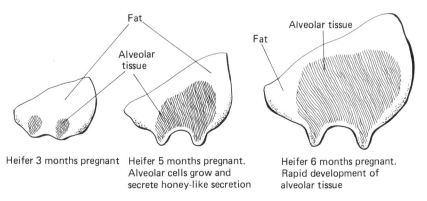

Heifer 3 months pregnant

Heifer 5 months pregnant. Alveolar cells grow and secrete honey-like secretion

Heifer 6 months pregnant. Rapid development of alveolar tissue

Fig. 1.5 Development of the udder in an in-calf heifer.

long to leave the cow straining without giving assistance.

Ropes should be tied above the fetlock joints, and the calf pulled downwards when the cow is pushing; when the pushing stops the pulling should stop.

(b) The cow is straining but no part of the calf appears; this may be due to the calf lying within the uterus in a wrong position (Fig. 1.7). A hand and arm smeared with disinfecting oils should be inserted into the uterus and the calf turned into the correct presentation (Fig. 1.6). If the situation cannot be easily corrected, a veterinary surgeon should be called immediately.

(c) The calf is born hind-legs first, this being referred to as posterior or breech presentation. Again birth will probably have to be assisted by pulling the calf. At the start the pulling should be designed to help the cow push the hips of the calf through the cervix and should in no way be severe or hurried. Once the hocks are outside the vulva, however, the hips have passed the cervix and the calf must then be pulled quickly, as the umbilical cord will probably have broken and the calf's oxygen supply cut off; the calf is in danger of suffocation and its front part must be brought out quickly for it to start breathing through its lungs.

It is essential that ropes used to draw calves

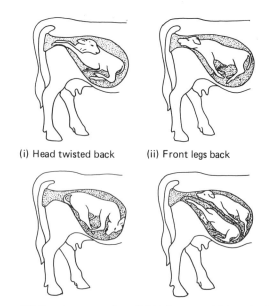

(i) Head twisted back   (ii) Front legs back

(iii) Breech presentation   (iv) Twins, one with head back

Fig. 1.7 Abnormal presentations of calf at birth.

should be sterilized and the hands of those assisting should be clean.

When the following abnormalities occur the cow should be left alone and a veterinary surgeon called:

i) no sign of the water bag after many hours;
ii) afterbirth hanging from the cow before calving;
iii) one limb appearing after the water bag has burst;
iv) the discharge of smelly fluid, which usually means a dead calf.

Care after Birth

A calf starts to breathe as a result of a shock stimulus, e.g. cold air or hitting the ground. The mouth and nostrils should be examined and any mucus deposit removed. If there are no breathing movements the calf should be laid on its side and the fore-legs moved vigorously in a circular motion. The umbilical cord should be disinfected with a suitable disinfectant and tied with a tape which has been immersed in a bottle of this solution.

Sometimes a cow will ignore her calf. A little salt or bran sprinkled on the back of the calf may induce the mother to lick her calf dry. If this is unsuccessful then the calf should be rubbed over with straw.

The cow and calf should then be left alone. If the udder is inflamed, massaging and hot

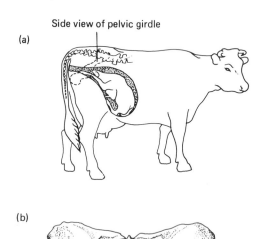

Side view of pelvic girdle

(a)

(b)

Fig. 1.6 (a) Normal presentation of calf in uterus. (b) End view of pelvic girdle (enlarged).

fomentation after milking may ease her suffering.

Colostrum

For the first 2–4 days after birth, a thick yellow fluid called *colostrum* is secreted from the udder. Colostrum is a mixture of milk and the honey-like secretion produced in the fifth month of pregnancy. It is very rich in vitamin A and easily digestible protein. It also contains antibodies which set up a resistance against disease. It is now known that the calf can only absorb these antibodies for the first 36 hours and in particular the first six hours of life; it is thus vital to feed it for at least two days. The combination of these materials makes colostrum an ideal food for the yet untried digestive system of the young calf.

Milk Production
(see Fig. 8.2 and chapter 8)

For the first 7–10 weeks after the end of colostrum production the quantity of milk produced from the udder gradually increases until it reaches a peak level of production. It is necessary to encourage as great a rise as possible in this production. This is normally achieved by lead feeding the cow with a quantity of food over and above the ration of food required for its present production of milk (see p. 93). In other words, the amount of food given to the animal is always more than is required at the moment.

After the cow has reached her peak level of production, it is desirable to maintain this level of production for as long a period as possible by feeding adequate, properly balanced rations of food. When a cow is not fed adequately, she will immediately begin to lower her milk yield according to her level of feeding.

The daily yield of the cow will then gradually drop until she dries off, in about 35–45 weeks from the onset of milk production. During this time the ration of the cow should be altered each week according to her milk yield and according to the yield of grass and other foods available. This will result in a considerable saving of costly feeding-stuffs.

Second Service

Some 20–21 days after the birth of the calf, the cow comes on heat once more. It is necessary for the cow's milk system to be rested before she delivers her second calf. A dry period of 6–8 weeks before the delivery of the second calf is desirable. How does the farmer achieve this?

Oestrus or heat period occurs every 20–21 days in the normal cow. After the egg has been shed from the ovary a yellow body is formed in the empty follicle 3 days (72 hours) after the beginning of heat, i.e. 1–2 days (24–48 hours) after the egg has been shed from the ovary (Fig. 1.8). It persists for 17–18 days and then withers and dies unless the shed egg has been fertilized in the meantime. Progesterone, which prevents the recurrence of heat, is formed by the yellow

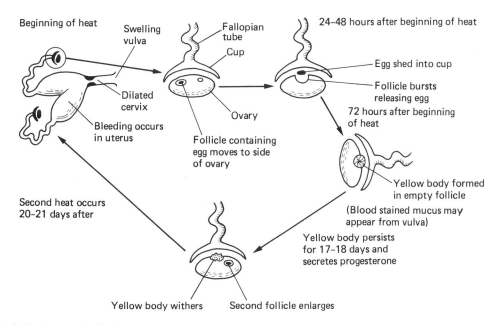

Fig. 1.8 The heat cycle of cattle.

body. When the yellow body disappears, no more progesterone is formed and the animal comes on heat once more; the heat cycle is thus completed in 20–21 days.

If three heat periods are allowed to elapse and the cow inseminated during her fourth heat period, the egg from the cow's ovary would be fertilized some 83 days after the birth of the calf.

This is calculated as follows:

21st day after day
   of birth   – onset of 1st heat period
41st   –   2nd
61st   –   3rd
81st   –   4th
83rd   – fertilization of egg, i.e. 12
weeks after birth of the first calf. The second calf would be born on the 52nd week after the birth of the first calf, i.e. 12 weeks plus the 40 weeks of pregnancy. In other words, the second calf is born 365 days after the first; this figure is usually referred to as the *calving index*, i.e. the average number of days between the birth of one calf and another. In practice a calving index of 365 days is a good figure because it shows that the cow is calving consistently once per year; if the index is higher, e.g. 400, it denotes less regularity in breeding.

Assuming the cow was in milk for 44 weeks during her first lactation, this would allow 8 weeks (52 minus 44 weeks) dry period before the birth of her second calf.

This dry period is essential for steaming-up the cow before her next calving. The dual strain of producing milk and feeding a calf growing enormously in size and weight during this period must be avoided.

Infertility

It often happens that a cow fails to come on heat, her heat periods may be irregular, or she fails to conceive after being served. All these upsets indicate that there is something wrong with the cow's reproductive system and they inevitably result in temporary infertility or even sterility; if the trouble cannot be corrected the cow will be sold off as 'barren'. Failure to conceive could also be due to an infertile bull.

The causes of infertility are many; they can be broadly classified as being due to: (a) failure of the reproductive mechanisms or anatomical deformities, or (b) infections, or faulty feeding and management; these are dealt with in chapter 16 (p. 220).

Reproduction is a very finely balanced mech-

anism, and a small disorder is usually sufficient to prevent fertilization and/or subsequent development of the embryo.

The precise nature of the disorder can only be detected, and if possible corrected, by a veterinary surgeon. The most common causes of infertility are as follows:

1. *Retention of the yellow body:* The yellow body fails to disappear from the ovary, and the cow does not come on heat. A veterinary surgeon can squeeze out this yellow body and the cow will come on heat within 2–6 days.

2. *Cystic ovaries:* The egg or ovum may not be shed from the ovary, but keeps on growing to form cysts; in other instances the yellow body may develop cysts. These lead to very frequent heats (nymphomania), very irregular heats, or no heats at all; when the cow is served, no calf develops because there is no egg produced. A veterinary surgeon can usually remove these cysts by feeling for the ovary through the rectum wall and squeezing them out; generally the cow will then return to her normal heat cycle.

3. *Delay in ovulation:* The cow comes on heat, but the egg is not shed until much later; if service is carried out during the heat period there will be no fertilization. Artificial insemination, about 6 hours after the end of heat, will usually be successful in ensuring fertilization.

4. *Too much 'yellow body' tissue:* When cows and heifers have been on heat many times without bulling, the ovary will often contain too much 'yellow body' type tissue; the animal will come on heat regularly but will fail to conceive. This too can be cured by squeezing out the yellow body.

5. *Anatomical deformities:* Any part of the reproductive system may not be properly formed, as in a freemartin, or may be sited in an incorrect position, or contain obstructions. A vagina may be slack and thus obstruct the penis of the bull. The cervix may be inclined downwards against the vaginal wall, preventing sperm from entering the uterus. A band of tissue may separate the vagina and uterus; this is usually found in maiden heifers. Artificial insemination is often effective in overcoming these deformities.

The Bull

Bulls used in Artificial Insemination Centres are carefully checked for fertility. When bulls are kept on farms they can occasionally be infertile or sterile, due to lack of sperm production; common causes are faulty nutrition, over-use of young bulls and under-use of old bulls.

SHEEP

Heat Period

The ewe lamb in lowland flocks may come on heat for the first time (i.e. reach sexual maturity) when she is around 7 months old. Ewe lambs from mountain flocks do not reach maturity in their first year, and some even fail to conceive when they are 18 months old. These differences are caused by differences in levels of nutrition and time of birth (see p. 178). In most of our breeds the heat period is confined to the second half of the year; this is due to the effect of longer nights and shorter days on the production of hormones which are responsible for the onset of heat. Ewes in lowland flocks come on heat early in this period, in upland flocks later, and mountain flocks in October.

Unlike the cow, the ewe shows no symptoms of heat recognizable to man. Heat can only be detected by the ram.

Service or Tupping

The structure of the reproductive system of the ewe and ram is basically similar to the cow and bull respectively. The process of fertilization is also similar (see Figs. 1.2 and 1.3.). The age of the ewe at the first service depends largely on her development. Ewe lambs from lowland flocks are often sufficiently developed to produce a satisfactory lamb if mated around October of their first year.

On the other hand, ewe lambs in hill flocks are not mated until their second autumn so that they are sufficiently grown to carry a lamb.

The majority of ewes in this country, however, are mated for the first time around 18 months old.

Ewes per Ram

Unlike cattle, lowland ewes are not brought to the ram, but the ram is left to run with the ewe flock for a period not greater than 7 weeks; the ram is allowed to run with highland ewes indefinitely. In lowland flocks this limits the length of the lambing season and reduces variation in ages of lambs within a flock.

It is important not to over-work the ram. The number of ewes allocated to one ram varies and is roughly as follows:

1. *Lowland flocks*
Ram lamb	50–70 ewes
Shearling (2 yr. old) ram	60–70 ewes

2. *Mountain flocks*
Mature rams: 30–50 depending on age of ram and whether tupping takes place in open hillside or in enclosed areas.

The heat period or oestrus lasts from 1 to 3 days, and if the ewe does not conceive, the next heat will occur 14–18 days later.

A shepherd can find out which of his ewes have been served by using a raddle or a marking crayon. This is a special colouring material smeared between the ram's front legs or attached by means of a special harness. It marks the ewe's rump on service. It is often changed to a darker colour every 2 weeks (e.g. red to blue to black), thereby indicating which ewes have returned to the ram.

The shepherd can make a note of the date on which each ewe is served; if a ewe does not return to the ram she can be expected to lamb about 147 days or 21 weeks afterwards.

Controlling Heat

It is possible to have all the ewes within a flock coming on heat within a 2 to 3 day period. This is done by inserting into the vagina of each ewe, using a special instrument, a pessary containing a synthetic 'progesterone' hormone. The hormone is absorbed through the lining of the vagina into the bloodstream, and prevents ovulation. The pessary is removed after 17 days, by pulling on a string attached to it. Most of the ewes come on heat within a few days after the pessary is removed from the vagina, and tupping can then take place. To prevent overworking the rams in this short period of time, the number of ewes per ram should be reduced to about 10–20.

The practical advantages of this technique are:

(a) Lambing dates can be determined to a limited extent.
(b) Since most of the ewes are in the same stage of pregnancy, flock 'steaming-up' is more effective.
(c) The lambing period is much shorter.
(d) A more even crop of lambs are marketed together.

Artificial Insemination

It is quite possible to inseminate ewes artificially. Sponges impregnated with progesterone are inserted into the vagina and left there for two weeks. When the sponge is removed the ewe is injected with Pregnant Mare Serum Gonadoptropin; the ewe is ready to be inseminated two days after the injection. Such a technique could be used to synchronize the heat periods of ewes for early or batch lambing; also the genetic qualities of a superior ram could be spread over a wider ewe population and his semen deep-frozen for future use.

Pregnancy

During the first 4 months of pregnancy the embryonic lamb makes very little growth in weight or size, and consequently the strain on the ewe is not very great.

During the last month, however, the embryo or foetus grows very rapidly, reaching anything up to 3.5–5.5 kg as a single, or 2.3–4.5 kg as a twin, according to the breed. It is during this period that the demand on the mother's food supply becomes increasingly heavy and she must be fed accordingly, i.e. 'steamed-up'.

Twinning

Twinning is far more common in sheep than in cattle, and is very much influenced by breed and environment. A breed of sheep in which twins are common is said to be a *prolific* breed, e.g. Finnish, Border Leicester. The twins are generally non-identical (see Fig. 1.3). The lowland shepherd wants as many twins as possible. On the other hand, not more than one lamb per ewe is desirable in mountain flocks, because of the limited amount and poor quality of food available.

The number of lambs reared expressed as a percentage of the number of ewes mated is known as the *lambing percentage*. This is markedly influenced by twinning. In lowland flocks the incidence of twinning can be increased by good husbandry. During the summer the ewes are put on a poorer diet; they are said to be *scavenging*. This diet keeps them in a good, lean condition and prevents them laying down fatty tissue around the ovaries, thus impairing formation of eggs. Egg production is related to the body condition of the ewe at tupping. Condition scoring at 6–8 weeks can assist in grouping ewes in the flock according to body condition; such groups can be fed according to their specific needs, thus levelling the whole flock to a target condition score of 3.5 (see p. 182).

Signs of Pregnancy

After the egg is shed a yellow body is formed in the empty follicle. The secretion of progesterone makes the uterus wall 'receptive' to the fertilized egg and prevents the ewe coming on heat.

A shepherd usually recognizes a pregnant ewe by the fact that she has not returned to the ram.

It is comparatively easy, for an experienced shepherd, to distinguish some weeks before lambing between barren ewes, ewes carrying single lambs and those carrying twins. Barren ewes usually put on weight and improve in condition; ewes carrying a single lamb are heavier than at mating time, but leaner when handled; ewes carrying twins are the heaviest and leanest.

Care during Pregnancy
(see Fig. 13.1, p. 172)

During the last 6–8 weeks of pregnancy the quantity of the ewe's food is gradually increased; better quality food is also fed, i.e. the ewes are 'steamed-up'.

This better feeding:

i) provides nourishment for the developing foetus and usually results in a strong lamb at birth;
ii) stimulates udder development and future milk production of the ewe;
iii) builds up body reserves of flesh on the ewe;
iv) normally prevents twin-lamb disease (pregnancy toxaemia, see p. 241).

Lambing

The pregnancy or gestation period is 21 weeks or 147 days; it varies only a day or two either way. The onset of birth depends on the disappearance of the yellow body and the consequent effects of the birth hormone produced in the pituitary gland. The udder may become bright red in colour as it becomes fully stocked.

During birth the bag of water appears first and usually bursts. The lamb is forced out, head and fore-legs first, by rhythmic contractions of the uterus. Finally the afterbirth is ejected.

If the ewe has been well cared for previously and is in a good condition, lambing presents no difficulty and it is wise to leave the ewe undisturbed.

If, however, no progress has been made after an hour's straining, the ewe should be caught quickly and attended to. The shepherd should carefully wash and disinfect his hands, before feeling inside the vagina for the lamb's nose and feet. If these are in the right position the difficulty is probably due to the size of the lamb. Help may be given by pulling the lamb downwards when the ewe is straining.

Care after Birth

After birth the ewe normally licks her lamb dry and stimulates breathing and circulation. When this is completed the lamb rises on its shaky legs and searches for the ewe's udder.

If the lamb is not breathing at birth, it can be induced to do so by clearing its mouth and nostrils, blowing down its nose, smacking its ribs and moving its fore-legs up and down. Once it starts breathing satisfactorily it should be placed in front of its mother.

If the lamb has not been licked dry by its mother it should be rubbed down. If the coat remains wet the lamb may quickly die in cold weather. If it is raining or sleeting, some form of shelter should be provided.

The navel cord should be disinfected since bacteria can quickly gain entry through it and cause navel or joint ill (see p. 230).

Colostrum

Colostrum is also produced by sheep and is particularly valuable to the young lamb because of its high nutritive and protective qualities.

Milk Production

It is very important that the ewe produces ample milk for the first 2 months of the lamb's life. Although the lamb starts to nibble grass at 3–4 weeks, and small amounts of concentrates are fed, it will be largely dependent on its dam's milk for the first 8 weeks. Thus the greater the amount of milk it receives, the quicker the lamb's growth rate.

Indeed, the lamb reaches its maximum capacity for milk consumption between 4 and 6 weeks of age, and it is essential that the ewe is well fed so that she can meet the demands of her lamb.

If, after 8 weeks, the lamb is provided with palatable and nutritious foods (e.g. young grass), the supply of the ewe's milk becomes of less importance.

Weaning

If the lambs have not been sold by the time they reach 14 weeks of age (i.e. as fat lambs), they must be weaned. This merely involves removing the lambs from their mothers and taking care that they are out of earshot. From now on they will be totally independent of their mothers.

Lambs should not remain with their mothers after they have reached 14 weeks, as big lambs often treat their dams roughly, resulting in damage of teats and udders.

The ewe's udder should be carefully watched after weaning as overstocking of the udder may lead to damage and mastitis. Mastitis can easily be avoided by prompt attention (see p. 226).

Rest Period

This is very important, because it gives the ewe a chance to rest and repair her body tissues in readiness for next season's lambing. The ewes are allowed to scavenge during this period.

The rest period occurs in the summer, during which time routine operations such as dipping, shearing and foot paring are carried out.

Unlike the cow, the heat period of the ewe does not occur within a few weeks of lambing. In lowland flocks, heat will commence in late summer; if the farmer requires his lambs on the market around Easter, tupping must take place in July or August.

Making up the Breeding Flock

As the tupping season approaches, the shepherd chooses ewes which have healthy udders, free from damage caused by mastitis and other causes; their feet must be free of foot rot. It is also important that their teeth are not badly worn and have not started to fall out, as this will prevent the ewes from making full use of food available. In addition each ewe must appear to be in good general health, and not in poor condition because of some chronic disease such as liver fluke or worms. Any ewes that do not reach the required standard are culled and sold off.

The chosen ewes are then flushed and the ram is turned in.

Second Service

The lamb, now a mature ewe, will get her second service approximately 1 year after the first. The year is divided as follows:

1st service

Pregnancy or gestation	5 months
Suckling lamb	3–3.5 months
Rest period	3.5–4 months

This offers an interesting comparison with the dairy cow. Once the cow conceives she never has a rest period; she is always milking and/or feeding a developing foetus. The ewe, on the other hand, has a period during the summer when she is doing neither of these things.

Causes of Sterility

Sterile or barren ewes are not very common under conditions of good husbandry and shepherding; under less favourable conditions they may become more common.

A barren ewe in a lowland flock results from a failure of the reproductive system to function properly, or reabsorption of newly formed embryos. It is rare to look for the cause of this failure, and the ewe is usually fattened off and sold.

In mountain flocks, infertility also results from failure of the reproductive mechanism. Very often this may be due to nutritional deficiency. In mountain flocks however, it is quite common for a ewe to be barren simply because the ram did not find her when she was in heat.

If a large number of ewes return to service, it is more than likely that the ram is at fault and a new one should immediately be substituted.

Possibly the most common causes of sterility in rams are:

i) malnutrition – a weak, anaemic ram is always of poor fertility, i.e. only produces a few, slow-moving sperms;

ii) a thick covering of wool on the scrotum, particularly in hot weather. The tubules of the testes which produce the sperms are very sensitive to high temperature; scrotal wool covering may prevent them from functioning properly as well as killing off those sperms already produced.

PIGS

Heat Period

The first heat occurs in a gilt when she is about 6 months old. A gilt selected for breeding (see p. 191) is mated for the first time at between 7 and 8 months old; she should weigh at least 110 kg; she will then farrow at 11–12 months old. The heat period lasts between 1 and 3 days and eggs are shed from the ovary some 24–36 hours after the commencement of heat. Heat is recognized by a swelling of the vulva; it gradually increases in size from the second day before heat and then decreases in size for some 2 days after heat. The animal is usually noisy and restless with other sows and may attempt to mount them. When alone a gilt or sow on heat is listless and quiet.

Boars should be 8 months of age before being used for service and it is generally recommended that they should not serve more than two sows per day or eight sows per week. It is best to serve sows twice during a heat period; the first service should be given 12–24 hours after the commencement of heat and the second service given 12–16 hours afterwards; this procedure increases the chance of fertilization taking place since ovulation can occur within a time span of 24–36 hours after the commencement of heat.

Mating in pigs is a prolonged process, lasting between 3 and 25 minutes. Semen is injected into the sow in waves of high and low sperm concentration. It is important that the mating animals should be left undisturbed so that the full quantity of semen is injected into the sow. After service the gilt or sow should be left undisturbed in case its movements expel the semen from its body.

Artificial Insemination

One artificial insemination centre has been established by the Meat and Livestock Commission; other centres also offer an insemination service.

Semen is collected from selected high-quality boars. It can be supplied, however, by rail and post to any pig producer in Britain. Licences are obtainable by centres on behalf of customers who wish to inseminate their own sows.

The key to successful artificial insemination of pigs is timing. Fig. 1.9 shows the best time for insemination. Although pigs differ one from the other, the broad pattern of oestrus is always the same and the vulva will redden and then swell as much as two days before the animal will stand.

The effective period for insemination is about one day: 12–36 hours after first standing to the boar, or in the absence of a boar when the pig stands to the riding test.

The Meat and Livestock Commission recommends the following:

Ordering the semen
As soon as the pig will stand to the boar, order the semen.

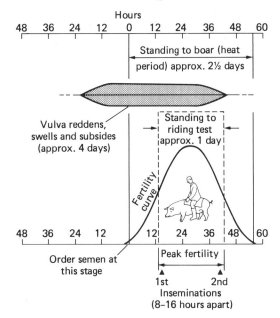

Fig. 1.9 Pig insemination – the vital time (source: Meat & Livestock Commission).

When to inseminate

The optimum time for insemination is shown in Table 1.2. The first insemination is carried out some 8 to 16 hours after the first standing to the boar or in the absence of a boar when the sow or gilt stands to the riding test. The time for the second insemination is 8 to 16 hours later. The second half-dose should always be used even if the animal is not standing and it should never be used to inseminate another pig.

Insemination is carried out by allowing the semen to run by gravity from a plastic bottle through a catheter (tube) into the uterus. The catheter is carefully inserted through the vagina and twisted anti-clockwise until locked in the cervix. The insemination process normally takes 5 to 10 minutes but this may be longer with some gilts.

Pregnancy
(see Fig. 14.2, p. 188)

The duration of pregnancy is between 110 and 118 days, i.e. 16 weeks. Many eggs are shed by the ovary during ovulation and as a result of fertilization, litters of between four and thirteen piglets are produced. The average number of piglets born per litter is between eight and twelve.

The recurrence of heat is watched for 20–22 days after service. If heat returns, then the sow must be served again.

During this period, a gilt or young sow may increase her body weight by 40–45 kg. The fresh weight of the unborn litter increases considerably from about the seventh week onwards; very little growth of the litter occurs up to about the fourth week. A normal gilt or sow must nourish about 14–18 kg of piglets inside her uterus during her pregnancy.

The twin demands of litter and sow growth mean that an adequate supply of well-balanced meal must be fed to the sow; correct feeding during pregnancy is vital in obtaining high litter numbers. On the other hand, too much food must not be fed, in order to prevent the sow getting over-fat; such fatness encourages wastage of embryo in the uterus.

In-pig gilts and sows can be managed in groups, 6 to 8 being ideal, so long as they are fairly equal in size. Sows in some herds are fed in individual feeder pens to allow sows at different stages of their pregnancy to be fed accordingly; this also prevents bullying by larger sows.

Farrowing

Due to variation in the duration of pregnancy, the sow is placed in a crate up to 7 days before she is due to farrow. Before placing her in the pen washing with a suitable parasiticide is recommended. Very few pig men allow their pigs to farrow out of doors. The farrowing house is scrubbed clean with warm water containing a few handfuls of washing soda, and well broken up fresh straw or wood shavings are placed on the floor. The house should be kept at a temperature of about 21.1°C to prevent any chill or discomfort.

Table 1.2. Optimum time for sow inseminations (source: Meat & Livestock Commission)

Animal first stands to boar	Method of dispatch	Order semen	First insemination	Second insemination
Morning Check-day 1	Rail Post	Before 0930 hours	late p.m. day 1 a.m. day 2	a.m. day 2 late p.m. day 2
Afternoon Check-day 1	Rail Post	Before 1600 hours	a.m. day 2	late p.m. day 2

During this period the sow should be handled quietly, left alone as much as possible, but watched frequently. It is advantageous to use short litter or sawdust to allow piglets to move freely around the pen.

Suckling Period

Some warm bran is usually fed to the sow over the farrowing period to prevent constipation. Plenty of water from a drinking bowl, some green food and limited quantities of balanced food will prevent indigestion and ensure an adequate flow of milk.

The sow normally suckles the litter from 3 to 6 weeks. The milk supply of the sow gradually increases for the first 3 weeks and then drops steadily until the piglets are weaned (see Fig. 14.2, p. 188). During this period the young piglets, born at some 1.1–1.5 kg live weight each, increase in size and weight until they are weaned at some 5.5 to 11.5 kg per piglet. Since the milk supply of the sow drops after 3 weeks, the litter is encouraged to eat pellet food from an early age so as to supplement the limited feeding requirement obtained from the sow's milk; this also prevents undue setback when the piglets are weaned. The pellets are placed in a trough or hopper in a corner of the pigsty behind metal bars or a gate. The piglets have easy access to the pellets but the sow is excluded; this is called creep feeding.

Nowadays it is possible to wean litters at 3 weeks old or when the pigs weigh about 5.5 kg. Appropriate pelleted foods are creep-fed, starting when the piglets are about 10 days old; they will be eating sufficiently to supply them with their nutritive requirements when they are about three weeks old. This form of weaning can, under high standards of management and hygiene, enable the sow to farrow three times in 15 months, thus increasing the number of litters born and reared per sow per annum to 2.5.

This system of artificial feeding is also valuable for rearing small litters; individual piglets in a large litter which cannot be fed by the sow; and litters left motherless because of the death of the sow or her inability to produce milk. The major problem associated with this form of management is infection.

During this period diseases such as agalactia, mastitis and pigging fever can cause complications.

Second Service

Heat normally occurs some 3–8 days after weaning and lasts for 2–3 days. If this service fails, then the sow is served again during her second heat, i.e. approximately 1 month after weaning.

After supplying the milk needs of her litter the sow is naturally run down. This is particularly true of sows which rear their litters well. Flushing prior to service cannot be practised, but her ration of food should be increased to 4 kg per day the day after weaning and remain at that level for 2 days after service. Since the growth of the foetal litter is very small at the beginning of pregnancy, this diet will enable the sow to get back into condition in readiness for the heavy demands made on her during the latter half of pregnancy.

Causes of Sterility

There are two possible causes of sterility. Frequently, small foetuses produced in the uterus shrivel up and disappear. It seems likely that this is due to the breeding 'make-up' of the sow or to over-fatness. Secondly, when boars are used too often, the motility and fertility of the sperms is reduced.

SECTION A

Breeding of Farm Livestock

2

Principles of Breeding

A young animal develops from a fertilized egg. The nucleus within this egg has been formed by the nucleus of the sperm from the male animal fusing with the nucleus of the egg from the female animal. Thus each parent transmits one nucleus to the young animal.

Cell Nucleus

What is a cell nucleus? When a cell divides, the nucleus is seen to consist of distinct threads called *chromosomes* (Fig. 2.1). There are 60 chromosomes in the body cells of cattle and these chromosomes are present in distinct pairs, members of each pair being identical in shape and length; such a pair of identical chromosomes are called homologous chromosomes. Thus there are 30 pairs of chromosomes in each body cell of cattle; 27 pairs in sheep; 20 pairs in pigs and 39 pairs in poultry. When a fertilized egg divides into two cells, each chromosome in the egg-nucleus splits along its length, the two halves separate, one half passing into each new cell (Figs. 2.1 and 2.2). This type of cell division continues until the complete embryo composed of millions of cells is formed. By this method of body-cell division, each nucleus in every body cell is identical with the original nucleus in the fertilized egg, i.e., in cattle every cell contains 30 pairs of chromosomes.

Formation of Eggs and Sperms*

Sperms are formed from body cells present in the testis; eggs are formed from body cells present in the ovary. Two sperms, or two eggs are formed from each body cell. When the body cell divides into two, the paired chromosomes

*This description has been simplified in order to avoid confusion.

separate, one chromosome from each pair moving into either one egg or one sperm (Fig. 2.2). In this way, the number of chromosomes found in an egg or sperm is half the number found in the body cell; in cattle there are 30 single chromosomes in each egg or sperm. This type of cell division is called *reduction division*.

Fertilization

When an egg is fertilized by a sperm, the two nuclei join together. In the case of sheep, the 27 chromosomes from the sperm join with the 27 chromosomes from the egg, forming a fertilized nucleus with 27 pairs of chromosomes, i.e., the original number present in the body cells of the parents. In this way, the number of chromosomes present in the body cells of sheep, pigs, cattle or poultry is kept constant.

Chromosomes

Chromosomes consist of nucleoprotein, i.e., a combination of nucleic acids and proteins. The nucleic acids carry genetic information and chromosomes can be thought of as a linear arrangement of 'units of information' called genes. Genes are present in pairs; one gene occupies a definite position on one chromosome and its partner gene is found in the same position on the homologous chromosome. Such pairs of genes are called alleles (Fig. 2.3). Many thousand pairs of genes are found in each body-cell nucleus.

Classification of Farm Animals

Before understanding the work performed by genes, it is necessary to appreciate how farm animals are divided up into types, breeds and individual animals.

(a) (b) (c)

(d) (e) (f)

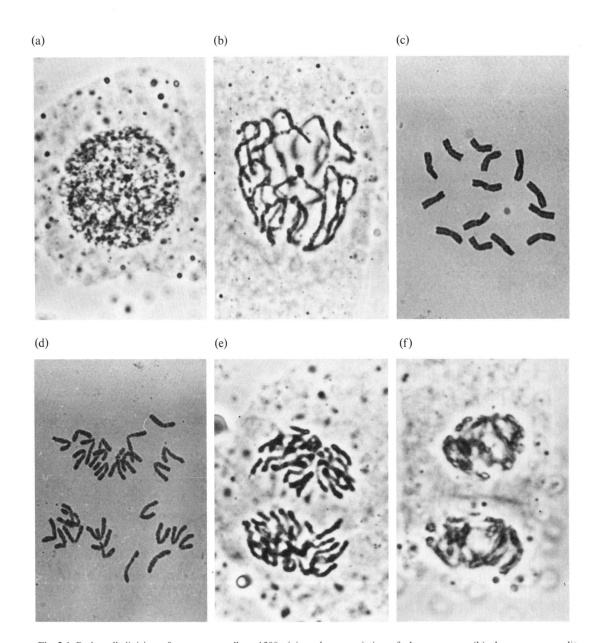

Fig. 2.1 Body cell division; fescue grass cells ×1300: (a) nucleus consisting of chromosomes; (b) chromosomes, split lengthwise, become visible; (c) chromosomes thicken and arrange themselves in the centre of the cell; (d) the two 'halves' of each chromosome separate and move to respective ends of the cell; (e) chromosomes 'bunch' together; (f) two new daughter cells with their nuclei.

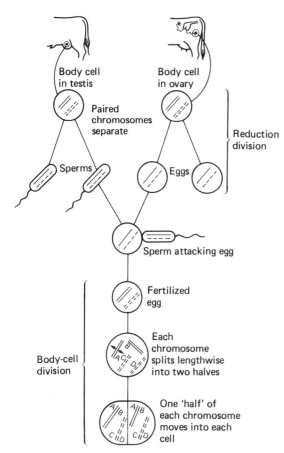

Fig. 2.2 The behaviour of chromosome pairs during reduction division and body cell division.

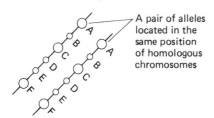

Fig. 2.3 A pair of homologous chromosomes.

Cattle, for example, are divided into three main types – dairy, beef and dual-purpose. The dairy-type animal is wedge-shaped, lean and leggy; a beef animal is stocky and well-fleshed with short legs; the dual-purpose type is intermediate between the two.

Each type or class of cattle consists of many breeds, for example:

beef: Aberdeen Angus, Hereford, Charollais, Limousin.
dairy: Friesian, Ayrshire, Jersey, Guernsey.
dual-purpose: Dairy Shorthorn, Welsh Black.

What makes one cow a Friesian and another cow a Hereford? Differences between breeds are judged by comparing 'points' of conformation and/or performance. Scientists concerned with breeding prefer to call such 'points' *characters* or *traits*. The expressions of characters possessed by the Friesian and Aberdeen Angus are listed in Table 2.1.

Table 2.1. Characters possessed by the Friesian and Aberdeen Angus

Character	Friesian	Aberdeen Angus
Body shape	Wedge	Block
Length of leg	Long	Short
Size of udder	Large	Small
Length of neck	Long	Short
Conditions of horns	Horned	Polled
Colour of coat	Red or black	Black
Condition of coat	Patchy	Uniform
Milk yield	High	Low

Within one breed of cattle, there are also differences of appearance and performance between individual animals. If two Friesian cows are compared, the following differences of character expressions could possibly be found (Table 2.2).

Table 2.2. Character expressions in individual animals

Character	Friesian A	Friesian B
Coat colour	Black	Red
Udder size	Large, pendulous	Small, well slung
Teat spacing	Even	Uneven
Average milk yield	5000 litres	3400 litres
Butterfat %	3.0	4.5

From the standpoint of breeding, it can be said that:

1. An animal consists of a collection of characters, e.g., coat colour, condition of horns, length of leg, milking capacity, etc.
2. Each character can be expressed in two or more ways, e.g., coat colour in Friesians can be either black or red; milk yield can vary from 550 kg, say, to 7000 kg; percentage of butterfat can vary from 2.8 to 8.5.
3. When a collection of cattle have some important character expressions in common they are called a breed.
4. When breeds of cattle have certain general character expressions in common they are called 'types'.

How do parent animals pass on these characters to their offspring? The only possible answer is by transferring chromosomes via gametes during fertilization. The inheritance of these characters can either be by additive or dominant gene action. (To simplify description, the epistatic interaction of non-allelic genes has not been described.)

Additive Inheritance

Consider the inheritance of coat colour in Shorthorn cattle (Fig. 2.4). If a red bull is crossed with a number of white cows, then all the calves born in the first generation are roan in colour, i.e., coats with a mixture of red and white hairs. If a roan bull was crossed with roan cows from this first generation of cattle it would be possible to get red, white or roan calves in the second generation. How is this possible?

In the parent bull there are a pair of alleles RR in each body cell and because of their presence the coat colour of the animal is red. The coat colour of the parent cow is white because of paired WW alleles present in the cells.

When two sperms are formed from a body cell in the testis, the two twin chromosomes bearing the genes RR separate, so that in one sperm there is only one R gene present. Similarly, in each egg formed from the ovary of the cow, there is only one W gene.

During fertilization the R gene from the sperm partners the W gene from the egg, so that RW genes lie side by side in the fertilized egg. By body-cell division the fertilized egg grows into a calf and eventually into a mature bull or cow. Each cell in either of these animals contains the twin genes R and W. Since there is only one R gene present, approximately a half of the number of hairs composing the coat are red in colour; the other hairs are white. This mixture of red and white hairs produces the roan colour effect. This form of inheritance is described as additive since the amount of redness in the coat is directly determined by the number of R genes present in the cells.

Number of R genes	Coat colour
0	white
1	roan
2	red

When a roan bull and roan cow of the first generation are mated together, the paired chromosomes bearing the R and W genes separate, when eggs and sperms are formed. This roan animal is capable of forming two types of sperms or eggs, i.e., one type containing the W gene and another type containing the R gene; such an animal is called a *hybrid*.

During service, the semen injected into the cow will contain many thousands of sperms; one half of them will contain the W gene, the other half of them the R gene. If there were two eggs present in the Fallopian tube of the cow, it would be possible for one of the two types of sperms to fertilize one of them as follows (Fig. 2.4):

Sperm No. 1 could fertilize egg No. 1 or 2
or Sperm No. 2 could fertilize egg No. 1 or 2

In other words, a sperm and an egg can join together in four possible ways to produce three kinds of fertilized eggs:

1 egg containing the genes RR
2 eggs containing the genes RW
1 egg containing the genes WW

Each of these fertilized eggs would form mature animals containing these genes.

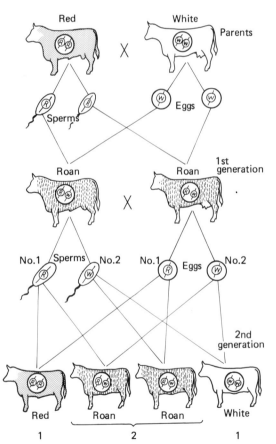

Fig. 2.4 Inheritance of coat colour in Shorthorn cattle.

Thus in the second generation, red, roan or white animals can be produced in the ratio of:

1 Red: 2 Roans: 1 White

Blue Roan Cattle produced by crossing a white Shorthorn with a black Aberdeen Angus are another example of this form of inheritance.

Dominant Inheritance

Pairs of genes do not always express themselves additively. If, for example, white-fleeced ewes are crossed with a black-fleeced ram, all the hybrids of the first generation are not grey-fleeced but white-fleeced. If ewes and a ram from this group of sheep were crossed, the lambs of the second generation would be born in the ratio of 3 white-fleeced lambs to 1 black-fleeced lamb. Fleece colours in these sheep still depend on the presence of a pair of alleles and these genes are handed on to first and second generation of sheep (Fig. 2.5).

In the first-generation hybrids of this cross the genes *B* and *W* are present in the body cells. The fleece colour of the animals, however, is white.

This means that the *W* gene is as effective in action when present alone (*W*) as it is when coupled with its allele (*WW*). The effect of the *W* gene completely masks or dominates the effect of the *B* gene.

When eggs and sperms are produced from these hybrid animals the *B* and *W* genes separate and recombine in four possible combinations:

1 *WW* (white-fleeced) – similar to the white-fleeced parent.
2 *BW* (white-fleeced) – similar to the white-fleeced 1st-generation hybrids
1 *BB* (black-fleeced) – similar to the black-fleeced parent

The above combinations of paired genes explain why lambs born in the second generation are in the ratio of 3 white-fleeced lambs to 1 black-fleeced lamb. (This ratio and all other ratios described can only be ascertained in practice when very large numbers of animals are counted. In any one act of fertilization the chances of the lamb born being black are 3 to 1 against.)

Many other character expressions are inherited in this way, some of which are listed in Table 2.3.

The Shorthand Language of Breeding

When crosses between animals are represented on paper, drawings of chromosomes and genes are not usually included. Thus a pair of alleles are represented simply by two letters. In the dominant white-fleeced parent sheep, in the above example, the genes are written down in capital letters as *WW*, i.e., the first letter of the word 'white'. The paired alleles responsible for the recessive character expression (black fleece) are written down in small letters as *ww*. Thus the inheritance of fleece colour in sheep represented in Fig. 2.5 can be written down in this form of 'shorthand' as follows (Fig. 2.6):

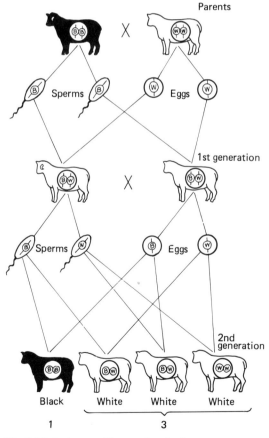

Fig. 2.5 Inheritance of fleece colour in sheep.

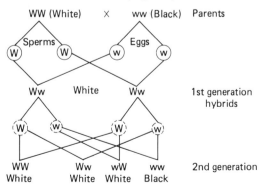

Fig. 2.6

Table 2.3. Inherited characteristics

Class of stock	Character	Dominant expression	Recessive expression
Cattle	Coat colour	Black	Red
	Coat colour	Black	White
	Coat pattern	Uniform	Spotted
	Coat pattern	Friesian	Ayrshire or Guernsey pattern
	Face pattern	Hereford white face	Plain face
	Horn colour	Black tipped	Clear tipped
	Horn condition	Polled	Horned
Sheep	Fleece colour	White	Black
Pigs	Shape of face	Long, narrow	Dished
	Coat colour	White	Red

SELECTION

Modern breeds of livestock have, in the main, been developed by selecting animals which look alike from assorted collections of animals which differ greatly in appearance. The breeder of farm livestock selects the animals he requires and crosses them together. From the animals born, he again selects for breeding those animals which look like the parent animals and discards the rest. In this way, by breeding through many generations, a collection of animals emerge which have certain character expressions in common. They are classified as a breed.

This is the basis on which most of our breeds have been moulded, i.e., the selection of what is required, and the discarding of the unwanted animals. How does this process operate genetically? Consider how it operates with additive and dominant inheritance of one character.

Additive Inheritance

Assume that the breeder has before him a collection of red, roan and white Shorthorn Cattle; it is known that their genetic constitutions are *RR*, *Rr* and *rr* respectively. If the breeder wants to breed red animals all he has to do is select red cows and bulls and cross them. In this way all his animals will be red in colour (Fig. 2.7).

He would thus, by accident, have selected animals which were homozygous for red coat colour; because of this the character will remain 'fixed' within the progeny. White coat colour could be selected for in the same way, but this is difficult or impossible in practice because white

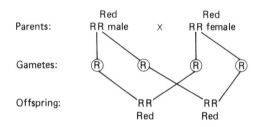

Fig. 2.7

Shorthorns suffer from reproductive defects generally known as 'white heifer disease'.

If, on the other hand, he wishes to produce pure-breeding roan cattle he would find this impossible. The roan animal is heterozygous because its cells contain two different alleles, *Rr*, which separate at gamete (egg or sperm) formation to produce two different types of gametes; one type will contain the *r* gene and the second type the *R* gene. These two genes will recombine together during fertilization in three possible ways (Fig. 2.8).

What is seen is the re-emergence of red and white animals because of the segregation and recombination of the *R* and *r* genes. It is thus not possible to 'fix' the roan character.

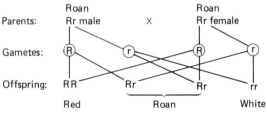

Fig. 2.8

PRINCIPLES OF BREEDING 23

With additive inheritance, the phenotype (appearance or performance of an animal) reflects the genotype (the genes which constitute an animal). By looking at the coat colour of Shorthorns it is known whether they possess the genes *RR, Rr* or *rr*. This is the principle underlying performance testing (see p. 29); the phenotypic performance of a parent animal is a reliable indicator of the genes it possesses and which it will hand on to its offspring.

Dominant Inheritance

Consider breeding for a character where one gene expression is dominant over another. Assume that a cattle breeder has before him a second generation (F_2) group of black and red cattle. From Table 2.3 it can be seen that black is dominant to red so that approximately three quarters of the animals are black and one quarter red. If the breeder wanted to produce a red breed of animals, all he would have to do is select red animals and cross them. In this way, all his offspring (100%) would be red in colour (Fig. 2.9).

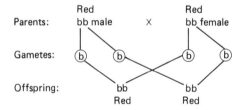

Fig. 2.9

It is thus easy to fix this character because it is a recessive one. If, on the other hand, he wishes to breed black-coated offspring he would have greater difficulty.

The black cows on average would consist of one-third *BB* and two thirds *Bb* genotypes; the black bulls would also consist of one-third *BB* and two-thirds *Bb* genotypes. If he allowed

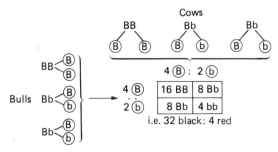

Fig. 2.10

indiscriminate matings between cows and bulls the resultant offspring could be predicted to be as in Fig. 2.10.

In other words, only 89% of the offspring would be black; the remaining 11% would be red. This fact highlights the difference between dominant and additive inheritance. With dominance, the phenotype does not reflect the genotype so that phenotypic selection of parents possessing a dominant character is not 100% effective in breeding offspring possessing this dominant character.

Because of this uncertainty the only way to assess the genotype of a particular parent animal is to observe the appearance (or performance) of its offspring; this is known as *progeny testing*. When selecting black cattle, the genes carried by the parent cannot be determined merely by looking at the animal. In other words, the only way to determine whether a black bull is carrying *BB* or *Bb* genes (whether the animal is homo- or heterozygous) is by looking at the coat colour of its calves.

The quickest way of determining the genotype of such a bull is to cross it with several red cows, i.e., with recessive *bb* animals. The possible results are shown in Fig, 2.11.

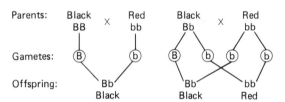

Fig. 2.11

If any red calves are thrown, then the bull is heterozygous with *Bb* genes; having discovered that it carries a *b* gene, it would not be used for further breeding, since the objective is to produce black animals giving rise to black offspring.

Continuous and Discontinuous Variations

All the characters which have been decribed so far are determined by one pair of alleles having distinct phenotypic effects. Because such characters are inherited in this way it is possible to classify the animals into distinct groups or classes; also the number in one class is a simple multiple of the number in another class. In the case of fleece colour inheritance (Fig. 2.5), the sheep of the second generation are either white (one class) or black (second class); there are three times as many white sheep as black sheep.

In the example of coat colour inheritance in Shorthorn Cattle (Fig. 2.4), there are three distinct classes distributed as follows: one quarter red, one half roan and one quarter white (see Figs. 2.4 and 2.13a). Because such variation of a character can be grouped into separate classes in this way it is described as a *discontinuous variation*.

Most of the characters which are of agricultural importance, such as milk yield, percentage butterfat, rate of liveweight growth, food conversion ratio, etc., are not determined by a pair of genes but many genes; any number from 2 to perhaps 100 genes may be involved, each gene contributing such a small amount to the total effect of a character that its individual effect cannot be detected; genes of this nature are called polygenes and such characters are said to be quantitively inherited.

To understand how polygenes influence the variation of a character (trait) within a population (a breed for example) reference can be made in the first place to the work of Nilsson Ehle.

Quantitative Inheritance

Nilsson Ehle found that in certain varieties of wheat grain, grain colour was determined by three pairs of alleles which have an additive effect. He crossed a wheat plant having deep red grains with a plant having white grains (Fig. 2.12). All the resulting first generation plants had grains that were intermediate in colour between the grain colours of the two parents, i.e., medium red. On allowing these first generation (F_1) plants to self pollinate and fertilize he found that the second generation (F_2) plants could be divided into seven classes according to the colour of their grains; some plants bore white grains, others deep red grains, etc.; the number of plants in each class occurred in the following proportions:

$$\frac{1}{64}\text{ Deep red}:\frac{6}{64}\frac{\text{Darker}}{\text{red}}:\frac{15}{64}\frac{\text{Dark}}{\text{red}}:\frac{20}{64}\frac{\text{Med.}}{\text{red}}:$$

$$:\frac{15}{64}\frac{\text{Light}}{\text{red}}:\frac{6}{64}\frac{\text{Lighter}}{\text{red}}:\frac{1}{64}\text{White}$$

To explain these results he assumed that the parent with the darkest red grains had three pairs of alleles – $R_1R_1R_2R_2R_3R_3$; the white-grain parent had no capital R genes but three pairs of alleles $r_1r_1r_2r_2r_3r_3$. At gamete formation each pair of alleles separate, only one entering each gamete. Thus the F_1 plant had three R genes and three r genes. Because this plant had only three R genes, the colour of its grains was

intermediate between darkest red and white, i.e., medium red.

The F_1 plant is capable of producing eight types of pollen grain nuclei and eight types of embryo sac nuclei – $R_1R_2R_3$, $R_1r_2R_3$, $R_1R_2r_3$, $R_1r_2r_3$, $r_1R_2R_3$, $r_1R_2r_3$, $r_1r_2R_3$, and $r_1r_2r_3$. The number of ways in which these male and female nuclei can join together is $(2^3)^2 = 64$; this is shown in the chessboard, Fig. 2.12; this results in seven possible gene combinations which can be arranged as follows:

Number of R genes	6	5	4	3	2	1	0	Total
Frequency	1	6	15	20	15	6	1	64

This frequency distribution corresponds to the proportions of plants with different coloured grains that occurred in the second generation. Thus colour of grain depended entirely on the number of R genes present. Each R gene controlled the synthesis of a certain quantity of the red dye which coloured the husk of the grain; progressive deepening of colour depended on the continued addition of R genes.

The above illustration demonstrates what occurs when a character is controlled by three pairs of alleles. If it is assumed that this character is controlled by five pairs of alleles, the ways in which male and female gamete nuclei could join together would be $(2^5)^2 = 1\,024$. The number of gene combinations, and consequently of colour classes, would amount to eleven and the frequency of occurrence in each class would be as shown in Fig. 2.13c. By proceeding one step further and assuming that the character is controlled by a hundred genes, then the distribution of phenotypes appears as shown in Fig. 2.13d. The difference in height between consecutive columns has become so small that a continuous curve rather than a stepped histogram is formed. It would not be possible to divide this population of plants into distinct classes according to the colour of their grain; a continuous range of colour pattern emerges between the extremes of white and darkest red; only a few plants possess grains with these extremes of colour. Variation of this kind in a given character is described as being *continuous*. The bell shaped curve is called a Normal Distribution Curve.

The above inheritance patterns are similar in nature to the inheritance of coat colour in Shorthorn cattle (see p. 20). They are all examples of additive inheritance and consequently phenotypic appearance reflects genotypes. In the case of grain colour determined by six genes (see Fig. 2.13b), the visual selection of a deep red grain

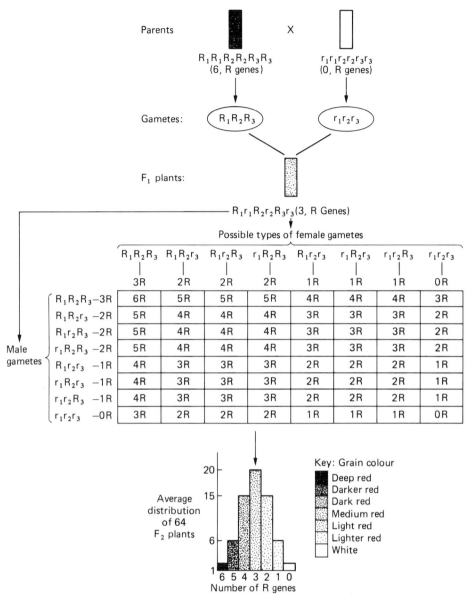

Fig. 2.12 Inheritance of grain colour in wheat (after Nilssen Ehle).

implies that 6 *R* genes are automatically selected. In the case of grain colour determined by 100 genes, selection of the deep red grain implies that 100 *R* genes are being selected; if a population of plants from this one plant is bred, all possess grains deep red in colour.

If, on the other hand, some of the polygenes acted in a dominant fashion, the phenotype would not reflect the genotype (cf. dominance, p. 23) so that selection of say deep red grain parents would not be 100% effective in breeding deep red grain offspring.

Heritability

Quantitative traits which are polygenically inherited are often greatly influenced by environmental factors. For example, the phenotypic performance of a cow as expressed by its milk yield depends not only on the number of polygenes which it possesses but also on all kinds of environmental influences. The cow may have received insufficient concentrates to supplement bulky food or she may have been affected by mastitis or hypomagnesaemia. These are just a

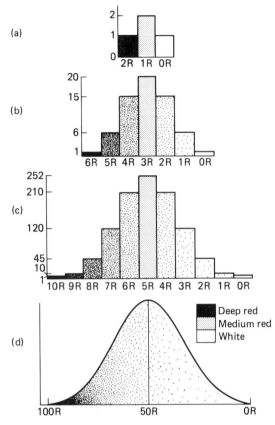

Fig. 2.13 The frequency of phenotypes in an F₂ population where a particular character is controlled by: (a) 2, (b) 6, (c) 10, (d) 100 genes respectively (assuming additive gene action).

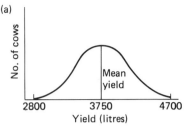

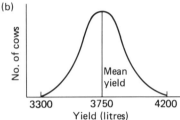

Fig. 2.14

few of the environmental factors which can influence milk yield.

When studying the variation of a quantitative trait such as milk yield in a breed of cattle it is only possible to see or measure the phenotypic variation that occurs. By graphically plotting milk yields against the number of cows possessing such milk yields, a normal distribution curve is formed. The average or mean milk yield can be calculated and the scatter or variation of milk yields around this mean can be seen.

Consider the two populations in Fig. 2.14.

The means of the two populations are the same; population A is obviously more variable than population B.

The phenotypic variation of such a character as recorded in a cattle population is due to genetic differences between cow and cow and to the differences in environmental conditions under which the cows are kept. How is it possible to determine the extent to which phenotypic variation in any character is due to (i) genetic differences and (ii) environmental differences?

Firstly consider additive inheritance in Short-

horn cattle; here the variation in coat colour is white, roan and red. This variation is due entirely to genetic differences, i.e., is due to *rr*, *rR* and *RR* genotypes. Environmental differences do not affect the coat colour in any way. Also it is found that the phenotype is an exact reflection of the genotype so that a population of red-coated animals could be formed by selecting red-coated parents. The heritability of this character is 100% because phenotypic selection of parents is 100% effective in producing what is required.

Next imagine the need to improve the yield of offspring from a variety* of pea seeds. The distribution curve of parent peas is shown in Fig. 2.15a. Peas weighing 800 milligrams can be selected and allowed to fertilize and produce first generation peas. The distribution curve of first generation offspring peas is shown in Fig. 2.15b. It can be seen that there is no difference between the distribution curves, i.e., the mean weight of both parent and offspring peas is the same. Selection of heavy peas had not produced any improvement. The heritability of this character is 0% because phenotypic selection is completely ineffective in producing any improvement in pea weight. All the variation in pea weight is due entirely to environmental differences.

Heritability (h^2) is defined as that proportion (or percentage) of total phenotypic variation which is caused by genetic differences. It measures the extent to which any improvement

---

*The variety is a Pure Line with each pair of alleles homozygous; the self pollinated, in-breeding pea species consists of a mixture of Pure Lines.

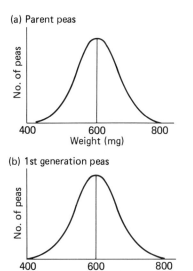

(a) Parent peas

No. of peas

400   600   800
Weight (mg)

(b) 1st generation peas

No. of peas

400   600   800
Weight (mg)

Fig. 2.15 Effects of selection on pea weight (0% heritability).

in a character can be handed on from parents to offspring. Any variation caused by differences in the environment cannot be handed on to offspring in this way.

Equationally, the situation can be expressed as follows:

Phenotypic = Genetic + Environmental
variation   variation   variation

$$V_P = V_G + V_E$$

Since heritability is more often than not expressed as a percentage it can be stated equationally as follows:

$$h^2 = \frac{V_G}{V_P} \times 100 \quad \text{or} \quad \frac{V_G}{V_G + V_E} \times 100$$

If heritability is high it implies that variation due to genetic differences (V_G) is high in relation to variation caused by environmental differences (V_E); also that such genetic differences are probably determined to a large extent by a limited number of genes acting additively. If heritability is low, genetic variation may or may not be additive, but environmental differences are certainly having the main effect on the phenotypic variation of the character. If heritability is medium it could be due to either (a) genetic variation being non-additive or (b) genetic variation being additive but environmental influences have a major effect.

One way of calculating heritability values is by the *contemporary comparison* method. Assume that it is necessary to calculate the heritability value of growth rate in beef cattle and that the weight of cattle at 400 days old is regarded as the criterion of growth rate (see Fig. 2.16a). From a population of cows and bulls having a mean weight of 400 kg select those bulls and cows that weigh more than 43 kg above this mean weight, i.e., those that weigh more than 443 kg. Assume that the mean weight of selected parents is 445 kg. Two groups of parents, group A consisting of animals with a mean weight of 400 kg (P_1) and group B consisting of animals with a mean weight of 445 kg (P_p) would thus be formed; the difference of 45 kg ($P_p - P_1$) is called the selection differential (ΔP). The mean weights of the calves at 400 days old produced from each group of parents could then be calculated and compared; such a comparison is called contemporary comparison. Assume that the mean weight of the calves (G_2) in group B was 18 kg greater than the mean weight of the calves (G_1) in group A; this difference in weight ($G_2 - G_1$) is called the genetic gain (ΔG). Heritability (h^2) could thus be calculated as follows:

$$h^2 = \frac{\text{Genetic gain } (\Delta G)}{\text{Selection differential } (\Delta P)} \times 100$$

$$= \frac{18 \text{ kg}}{45 \text{ kg}} \times 100 = 40\%$$

Thus phenotypic selection has been 40% effective in improving live weight. This implies that 40% of the phenotypic variation in weight of this cattle population is due to genetic differences; 60% is due to environmental differences.

If only the bull parents had been divided into two groups with a selection index of 45 kg (as is the case when bulls are progeny tested) and then mated at random to a population of 'average' cows, the genetic gain as recorded in the two calf groups would be around 9 kg, i.e., a half of the genetic gain obtained when both parents are selected on a weight basis. Thus to calculate the heritability value using only a single parent the genetic gain of the progeny needs to be doubled.

Examples of heritability values for some important characters are listed below.

Conception rate in cattle	5%
Egg production in poultry	20%
Milk production in cattle	30%
Fleece length in sheep	40%
Egg weight in poultry	60%
Slaughter weight in cattle	85%

What is meant by high or low heritability is not rigidly defined, but the following values are generally accepted:

High heritability	Greater than 50%
Medium heritability	Between 20 and 50%
Low heritability	Less than 20%

IMPROVEMENT OF ECONOMIC TRAITS

Today, livestock improvement is mainly concerned with the improvement of a limited number of economically important traits within existing breeds of livestock. Milk yield and quality are the main characters being selected for in dairy cows; live weight gain, food-conversion ratio and carcass quality are those selected for in pigs, sheep and cattle being reared for meat production.

Selection technique as it applies to growth rate in beef cattle is shown in Fig. 2.16a when two-parent selection is adopted.

If only bulls weighing over 443 kg had been selected and mated to the cows in the population as a whole, then the heritability of the character under these conditions would be a half of the heritability value, namely 20%. The expected genetic gain would thus be:

$$\Delta G = \Delta P \times h^2$$
$$= 45 \times \frac{20}{100} = 9 \text{ kg}$$

The offspring from cows mated to such selected bulls will have a mean weight of 9 kg greater than the offspring from cows mated to non-selected bulls (Fig. 2.16b). The rate of improvement by phenotypic selection will thus depend on the heritability value of the trait being selected. If the heritability value is high, selection will result in an immediate improvement in the progeny and rapid continued improvement by further selection in succeeding generations. If the heritability value is low, then little, if any, improvement will result from selection technique; improvement will be attained by correcting any environmental limitations (managerial weaknesses).

In practice, breeding plans for improving quantitative characters can only be constructed if records are available, as it is from such records that mean values and heritability values are calculated. In the absence of such records only limited progress can be made for improving quantitative characters by breeding techniques. It is because of these basic facts that many breeding programmes have in the past produced such disappointing results. Even the pedigree breeder who has bred high-quality animals is now appreciating that continued progress can only be achieved by pooling his livestock resources with other breeders and using outside agencies who employ skilled geneticists. Agencies such as the Milk Marketing Board and the Meat and Livestock Commission are helping

and will continue to help individual farmers to breed better livestock.

Progeny Testing

The genetic principle underlying this form of testing has already been described. The main purpose of progeny testing is to assess quantitative traits which:

i) can be expressed in one sex only, e.g., estimating the genes for milk production possessed by a bull;
ii) cannot be measured until after slaughter, e.g., carcass characteristics;
iii) have low heritabilities, i.e., where individual selection is apt to be highly inaccurate.

Testing is usually carried out on male animals since one sire is mated to many females; the

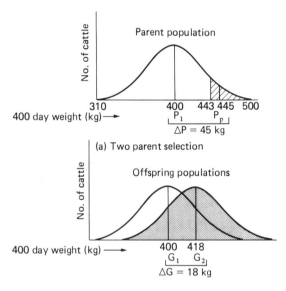

(a) Two parent selection

(b) One parent selection

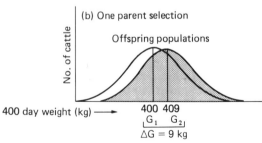

Fig. 2.16 Genetic gain resulting from (a) two parent selection; (b) one parent selection.

male's effect on the genetic constitution of the breed as a whole is thus much greater than that of the female. Testing is usually undertaken by comparing the performance of the offspring of a particular sire with the performance of the offspring from other sires under similar environmental conditions; such a comparison is known as an improved contemporary comparison. The genetic gains referred to concerning beef cattle (Fig. 2.16) are examples of contemporary comparisons.

When dairy bulls are progeny tested, a milk index, which is another name for contemporary comparison, is allocated to each bull. This milk index measures the average difference in milk yields between the daughters of a bull and the daughters of other bulls which are milked in the same herds and in the same recording year. It is important that these comparisons are made in the same herds as the differences in milk production brought about by different levels of feeding and management are eliminated. The accuracy of this assessment depends on the number of daughters which have been tested. The larger the number of daughters tested, the higher the test accuracy figures and consequently the more reliable the milk index assessment given. Thus an improved contemporary comparison rating needs to be judged in the light of the test accuracy figures given. A bull with an accuracy rating (scientifically called weighting) of under 20 needs to be regarded with extreme caution; if it is less than 7, the improved contemporary comparison rating has little or no value. These principles can be appreciated by referring to Table 3.8.

The disadvantage of progeny testing sires is the time it takes to assess their breeding value, e.g. dairy bulls are at least four years old. The technique of deep freezing semen can increase the working life of a valuable sire since frozen semen can be used long after the sire's death.

Performance Testing

This form of testing applies to traits that are highly heritable and can be easily measured in animals; the phenotypic performance of a young animal can be regarded as a fairly reliable reflection of its genotype and of the genes which it will hand on to its offspring. The underlying genetical principle has been described under additive inheritance (see p. 22). In practice this form of testing mainly applies to sires; it enables a large number of potential sires to be reduced to

a reasonable number for further progeny testing. It is important that potential sires are tested under similar or standard environmental conditions. This reduces phenotypic variation due to environmental differences so that any variation recorded in a group of sires is due mainly to genetic differences. In practice, the most effective way of doing this is to centralize potential sires at Performance Testing Stations.

Sib Testing

'Sibs' is the term used to describe full brothers and sisters, i.e., progeny that have two common parents. Half-sibs are step-brothers or sisters, i.e., progeny that have one parent in common.

If a young male animal is being considered as a possible replacement for future breeding and the traits being selected for can either (a) only be observed in female animals, e.g., prolificacy, or (b) only be assessed in the slaughtered animal, e.g., carcass quality, then information on its close relatives can be a valuable guide as to his likely genotype.

The principle here is that relatives have some proportion of their genes in common. A parent and an offspring share one half of their genes. Two full brothers will on average possess one half of their genes in common; all of the genes come from the same two parents but the contribution of genes from both parents will not normally be identical. Thus if the phenotype of one animal can be measured, thus obtaining a prediction of its breeding value, something can be inferred about the breeding value of its close relative.

Progeny testing is a type of half-sib testing, i.e., the genetic value of the parent sire is being assessed on the performance of his daughters, all of whom are half-sibs. In other types of sib testing, a young potential sire may be selected according to the performance of its half sisters.

Selection Index

Selection is seldom made on the basis of one trait only. Breeders usually need to select for several traits at a time, as is the case with pigs when growth rate, food conversion ratio and carcass quality are selected simultaneously. The more traits selected for, the less selection 'pressure' can be exerted on each trait. It is probable that individuals scoring high on trait A will be mediocre or poor for trait B unless the two traits are genetically correlated, i.e. tend to be inherited together. The breeder must therefore make compromises, selecting some individuals on a 'total merit' basis which would probably not be saved for breeding if selection was based on a single trait. In selecting on a total merit basis it is desirable to reduce the records of performance on important traits to a single score called the Selection Index. The index number has no meaning in itself but is valuable in comparing individuals on a relative basis. The methods used in calculating an index usually take into consideration the heritability, the relative economic importance of each trait and any genetic or phenotypic correlation between traits; traits will be correlated when they are affected by the same genes linked close together on the same chromosome.

In more concrete terms it can be said that the selection pressure on any one trait depends on the number of traits being selected for. If there was simultaneously selection for two characters of equal importance, the selection applied to either of them would be approximately $1/\sqrt{2}$ or 71% of that possible if only one trait was selected; the general formula becomes $1/\sqrt{n}$ when the number of traits being selected for is n.

Pedigree Breeding

Historically speaking, early breeders started with breeding material in which standards were low and genetic variation high. By acute observation and careful, rigorous selection they fixed improved types which were the progenitors of our present breeds. Although colour marking and conformation were the main criteria for selection, the principles of performance and progeny testing were employed by pioneer breeders. The maintenance of the high standards of attainment in our present-day breeds is largely the responsibility of pedigree breeders and breed societies. The refined techniques of performance and progeny testing, particularly as they apply to sires, can only be applied to young stock that potentially are likely to hand on desirable genetic qualities to their offspring; pedigree animals are the ones most likely to possess such qualities.

Pedigree breeding implies that individual animals of known ancestry are selected for crossing to produce offspring. Each pedigree animal possesses a pedigree record which describes the name, breed, date of birth, appearance and possible performance of its ancestors.

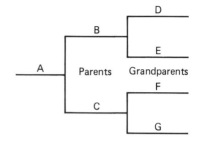

Fig. 2.17

The form of the record is shown in Fig. 2.17; the sires appear on the upper lines (B, D and F) and dams on the lower lines (C, E and G).

When pedigree records are judged for breeding purposes the main features looked for are:

i) consistently high performance over several generations;
ii) regular and sustained breeding on the part of the females.

In the pedigree shown in Table 2.4, the above factors are present in the dam and grandmothers of the bull. It is a record of consistency in milk production, butterfat percentage, regular breeding and longevity; note the progeny test data included in the pedigree record.

It needs to be emphasized that the records of near relatives are of the highest value as indicators of the animal's probable breeding value. The further back one looks in the pedigree the less valuable the recorded information.

When an animal is purchased for breeding it is important to ensure that the management, particularly the feeding, should be similar to that on the buyer's farm. This decision equates environmental conditions so that the genetic qualities of the animal are manifested in the offspring.

Inbreeding

Inbreeding is the mating of individuals more closely related than the average of the population to which they belong.

The most intense form of inbreeding is the repeated mating of brother and sister, mother with son or father with daughter. Other forms of inbreeding are listed below in descending order of intensity:

i) half-brother and sister;
ii) one-sire herd;
iii) two-sire herd;
iv) first cousins;
v) half first cousins.

Table 2.4. Pedigree of Kirkhammerton River Thames (source: Milk Marketing Board)

FRIESIAN

Born: 12. 4.82

Bred by: T J Pick
Close House, Kirk Hammerton, York YO5 8DA

SIRE: MMB THAMESDALE SUPERSTAR 393715

Born: 2.11.74

June 82		Eff. Dtrs	ICC	
MILK	No. Dtrs 74	65.7	+436	kg
BUTTERFAT		65.7	+ 29.8 kg + 0.25 %	
PROTEIN		65.7	+ 12.8 kg - 0.03 %	

Number of herds 62

Percentage of dtrs in the two herds with highest and second highest number of dtrs 4 : 3

CONFORMATION OF PROGENY (MMB Panel and Livestock Officer Assessment)

Date last summarised 1982 Number inspected 58

DAUGHTER AVERAGE			
Lact	1	2	3
Dtrs	79	49	11
Age	31	43	49
kg	5255	5812	6006
Days	299	297	293
BF %	4.13	4.09	3.99
kg	217	238	240
Ptn %	3.29	3.30	3.23

Scorecard Breakdown		
Legs		101
Feet		100
Udder Shape	Fore	107
Attachment	Rear	110
Teats	Shape	109
	Position	111

DAM: KIRK HAMMERTON CHARMAINE 29TH 4450740

Born: 21. 7.76

Lac			Days	% BF	No of Tests	%Ptn	PI
1	20.10.78	6139	305	4.11	10	3.41	121
2	23.11.79	9283	305	3.75	10	3.23	158
3	19. 2.81	8819	279	4.05	9	3.29	143
4	12. 4.82						

COW GENETIC INDEX 956

DAM'S SIRE: MMB RIVERDOWN JESTER 381411

Born: 5.10.72

Dtrs	Lac	Age	kg	Days	% BF	%Ptn
98	1	30	5517	301	3.84	3.20
83	2	42	6248	296	3.90	3.31
67	3	55	6886	295	3.76	3.27

DAM'S DAM: KIRKHAMMERTON CHARMAINE 15TH 3749994

Born: 2. 4.73

Lac	Date	kg	Days	% BF	No of Tests	%Ptn
1	31. 7.75	3016	225	3.86	7	3.44
2	21. 7.76	5507	301	4.24	10	3.38
3	7. 7.77	6612	281	3.60	10	3.22
4	9. 6.78	6632	305	3.81	9	3.21
5	11. 7.79	6703	305	3.87	10	3.30
6	17. 7.80	5539	293	4.20	9	3.26

Pedigree produced August 1982

KIRKHAMMERTON RIVER THAMES

(ESTIMATED TRANSMITTING ABILITY
+27.4 kg Fat, +16.4 kg Protein)

SIRE'S SIRE: FAIRLEA ROYAL MARK 299855 HFC

2698 DSC DAUS: MILK +8 (+.05% FAT)
3329 DAUS: 59% GP (RATING: 3005/+3)

SIRE'S DAM: NINE-ELL TELSTAR DILLYANN VG 2281905

Lac	Date	kg	Days	% BF
1	2yr	7154	305	4.36
2	3yr	9002	305	3.99
3	5yr	7907	305	4.17
4	6yr	9585	305	4.49
5	8yr	8156	305	4.45
6	10yr	6748	305	4.03

The information given in this document is correct to the best of knowledge and belief of the Board who do not accept any liability for losses, which may result from any error.

Inbreeding is not a method of improvement. It reduces fitness and fertility and increases the mortality rate; although it may be necessary on occasions, it is never desirable in itself. It may be used to increase the uniformity in a population and is an attempt to breed a group of animals which are genetically homozygous for certain characters. One specific effect of inbreeding is to reveal defective characters which were masked or dominated in the original group of animals used.

In the Dexter breed of cattle, two types of cattle exist, a short-legged type and a long-legged type. These character expressions depend on the presence of one pair of genes. The long-legged type is the result of two dominant genes *LL*. The short-legged type is due to the presence of a dominant and a recessive gene *Ll* (similar to roan-coated Shorthorn cattle).

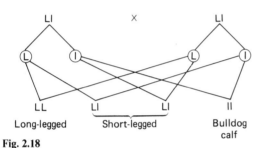

Fig. 2.18

When two short-legged types are mated together their genes can recombine as in Fig. 2.18.

When two *ll* genes are present the calf produced is a bulldog, i.e., a calf whose underjaw sticks out like a bulldog, whose tongue protrudes between the teeth, the leg bones are curved; the calf is aborted usually about the seventh month of pregnancy.

In this particular breed, if short-legged animals are inbred together, the defect (due to the

l gene), masked in the parents, is brought into a pure form (*ll*) and the defect shows itself.

Another example is the occurrence of 'oedematous calves' in Ayrshires; this abnormality is controlled by a pair of recessive alleles.

These examples illustrate that inbreeding in itself cannot produce defects but merely shows up more quickly the possible defects hidden in the cattle originally used. Recessive abnormalities are difficult to clear from a breed because it is impossible to identify animals carrying one recessive gene without extensive test mating. The only way to reduce the incidence of such defects is to remove any animal shown to be a carrier, along with close relatives.

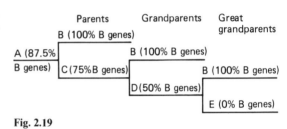

Fig. 2.19

Line Breeding

This is a special form of inbreeding used for the purpose of maintaining a high genetic relationship to a desirable ancestor. The pedigree in Fig. 2.19 shows that close line breeding to B has been practised. If we assume that 50% of parents' genes are handed on to offspring, then animal A possesses 87.5% of the genes found in ancestor B.

As is the case with inbreeding, line breeding is not a method of improvement. It may be resorted to on occasions to fix desirable characters possessed by a particular ancestor. It may lead to reduced vigour and reappearance of defective characters.

CROSS-BREEDING

Up to this point selective procedures for improving economic characters within breeds of livestock have been discussed. Often in farming, out-crosses are made between two distinct breeds; the resulting animal is known as a first cross, a first-generation hybrid or a half-bred. All these words mean the same thing. It is an

animal combining the genes of its two dissimilar parents. In other words, half the genes from the mother and half the genes from the father are expressed in the animal. For example in dairy cows, colour-marked calves can be produced by crossing cows with either an Aberdeen Angus, a Hereford, a Galloway bull or a Charollais. Such markings indicate to the buyer that the calves probably possess beefing qualities inherited from the father.

Three important breeding concepts need to be appreciated with this form of breeding:

1. Cross-breeding gives rise to hybrid vigour, i.e., an improvement in fertility, thrift, viability and growth rate; it is the reverse of the loss of vigour resulting from close inbreeding. The effect of cross-breeding is to bring an increasing number of alleles into a heterozygous state; the increased fitness of such individuals is often called *heterosis*. Crossing of breeds is often adopted in commercial practice because the effects of heterosis are so marked on certain specific characters, e.g., the number of pigs born from first cross hybrid sows is 5% greater than the average number of pigs born to sows of the two parent breeds from which the hybrid sows originated (see p. 69); it needs to be appreciated that this can only be an advantage if the prolificacy of the cross-bred exceeds the prolificacy of the best of the two parent breeds.

2. It is not possible to cross half-breds so as to obtain all the offspring resembling themselves.

3. When half-breds are crossed, some off-spring appear that resemble neither the half-breds not the parents from which the half-breds originated.

The principles outlined in (2) and (3) above can be appreciated by studying the inheritance of two pairs of characters.

Inheritance of Two Characters

Fig. 2.20 illustrates the crossing of a plain-faced black cow with a red white-faced Hereford bull. All the calves born in the first generation are white-faced and black. The genes present in the mother cells of the parents can be represented thus:

$$\text{Bull} \begin{cases} \text{white face} - WW \\ \text{red coat} - bb \end{cases}$$
$$\text{Cow} \begin{cases} \text{plain face} - ww \\ \text{black coat} - BB \end{cases}$$

When the cow forms eggs, the BB alleles responsible for the black coat colour separate, one into each egg; similarly the ww alleles responsible for the plain-face separate, one into each egg. In the bull, one gene from the WW pair and one gene from the bb pair are found in each sperm.

The fertilized egg from this cross thus contains two pairs of alleles, $Ww\ Bb$. The cow or bull containing these four genes in its body cells is capable of forming four types of eggs or four types of sperms, respectively.

These eggs and sperms can combine together in sixteen possible ways to produce nine gene combinations and four phenotypes. To illustrate these combinations it is best to arrange them in chess-board form as shown in Fig. 2.20.

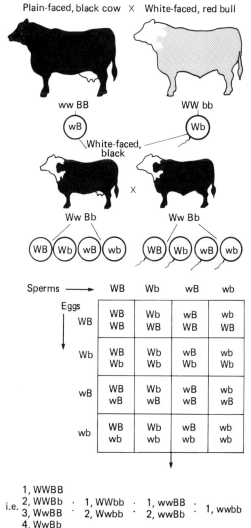

Fig. 2.20 Inheritance of face pattern and coat colour in cattle.

What do these animals look like? They can be sorted out as follows:

1. Each animal with one W and one B gene will be black and white-faced (because they are dominant).

2. Each animal with one B and two w's will be black and plain-faced.

3. Each animal with two b's and one W will be red and white-faced.

4. Each animal with two b's and two w's will be red and plain-faced.

It can thus be seen that when F_1 hybrids are mated, some of the offspring resemble their parents, others resemble neither, i.e. the plain-faced, red animals. Under normal farming conditions hybrids cannot be used for further breeding and a nucleus of pure breeds is always necessary to recreate cross-breds.

The appearance of the plain red animals illustrates how a new breed could be formed. If such animals were selected and multiplied by mating males and females together, a new breed of red, plain-faced animals could be formed. Initial crossing between breeds creates a greater range of variation because different combinations of the characters constituting the parent breeds occur. From such a range of combinations it is then possible to select that combination of characters which meets the requirements of the breeder.

The basic procedure, but at a more sophisticated level, has been adopted in breeding the new Cambridge breed of sheep which was started in Cambridge in 1964 and has continued since 1972 at Aberdeen. The aim was to form a lowland breed with high prolificacy and growth rate (Fig. 2.21).

Initial selection of ewes, who had produced consecutive sets of triplets in three lambings preceding selection, was made from nine breeds

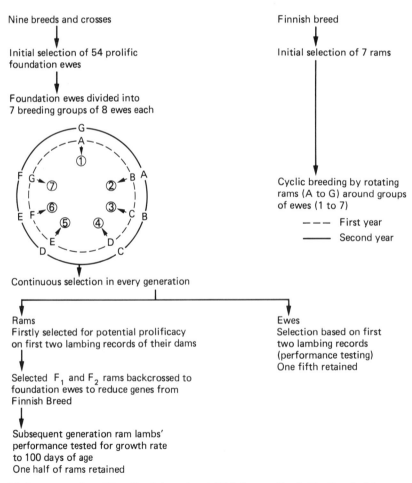

Fig. 2.21 Simplified representation of Breeding Scheme to establish the new Cambridge Breed of sheep.

and crosses to form a foundation group of 54 ewes – 34 Clun Forest, 6 Llanwenog, 3 Lleyn, 2 Radnor, 1 Kerry Hill, 3 Suffolk × Welsh Half-Bred, 1 Ryeland, 3 (Suffolk × Border Leicester) × North Country Cheviot and 1 Blue-Faced Leicester. Initial ram selection came from the Finnish breed known to have a high prolificacy; each of the seven rams selected was mated to a group of eight ewes thus forming seven breeding groups.

For the first eight years of crossing, inbreeding depression was avoided by mating the rams in a strict cyclical form with the seven breeding groups of ewes and after this period inbreeding was minimized by ensuring that total ram numbers did not fall below 10 in any season, and by using a computer mating system to confine mating to individuals that did not have a common ancestor nearer than one great-grandparent. Also the F_1 (Finnish/British) ram-lambs and the resulting F_2 rams were backcrossed to the foundation ewes so that the genetic contribution of the Finnish breed was markedly reduced.

Subsequent selection of rams for prolificacy was based mainly on the first two lambing records of their dams. These ram-lambs were then removed from their dams on the second day of life and performance tested by artificial rearing. Each was fed a restricted amount of milk substitute for 30 days and given *ad lib.* access to complete diet pellets from 14 days old; approximately 50% of ram-lambs were culled on the basis of growth rate to a hundred days.

Initially, no ewes were culled until they had lambed twice but subsequently four-fifths of the ewes were culled and one-fifth retained for breeding based on the first two lambing records.

By this method of initial crossing and subsequent selection with limited objectives, a new breed – the Cambridge – has emerged. It is a reminder of the history of animal breeding in this country. A phase of collection and crossing of genetic material is followed by selection with the formation of a new breed. When the new breed is no longer satisfactory, either because of a lack of genetic variation or because new or better combinations of traits are required, then cross-breeding with another local or imported breed is undertaken, followed by renewed selection.

3

Breeding for Milk

The aim of breeding, whether at national or farm level, is to produce a cow which is superior to its contemporaries in terms of milk yield and quality, fertility, longevity and wearability, conformation and efficiency of feed utilization. All these factors have an effect on the net margin of the herd.

FACTORS AFFECTING OUTPUT

1. Milk Yield

Yield varies considerably between breeds and within breeds (Table 3.1). Since most farms are concerned with one breed the aim is therefore to improve within that breed by careful selection of dam and sire. It needs to be remembered that two cows of very similar breeding may perform differently because the environmental factors of management and stockmanship are dissimilar. Since milk yield is the main component of the cow's output, it has the biggest impact on financial margins. Table 3.2 shows how milk yield per cow in recorded herds has risen consistently since 1959 due to improved breeding and management. The effect of yield on the gross

Table 3.1. Milk yield and butterfat (1979–80) of recorded herds in England and Wales by breed or breed types (October to September year) (source: Milk Marketing Board)

Breed or breed type	Average yield (kg)	Average butterfat (%)
Ayrshire	4938	3.90
British Friesian	5523	3.77
British Holstein	6233	3.73
Dairy Shorthorn	4834	3.58
Dexter	2189	4.09
Guernsey	3974	4.62
Jersey	3814	5.13
Northern Dairy Shorthorn	4733	3.59
Red Poll/British Dane	3831	3.68
South Devon	3518	4.18
Welsh Black*	3295	3.90
Mixed and others	5259	3.80
All breeds	5428	3.81

Official Milk Recording Scheme.
Lactation herd averages for full year herds.
From 1978/9 Poll Friesian and Red and White Friesian included in British Friesian.
*One herd only.

Table 3.2. Milk yield per cow in official recorded herd schemes (source: Scotland: S.M.R.A.; N. Ireland: D.A.N.I.) (kilograms)

October to September	England and Wales	Scotland*	Northen Ireland*
1959–60	4003	3912	4192
1964–5	4157	3987	4358
1969–70	4318	4172	4599
1971–2	4543	4344	4850
1972–3	4636	4421	4868
1973–4	4579	4462	4953
1974–5	4668	4602	5029
1975–6	4851	4733	5050
1976–7	4908	4749	5578†
1977–8	5249	5056	5255‡
1978–9	5335	5092	N.A.
1979–80	5428	5136	5118

Lactation herd averages for full year herds.
All breeds cows and heifers.
The lactation period in England and Wales and in Scotland is 305 days. In Northern Ireland it was changed from 315 to 305 days commencing with lactations from 1 May 1967.
* Calendar year figures.
† Jersey cows not included.
‡ Average for nine months period only Jan.–Sept.

Table 3.3. The effect of yield on the gross margin of a cow

Performance level	4000 litres	4500 litres	5000 litres	5500 litres	6000 litres
Milk price 13p/litre	£520	£585	£650	£715	£780
Plus calf £70, less mortality	64	64	64	64	64
Less cow depreciation	−30	−30	−30	−30	−30
Enterprise output	£554	£619	£684	£749	£814
Less concentrates @ £145 per tonne	163	196	232	272	314
Sundries	40	40	40	40	40
GROSS MARGIN	£351	£383	£412	£437	£460

margin of a cow (see p. 124) is illustrated by Table 3.3.

2. Milk Quality

The national average composition of supplies from non-Channel Island milk is:

Fat		3.87%
Solids—not-fat		
Lactose	4.65	} 8.70%
Protein	3.30	
Minerals	0.75	
Total solids		12.57

This again varies from breed to breed and within breed (Table 3.1). Every farm receives monthly a quality slip which indicates levels of

Table 3.4. Milk supplies (quality). Monthly simple averages of butterfat and solids-not-fat in milk in England and Wales (excl. Channel Island herds), 1980–81.

Month	Fat (%)	S.N.F. (%)	Total solids (%)
April	3.76	8.63	12.39
May	3.61	8.78	12.39
June	3.72	8.79	12.51
July	3.79	8.74	12.53
August	3.84	8.70	12.54
September	3.93	8.74	12.67
October	4.04	8.79	12.83
November	4.11	8.72	12.83
December	4.07	8.66	12.73
January	3.96	8.62	12.58
February	3.89	8.61	12.50
March	3.88	8.61	12.49
Annual Ave.			
Simple	3.88	8.70	12.58
Weighted	3.87	8.73	12.60
Incl. Ch. I. herds			
Simple	*3.92*	*8.71*	*12.63*
Weighted	*3.90*	*8.73*	*12.63*

Figures are based on test results for all supplies, under the Joint Committee Quality Payment Scheme.

fat and solids-not-fat achieved during the month. Typical results are illustrated in Table 3.4. When selection for breeding occurs it is necessary to resort to fat and protein figures since the solids-not-fat component of milk is not measured in individual cows in National Milk Records. There is, however, a high positive correlation between protein percentage and solids-not-fat percentage, which means that selection for the former will result in improvement of the latter.

Quality has a direct impact on financial output since the Board pay what is virtually a standard price per kg fat produced, and a lower standard price per kg solids-not-fat, almost regardless of the percentage of either fat or solids-not-fat in the milk. Minimum values of 3.90% fat and 8.70% solids-not-fat apply to the basic grade of milk, and adjustments to the price are made for each change of 0.1% of each component.

Factors which affect composition

(a) *Age of cow* – the percentage of fat and solids-not-fat tends to decline with the advancing age of a cow; on average fat drops by 0.04% per lactation and solids-not-fat by 0.07%. This is linked to the progressive increase in milk yield as the cow gets older (see Fig. 3.1).

(b) *Stage of lactation* – fat and solids-not-fat levels are very high after calving but fall with rising milk yield, reaching their lowest six to ten weeks later. Fat content increases slowly thereafter to reach the lactation average value at about six months. Solids-not-fat remains fairly constant at about the eight to ten weeks level and the degree of improvement thereafter largely depends on whether the cow is in-calf (see Fig. 3.2).

(c) *Calving interval* – an interval of more than 120 days between calving and conception delays the rise in solids-not-fat.

(d) *Seasonality* – butterfat tends to be highest between October and December and lowest in May and June. Solids-not-fat is highest in spring and autumn (with a slight fall in July and

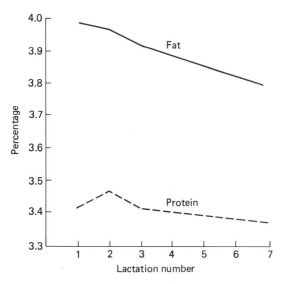

Fig. 3.1 Analysis of fat and protein % by lactation number (Friesian).

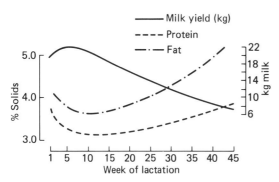

Fig. 3.2 Lactational variation.

August) followed by a general decline throughout winter (see Fig. 3.3).

(e) *Feeding* – the quality and quantity of food eaten by the cow not only affects yield but quality as well.

(f) *Milking technique* – equipment correctly used and maintained makes for quick and efficient removal of quality milk.

(g) *Health* – the ability to resist disease is not a highly heritable characteristic but some evidence suggests that some cow families are prone to certain disease. Mastitis in particular has a detrimental affect on not only yield but butterfat and solids-not-fat as well. The loss of yield is estimated to be at least 10% of total production and in an individual cow solids-not-fat may be depressed by as much as 1% in an affected quarter; this may persist for the remainder of the lactation unless it can be cleared up promptly.

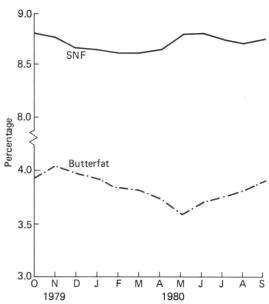

Fig. 3.3 Simple average butterfat and solids-not-fat of all supplies in England and Wales.

The financial effects of compositional quality is illustrated in the following example:

Example 1:
Assumptions – basic price 13p/l for milk with 3.9% fat and 8.7% solids-not-fat (s.n.f.)

butterfat (b.f.)	0.135p/0.1%
s.n.f.	0.082p/0.1%

(a) 5000 litres @ 4.12% b.f.
      8.80% s.n.f.

basic price 5000 litres @ 13p/l	=	£650.00
b.f. 5000 × (0.135 × 2)	=	13.50
s.n.f. 5000 × (0.082 × 1)	=	4.10
Total		667.60

(b) 5000 litres @ 3.50% b.f.
      8.93% s.n.f.

basic price 5000 litres @ 13p/l	=	£650.00
b.f. 5000 × (0.135 × − 4)	=	− 27.00
s.n.f. 5000 × (0.082 × 2)	=	8.20
Total		631.20

3. Fertility

Regular calving, monitored as calving index can have a pronounced effect on the annual milk yield of a cow. Since fertility has a low heritability, stockmanship must be of a high standard. The aim is a calf a year giving a calving index of 365 days but indices in excess of 400 days are not uncommon. Failure to achieve the objective means a loss of annual milk yield and calves, but possibly more important is the change of calving pattern for herds with a strict seasonal pattern. The effect of calving index on the annual yield of milk and on gross margins is illustrated in the following example:

Example 2:

(a) Effect on annual yields (litres)

Index	365 days	380 days	400 days
	4500	4323*	4108
	5000	4800	4562
	5500	5277	4808

*4500 × 365 ÷ 380.

(b) Effect on gross margin
Assumption – annual gross margin per cow = £400

365 days	380 days	400 days
400	384*	365

*400 × 365 ÷ 380

4. Longevity and Wearability

There is little purpose in breeding high-yielding cows if they have a herd life of only one or two lactations. Weakness of legs and feet is a charateristic that can be transmitted. Before using an unknown bull in the herd these characters should be checked. The udder and in particular udder attachment, is another character which brings the herd life of potentially excellent cows to an abrupt end.

Planned culling is a feature of all herds; the above factors can, however, lead to unplanned culling which can have adverse effects on the net margin of herds. The greater the number of cows that have to be culled the greater number of replacements required and consequently additional hectares of land are needed for the heifer rearing enterprise; this is illustrated in the following example:

Example 3:

Assumptions –	£
downcalving heifer value	600
cull value	300
Total depreciation	300

Annual depreciation per cow if herd life is:

(a) 3 lactations
  (33% depreciation rate) = 300 ÷ 3 = £100
(b) 4 lactations
  (25% depreciation rate) = 300 ÷ 4 = £75
(c) 5 lactations
  (20% depreciation rate) = 300 ÷ 5 = £60
(d) 6 lactations
  (16% depreciation rate) = 300 ÷ 6 = £50

No. of heifers of different ages undergoing rearing/100 cows:

Replacement rate	Calving at:		
	2 years	2½ years	3 years
15%	30	38	45
20%	40	50	60
25%	50†	63	75

†25 calves + 25 yearlings = 50.

Consider a 15% becoming a 25% replacement rate. With 2 year calving this means an extra:

	LUs
10 heifers from 0 to 1 yr old × 0.30 =	3.0
10 heifers from 1 to 2 yr old × 0.54 =	5.4
	8.4

Extra land required to carry 8.4 LUs (livestock units) if stocking rate is 2 LUs per hectare = 4.25 ha which must be released from the dairy herd to accommodate the heifer replacement enterprise, i.e. the substitution of a low gross margin per hectare for a higher one.

5. Conformation

A cow needs to be able to accommodate a large rumen to deal with a higher forage diet for conversion into milk. Udder attachment, teat placement, legs and feet are all important; a sound cow will perform well over many lactations.

GENETIC CONSIDERATIONS

Breeds

The popularity of each breed is shown in Table 3.5 as measured by the number of inseminations from Milk Marketing Board centres. Some of the main breeds kept for milk production are as follows:

Ayrshire. Animals are medium-sized and very hardy, being able to adapt themselves to a

Table 3.5. Number of inseminations by breeds from board centres in England and Wales and Scotland (April to March years) (source: Milk Marketing Board).

Breed		England and Wales 1980–81		Scotland 1980–81	
		('000)	(%)	('000)	(%)
Dairy					
Ayrshire		18	1.0	12	10.3
Friesian/Holstein*		1093	60.3	65	56.0
Guernsey		20	1.1	–	–
Jersey		25	1.4	–	–
	Total	1156	63.8	77	66.3
Dual purpose					
Dairy Shorthorn		4	0.2	–	–
Welsh Black		4	0.2	–	–
Others†		2	0.1	–	–
	Total	10	0.5	1	0.9
Beef					
Aberdeen Angus		62	3.4	6	5.2
Beef Shorthorn		–	–	1	0.9
Blonde d'Aquitaine		3	0.2	–	–
Charolais		130	7.2	9	7.7
Chianina		1	0.1	–	–
Devon		6	0.3	–	–
Hereford		351	19.3	11	9.5
Limousin		57	3.1	5	4.3
Murray Grey		13	0.7	1	0.9
Simmental		18	1.0	4	3.4
South Devon		2	0.1	–	–
Sussex		3	0.2	–	–
Others‡		2	0.1	1	0.9
	Total	648	35.7	38	32.8
	All Breeds	1814	100.0	116	100.0

First inseminations.

*Includes Red & White Friesian.

†Includes Brown Swiss, Dexter, Kerry and Meuse Rhine Issel, Northern Dairy Shorthorn, Shetland; also, in E. & W. only, British White, Danish Red/British Dane, Gloucester, Normande and Red Poll; also, in Scotland only, Rotbunt and Pinzgauer.

‡Includes Beevebilde, Brahman, Galloway (inc. Belted), Highland, Lincoln Red, Luing, Maine Anjou, Marchigiana and Romagnola. Also in E. & W. only, Beef Shorthorn, Belgium Blue, Chartley, Longhorn, Pinzgauer and Rotbunt. Also, in Scotland only, Bison, Meuse Rhine, Shetland and Welsh Black.

variety of managerial conditions; the breed does extremely well under adverse weather conditions and poor fodder. It is famous for its pronounced wedge-shaped appearance, flat compact udder and uniform, well-placed teats. Milk yields from mature cows are the second highest of all British breeds; average butterfat is just under 4%. The fat globules are small – unsuitable for butter making but suitable for cheese making.

British Friesian. Animals have large frames and barrels capable of eating large quantities of grass and forage crops. The Friesian/Holstein out-yields all other British breeds. Quality, by careful breeding, has reached acceptable levels. The breed is widely used for crossing with beef bulls, in particular the Hereford. This factor together with the value of culled cows has given the breed a considerable economic advantage over other breeds.

Guernsey. Animals are medium-sized dairy types able to thrive in much more exposed districts than one would expect. Although the yield is not as high as the two previous breeds the butterfat percentage of 4.5–5.0 is very high. The fat globules are large, being ideal for cream or butter production.

Jersey. Animals are more delicate and able to thrive in mild climates. The quality of the cow's fine appearance is matched by the quality of its milk. Milk yield is not as high as other breeds but the yellow, rich, creamy milk is much in demand; average butterfat content is just below 5%. The large fat globules are ideal for butter production.

Heritability

Milk yield and compositional quality have medium to high heritability values, e.g. the heritability of butterfat yield is 48%. Although profoundly affected by environmental factors, long-term improvement can be effected by selective breeding.

Data on milk yields are plentiful, so that mean values, range of variation and percentage heritability (Table 3.6) within breeds can be calculated. There is some evidence to suggest that both total solids and solids-not-fat tend to be associated with high fat. While this is true on average it would be unsafe to rely on this correlation concerning individual cows. Where an attempt is made to raise the total solids of a

Table 3.6. Heritability estimates – Friesians (source: O'Connor, MMB).

	Yield	Percentage
Milk	0.31	–
Fat	0.48	0.58
Protein	0.41	0.44
S.N.F.	0.34	0.47
Total solids	0.38	0.48

herd, it is necessary to have figures for both fat and solids-not-fat; the basic solution lies in culling cows giving poor quality milk and breeding replacements from stock with high compositional records.

Some conformation characteristics are highly heritable, as can often be seen when a bull stamps his characteristics on his daughters.

Selection of Foundation Cows

When a farmer decides to improve his dairy herd, he must firstly select from his herd those cows which will act as foundation stock for producing heifer calves as herd replacements. Cows in most herds can be broadly divided into two, three or four groups or families. Usually, each family originates from one mother cow; one or two families are selected for mating to good bulls to produce herd replacements. If cows in a herd are not good enough as foundation stock, additional cows are purchased; two good foundation cows are far more valuable than a dozen moderate cows.

Foundation cows are selected on the basis of (a) appearance and (b) their performance records and those of their families.

Three aspects of conformation are really important – legs, feet and udders. Good feet and hind legs which are well spaced and not too straight are vital characteristics since the cow spends most of her life standing on her four feet. Low-slung udders invariably mean muddy and sore teats; also when teats are set far apart it causes difficulty at milking (see Fig. 3.4).

Performance records of the cow herself and of her sire and dam can be studied. The record of the latter two are important because each has contributed 50% of the cow's genes. Six main character expressions should be looked for when studying records:

i) high milk yield,
ii) high butterfat percentage,
iii) high number of calves produced by the cow's dam,
iv) regular calving,
v) freedom from disease, and
vi) fast milking.

The Milk Marketing Board provides a comprehensive set of National Milk Records which aim to highlight all these factors. The conformation characteristics are expressed on their Type Evaluation Report and a report similar in many respects is compiled by the British Friesian Cattle Society, and others.

Furthermore, the Board have developed a cow index-system to help individual farmers make decisions concerning the selection of cows for either breeding or culling (Table 3.7). The Production Index places the production records of all cows on an equal basis, thus making direct comparisons between cows possible. Individual cow records of milk, fat and protein yields are adjusted for age, lactation number and month of calving, to give a corrected weight of measured solids.

To enable an individual to be compared with the rest of the herd the average adjusted weight of measured solids for the whole herd is calculated each month by averaging the adjusted

Table 3.7. Which is the profitable cow? (source: Milk Marketing Board).

Line No. 196	Line No. 135
Calving date: 16:09:80	Calving date: 07:09:80
Age: 36 mths	Age: 73 mths
Lactation number: 02	Lactation number: 05

Their production seems almost identical:

Milk yield 5600 kg	Milk yield 5640 kg
Fat yield 204 kg	Fat yield 206 kg
Protein yield 180 kg	Protein yield 179 kg

But when corrected for age, lactation number and month of carving their yields are:

Milk yield 5432 kg	Milk yield 4559 kg
Fat yield 197 kg	Fat yield 169 kg
Protein yield 172 kg	Protein yield 145 kg

Their corrected weight of measured solids when compared to the herd base of 100 gives index values of:

118	**101**

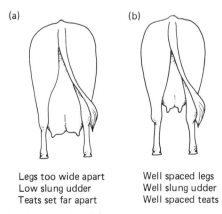

(a)
Legs too wide apart
Low slung udder
Teats set far apart

(b)
Well spaced legs
Well slung udder
Well spaced teats

Fig. 3.4 Aspects of conformation in two cows.

records of all the cows in the herd. This herd average recorded in kilograms is known as the Herd Base. The Production Index of each cow, expressed as a percentage of the Herd Base, is calculated as follows:

Herd Base = 355
A cow's adjusted weight of measured
  solids = 375
Its Cow Production Index = $\frac{375}{355} \times 100$ = 106

The Choice of Bull

The Improved Contemporary Comparison (ICC) method is used to determine the relative breeding value of bulls (see Table 3.8). An index figure enables bulls to be ranked for weight of milk, butterfat and protein as well as the percentage of protein and butterfat. The method aims to eliminate as far as possible the effects of management from herd to herd, by comparing the heifer records of a sire's daughters with their contemporaries from other sires milking in the same herd at the same time; all the records are corrected for age and month of calving, and then classified according to the season of calving by restricting comparisons to those between a bull's daughters and their contemporaries in three 4-month calving periods. The ICC figure is expressed in either (a) kg, which shows by how many kilograms the sire's daughters are above or below the average figure of their contemporaries; or (b) %, which shows by what percentage the sire's daughters are above or below the average figure of their contemporaries. The reliability of the ICC figure can be assessed by reference to a weighting figure and a herd distribution figure. The former indicates the number of comparisons which have been made; the higher the number of comparisons, the greater the reliability of the ICC index. The Sire Herd Distribution figure measures the scatter of comparisons made within the breed population; the higher the scatter figure, the greater the reliability which can be attributed to the ICC figure.

ICC assessment figures are also made for a range of conformation characteristics. Rankings are made to a base, 'mean' figure of 100; the weighting figure determines the reliability of the ICC figure.

Details of size of daughters, colour and beef shape with relative weightings are also given.

If continued herd improvement is required in successive generations it implies that a succession of bulls each better than his predecessor has to be found. Example 4 highlights this problem in respect of fat weight in kg.

Example 4:

Generation	Bull		Cow genetic merit	Progeny merit	Change per generation
	ICC	Genetic merit*			
1	+10	+20	0	+10	+10
2	+10	+20	+10	+15	+5
3a	+10	+20	+15	+17.5	+2.5
3b	0	0	+15	+7.5	−7.5

*Genetic merit = ICC × 2   (source: MMB)

Table 3.8. Relative breeding values of a sample of premium Friesian/Holstein bulls (Spring 1982) (source: MMB).

MILK		FAT				PROTEIN				SIRE/HERD DISTRIBUTION		BULL DETAILS	
W'ting	ICC (kg)	W'ting	ICC (kg)	ICC (%)	Dtr. ave. (%)	W'ting	ICC (kg)	ICC (%)	Dtr. ave. (%)	No. herds/ No. dtrs.	% in herds 1%2	Name	H.B. No. & MAFF App. Categ.
37	+571	37	+19	−0.05	3.66	37	+13	−0.11	3.10	36/46	7/4	Hully Mastermind	373077(1)
390	+294	390	+9	−0.05	3.87	385	+8	−0.04	3.27	150+/552	–	Ironside Alpha	348975(1)
37	+205	37	+10	+0.04	3.87	37	+7	0	3.31	36/41	7/5	Lyngate Regal Prince	385475(1)
38	+218	38	+17	+0.18	4.05	38	+8	+0.01	3.27	36/46	9/7	Masbury Rio Grande	370457(1)
28	+197	28	+11	+0.07	3.89	28	+9	+0.06	3.36	28/34	9/6	Melcourt Veidor	365787(1)
73	+391	73	+14	−0.03	3.81	72	+10	−0.05	3.21	62/82	6/5	MMB Cherrylane Pilot	370651(1)
89	+314	89	+16	+0.07	3.93	88	+8	−0.04	3.26	69/102	6/5	MMB Dunco Bootmaster	382377(1)
93	+673	93	+22	−0.09	3.78	93	+18	−0.07	3.21	85/106	4/3	MMB Highpoint Boy	381773(1)

Key: R = Red Carrier; CA = Check availability of semen; H = 50% or more Holstein blood.

(a) Consider line 2:

the bull's own intrinsic genetic merit is $\quad + 20$ kg fat

the cow's genetic merit is $\qquad\quad\underline{+ 10}$ kg fat

$$\text{Total } + 30 \text{ kg}$$

This is halved to determine the genetic merit of the progeny = 15 kg. The gain from generation 1 to generation 2 is $15 - 10 = 5$ kg. To maintain a change per generation of 10 kg fat, the bull used in second generation would need an ICC of $+ 15$ kg fat, i.e., a genetic merit of 30.

(b) Consider lines 3a and 3b:

      3a: the merit improvement is marginal

      3b: the merit is negative

It is important therefore to know the genetic merit (average improved contemporary comparison) of the bulls being used in the herd. The Milk Marketing Board aims to provide members with information relating to the average ICC of the sires of cows and heifers completing lactations in the previous recording year.

Testing Young Bulls

The MMB progeny-tests about 150 Friesian and Holstein bulls each year in its Dairy Progeny Testing Scheme. This scheme involves about 2500 farmers who draw up contracts with the Board.

On completion of the test a bull is transferred to a lay-off station to await the results. Statistics indicate that only about one in eight of bulls that enter the scheme achieve mature stud status. The majority of these young bulls come from contract matings of proven bulls to cows outstanding in terms of yield, butterfat and conformation.

Breeding programmes, in the main, are products of Contract Mating Schemes. The method of selecting suitable cows is being continually improved and the latest genetic index for production is a most valuable innovation. This is an indicator of the cow's genetic potential and not a historical record of her ancestors.

According to Board statistics, an index of 115 or more represents the top 12% of any breed. Dams of bulls born in 1979–80 had average genetic indices of 118 for weight of fat and 115 for weight of fat plus protein; in 1974–78 the indices were 108 and 106 respectively.

Embryo Transfer

Since the improvement of genetic merit through the male is rather slow, the technique of embryo transfer could increase this rate. This new breeding technique allows the elite females in the herds to multiply their genetic contribution for herd or breed improvement. Instead of producing four or five calves in her lifetime, a cow could produce 20 or more.

The donor cow is injected with hormones to encourage a number of eggs to be shed (superovulation). At six to seven days following insemination the embryos are flushed out and are either transferred by surgery to foster mothers (recipients) or frozen and stored for later use.

THE BREEDING SITUATION

The general genetic standard of dairy cows in this country is high. One of the main factors which has made this possible is the inception of an Artificial Insemination Service. It has enabled genes from bulls of known quality to be spread over a large population of dairy cows; in the past

DAUGHTER TYPE ASSESSMENT – ICC BASIS										SIZE	COLOUR	BEEF SHAPE		NOTES
Head, neck, shoulder	Body cap.	Top line rump	Legs	Feet	Fore udder	Rear udder	Teat shape quality	Teat posn.	W'ting	Ave. of dtrs.	% Black in dtrs.	Score	W'ting	See key
101	102	101	105	105	102	101	102	106	40	M	50	111	32	
99	97	103	99	101	101	102	107	107	73	M/S	71	100	73	R
106	103	106	106	100	105	108	101	104	41	M/S	55	99	41	R
104	102	108	104	100	104	109	106	106	37	M/S	80	106	25	CA
103	103	103	103	101	101	101	104	104	32	M/L	63	106	14	CA
100	104	99	98	100	105	100	105	105	72	M/L	56	93	31	H
102	99	98	98	102	103	102	101	102	66	M/L	82	92	57	H
103	105	99	99	99	102	103	101	103	65	M/L	68	87	65	H

only a limited number of cows were naturally served by high-quality bulls, whilst the majority were served by bulls of unknown genetic qualities. The breeding policies of farmers have also become more effective because they are able to nominate specific progeny-tested bulls for their particular requirements.

The dairy herds in this country fall into two categories -- pedigree and commercial.

Pedigree Herds

Each animal is registered with a breed society and its pedigree entered into a herd book (see p. 30); due to this method of recording it is possible to trace the ancestry of any animal over many generations. Breeding is thus based on the selective mating of animals with known ancestors. Most breed societies permit artificial insemination as a form of service so that the disadvantages accompanying the use of natural service by a bull on a limited cow population is discarded. This technique also enables pedigree bulls to be progeny tested by the contemporary comparison method; such bulls can thus be used for mating to pedigree cows within the registered breed. Thus the main contribution of the pedigree breeder to the commercial breeder is:

(a) the supply of sound foundation cows which can form the nucleus for further herd improvement; and

(b) the supply of young sires whose genetic potential can be screened by contemporary comparison methods; they form the most likely nucleus from which progeny-tested bulls emerge for use at cattle breeding centres.

Commercial Herds

The basic needs are good, sound cows producing high yields of milk having high compositional quality. Replacements are usually bred by nominating progeny-tested bulls from cattle breeding centres. This is a comparatively cheap method of maintaining and improving the performance of commercial herds. It highlights the advantages of collaboration between the farmer and the Milk Marketing Board. The Board possess the resources to progeny-test bulls and set up an artificial insemination service; the service is paid for by the levy and insemination fees collected from the farmers.

4

Breeding for Beef

The end products of beef production systems are carcasses of beef. Each carcass is characterized by two properties, weight and quality. Weight can vary enormously from say 180 kg to 360 kg. Quality refers to the relative proportions and distribution of meat, fat and bone within the carcass; the best cuts of meat are obtained from the hind quarters of the carcass (Fig. 4.1).

PRINCIPLES OF GROWTH AND DEVELOPMENT

The time taken for a calf to grow into a finished beast ready for slaughter into a carcass of beef depends on the interaction of two factors, namely rate of liveweight growth and rate of maturity.

Rate of Liveweight Growth

This is usually expressed as the number of kilograms liveweight gain per day; it can vary from 0 to 1.36 kg per day.

Genetic control. The rate of liveweight growth varies widely from breed to breed and amongst animals within a given breed; bulls grow faster than steers and steers grow faster than heifers.

Environmental control. Potential growth can only be realized if an animal consumes sufficient highly digestible food; growth rate can be inhibited by restricting such a food intake at any stage in the animal's development.

Rate of Development

This is defined as the successive development of bone, muscle and fat in the animal. In the young beast the growth rate of the skeleton is high and as the animal ages, deeper muscling of the skeletal frame occurs; during the latter stages of maturity or finish, fat is deposited under the skin and around the muscular carcass; fat marbling of the muscular tissues may also occur. Beef animals vary in their rates of undergoing these developmental changes; some are early maturing and others late maturing.

Genetic control. The rate of development varies widely from breed to breed and amongst animals within a given breed; heifers mature earlier than steers. There is no correlation between growth rate and maturation rate, e.g., some breeds are fast growing and late maturing whilst others may be fast growing but early maturing.

Environmental control. If feeding is restricted any time after three months of age, fatty tissue growth is greatly reduced, muscle tissue growth is reduced to a lesser extent, but skeletal growth continues normally. If the level of feeding is again raised, muscle tissue growth recovers quickly followed later by fat deposition. Winter feeding, however, needs to be controlled for around 0.5 kg daily liveweight gain so that liveweight gain at subsequent grazing is not depressed and finishing is possible by the end of the grazing season ('compensatory growth', p. 157).

Food Conversion Ratio

Since rate of growth and maturity depend partly on the amount and quality of food eaten, it is important to assess the efficiency of food utilization in the animal. The measure used to assess such efficiency is the food conversion ratio.

This is defined as the amount of food required per kilogram liveweight gain. This ratio increases as the animal grows older and heavier for two reasons.

45

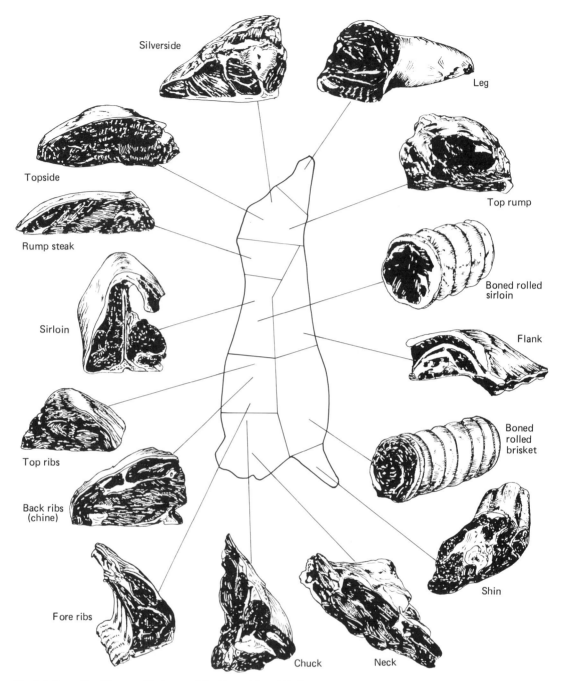

Fig. 4.1 Cuts of beef (source: *Dictionary of Cooking* – Aileen King).

1. Larger quantities of food are required for body maintenance (chapter 8); it is food eaten in excess of this requirement which forms body tissue recorded as daily liveweight gain.

2. The amount of fat desposited, relative to muscle, increases during ageing. Because more energy food is required to lay down a kilogram of fat than a kilogram of muscle, the food requirement per kilogram liveweight growth increases greatly during the later finishing stage.

Thus the efficiency of food conversion improves if (a) the animal is allowed to grow to slaughter weight and condition in the shortest time possible, thus reducing the overall food maintenance requirements. This implies adequate nutrient intake for rapid liveweight growth; and (b) the animal is not allowed to be over-finished, resulting in a fatty carcass.

GENETIC CONSIDERATIONS

From a breeding point of view, improvement in beef performance has to originate by selective procedures within pure breeds of cattle. If qualities within breeds can be improved, then subsequent crossing of such breeds for specific purposes can only lead to more promising results than hitherto. The characteristics of the most common breeds are described in Table 4.1.

A wide range of variation exists between and within breeds. This is illustrated in Table 4.2.

It is obvious that management and genetic factors contribute to variations from herd to herd within each breed. But even within single herds the 400-day weights have varied widely for bulls kept under similar management; this variation can only be due to genetic differences within the group of animals being compared. It is this genetic component of phenotypic variation that can be improved by selective procedure.

Heritability Values

In beef cattle, approximate heritable values are known for some characters but a great deal of further investigation is required to obtain more precise measurements related to specific breeds of beef cattle. Examples of heritability estimates for single suckled pure-bred beef are as follows:

		%
Low	Conception rate	0–5
	Calving interval	0–15
Medium	Weaning weight	20–40
	Carcass grade	25–45
High	Milk yield	30–50
	Liveweight gain	30–50
Very high	Killing-out percentage	65–70
	Final weight	65–70

Table 4.1. Breeds for beef production

HILL BREEDS

Galloway. Polled, black or dun coloured cattle. Slow to mature under severe hill conditions but earlier maturing strains have been developed.

Highland. Horned, long-haired cattle. Conformation and late maturity are characters which have improved in recent years.

Welsh Black. Horned, black cattle; a polled strain exists. The lactation curve is long and gradual. Calves grow and mature quickly.

LOWLAND BREEDS

Aberdeen Angus. Polled, black cattle. Calves grow rapidly and mature early, producing compact animals at an early age.

Beef Shorthorn. Horned, red, white or roan cattle. Calves grow and mature rapidly. The larger, more rugged bulls are often used for crossing.

Charolais. Horned and polled, buff-coloured cattle. Calves are rapid growing and late maturing, producing large, lean carcasses. The bulls are widely used for crossing but the pregnancy period is longer and calving difficulties have been experienced; the latter tend to be associated with particular bulls rather than with size of calf.

Devon. Horned, ruby coloured cattle. They have large frames and grow rapidly.

Friesian. Horned, black and white cattle. Steer calves are rapid growing and late maturing.

Hereford. Horned and polled, red-coated animals with white face and breast. Natural foragers, noted for size and fleshing. Calves grow rapidly and mature early.

Lincoln Red. Horned, red coloured cattle but polled animals are now available. They have large frames and grow rapidly.

Limousin. Horned, rich golden-red colour, shading to a lighter tan under the belly, legs, inner thighs and muzzle. One of the main characteristics is the ability to produce marketable meat at any age from three months to three years.

Simmental. Horned, yellowish brown or red coat combined with white markings; the head is always white and the muzzle is flesh coloured. A dual-purpose breed on the Continent but has been introduced into Britain for beef production. Late maturing. Calving difficulties have been experienced and bulls should not be used on maiden heifers.

Sussex. Polled, red coloured cattle. They grow and mature rapidly. They can withstand extremes of heat and cold and are able to survive on coarse, scanty lowland herbage.

Table 4.2. Two-year average weights (kg) for the principle beef breeds (source: MLC)

Age in days:	Heifers				Bulls				Weight range* (kg)
	100	200	300	400	100	200	300	400	
Aberdeen-Angus	103	181	238	289	113	210	301	388	(308–536)
Beef Shorthorn	121	199	250	301	127	233	325	413	(399–534)
Blonde d'Aquitaine	142	231	315	379	154	260	370	504	(377–699)
Charolais	151	259	348	421	166	297	429	556	(470–780)
Devon	111	183	240	294	122	209	310	450	(346–605)
Hereford	115	191	253	302	125	222	322	422	(344–603)
Limousin	135	226	296	356	148	251	357	475	(382–658)
Lincoln Red	126	212	278	339	143	249	363	496	(402–625)
Simmental	149	250	330	394	166	290	415	544	(439–730)
South Devon	138	230	301	356	154	268	380	528	(419–715)
Sussex	112	190	261	317	121	211	330	458	(367–601)
Welsh Black	124	200	255	303	135	230	315	430	(332–623)

* Excluding the lowest 5% of weights.

Performance Testing

The performance test is based on the fact that phenotypic performance reflects the genotype of the animal being observed. If the performance of a character is good, then it is distinctly possible that the genes responsible for it will be handed on to its offspring. Such testing is only valid if the character is not only highly heritable but is also capable of being observed or measured in the parent animal.

Characters which are measurable in bulls are beef conformation, liveweight gain, food conversion efficiency, withers height and fat depth.

Comparison of bulls with respect to the above characters can only be made if they are kept under the same regime of feeding and management. The only effective way of comparing bulls from different herds is to collect them at a testing station and rear them under standard conditions of feeding and management.

Bull Performance Testing at Central Station

The MLC tests are based on animals that enter at between 150 and 190 days of age. As well as measuring liveweight gain, food intake and food conversion, withers height is taken as a guide to stage of maturity and backfat thickness is measured ultrasonically as a guide to carcass classification. These tests last for 7 months, by which time the animals are around 400 days old and at this point are type-scored by a panel of breeders. Table 4.3 illustrates the type of result obtained.

Table 4.3. Example of MLC performance test results. Summary of main results – the bulls ranked according to their 400-day weights

Pen No.	Bull's name	Withers ht (cm) at 365 days	400-day wt (kg)	Rel. Perf.	Daily gain (kg) Pre-test	On test	Feed conversion efficiency, % better (+) or worse (−) than average 350–450 kg	400–500 kg	Conf. score	Fat measure Ave. depth (mm)	%
9	Nominee	119.4	583	+57	1.0	1.8	+14	+14	79	5.3	84
10	Night Hawk	116.2	529	+ 3	0.9	1.7	+10	+16	65	4.5	72
11	Natty Lad	114.9	524	− 2	1.0	1.5	+ 7	+ 8	76	8.3	133
7	Punch	114.9	500	−26	1.0	1.4	− 9	−18	67	7.3	117
8	Senator	115.6	496	−30	1.0	1.4	−10	−21	62	5.8	93
	Mean:	116.2	526		1.0	1.6	FCR 6.36	6.94	69	6.2	—
Overall breed average			425								

Note how the bulls rank at 400 days – their weight at this age gives a good indication of their overall growth from birth and it is highly correlated with subsequent growth. Bulls with low fat and high withers height measurements are more likely to continue their growth. Note also how bulls with better growth rates tend to have better feed conversion.

Table 4.4. Breed average results from performance tests (source: MLC)

Breed		400-day wt (kg)	Withers ht (cm)	Backfat depth (mm)
Aberdeen-Angus	Average	472	112.7	8.3
	Range	390–532	103.5–120	5.5–12.7
Blonde d'Aquitaine	Average	575	126.9	1.7
	Range	490–671	115–135	1.1–2.6
Charolais	Average	608	125.1	2.5
	Range	509–692	119–134	1.3–4.4
Devon	Average	528	116.0	6.8
	Range	457–609	111–121	3.9–11.1
Hereford	Average	478	111.5	6.5
	Range	364–594	105–119	2.6–11.1
Limousin	Average	544	122.2	2.4
	Range	451–626	118–129.5	1.6–3.8
Lincoln Red	Average	543	123.0	7.9
	Range	499–624	117–129.5	4.7–11.9
Simmental	Average	606	128.5	3.4
	Range	509–717	122–137.2	1.8–8.5
South Devon	Average	611	126.9	4.1
	Range	541–703	119.5–131	1.8–7.5
Sussex	Average	541	117.5	5.2
	Range	476–601	113–122	3.0–7.6
Welsh Black	Average	504	117.5	4.2
	Range	434–571	112.5–122.5	2.0–6.4

Tests have highlighted the variation that occurs between and within breeds. Table 4.4 illustrates the breed average results obtained by MLC.

Progeny Testing

As mentioned in chapter 2, this is a method of determining the genotype of a parent by observing and recording the performance of its offspring. In beef animals this type of testing is confined to performance tested bulls. The MLC undertake the testing of progeny from pedigree and some commercial herds; they are artificially reared at a testing station and recordings made of weights at 200, 300 and 400 days old. Male and female are tested and compared with their contemporaries. Care is taken that calves are not grouped according to sire but lodged at random so that variations due to slight differences in environmental conditions are accounted for.

Bulls can be used either for natural service within beef herds or for artificially inseminating dairy cows. The MMB, having appreciated the latter, set up a testing station at Warren Farm in Berkshire where beef bulls are crossed with Friesian and other dairy breeds and the offspring are collected to be reared on the 18 month old grass/cereal system. The disadvantage of the scheme is the fact that the 'protected' environment may not be in the interest of the eventual user. Tests on commercial farms have the advantage of providing a more realistic environment but the accuracy may be questionable unless the sample group is large enough; it has a distinct advantage, however, when a factor such as ease of calving is considered.

THE BREEDING SITUATION

The above breeding procedures are adopted to improve the breeding qualities of beef stock and ensure economic returns in beef production. There are less than 5000 herds of pure-bred cattle, including hill cattle, to be found in this country. In addition to the small number of herds, the number of cattle per head is also small. Included within this beef cattle population are a limited number of pedigree cattle which form the genetic core from which any breed improvement programme stems.

MLC Scheme for Herd Analysis

This scheme aims to:

(a) identify bulls and heifers who show superiority or inferiority at the 400 day weight. This aids selection of stock for breeding and those for culling;
(b) provide an updated cow summary giving details of calf weight at each 100 day point, and the amount this varies from herd contemporaries and the number of contemporaries involved. At each point of age an overall value is given which has been adjusted for the number of calves produced by the cow and the number of calves with which they have been compared (see Table 4.5a);
(c) provide an up-dated sire summary (see Table 4.5b).

Table 4.5. Examples from MLC scheme for herd analysis

(a) Cow ranking list

	Cow identity	No. of calves	Contemporary comparisons at 200 days (kg)
1	L1	8	+13
2	T13	3	+ 7
3	S37	5	+ 4
4	S41	3	+ 1
5	P6	6	0
6	N11	6	− 3
7	M8	2	− 6
8	T50	3	−11

(b) A sire progeny record

	Bulls	Steers	Heifers	Progeny with contemporaries		Breeding value
100 days No.	7	—	10	No	10	
Ave. wt (kg)	125	—	113	CC	+13	+4.1
200 days No.	8	—	11	No	12	
Ave. wt (kg)	222	—	207	CC	+14	+4.5
300 days No.	7	—	12	No	10	
Ave. wt (kg)	288	—	281	CC	+46	+13.3
400 days No.	7	—	10	No	9	
Ave. wt (kg)	380	—	319	CC	− 10	− 2.5

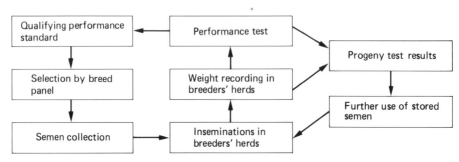

Flowchart 4.1 Young bull proving-scheme (source: MLC 1979).

The Meat and Livestock Commission have also introduced a Young Bull Proving Scheme to assist breeders with the improvement of their herds (Flowchart 4.1). The Scheme's aim is to promote promising young bulls by performance-testing for use in breeders' herds by the use of artificial insemination. The calves from such matings are either recorded or performance tested. The main objective is to stimulate the use of good bulls to improve the most desirable characteristics.

The selection of bulls is based on criteria which demands bulls to be sound in jaw, legs and feet and must exceed minimum performance standard agreed with the breed society. Normally, a requirement of 35 kg above test mean for performance tested bulls and 55 kg for farm recorded bulls at 400 days has to be satisfied. The breed panel inspect and make final selection based on type assessment.

Forty per cent of home-produced beef originates from dairy and cross-bred dairy calves. Friesian calves are often used, but under systems relying heavily on grass and forage feeding, cross-bred calves are generally preferred. Cows from dairy or dual-purpose breeds are thus artificially inseminated by pure-bred beef bulls. Since about 75% of home-bred beef is produced from the Friesian breed, a small minority of dairy producers are becoming much more selective in their choice of beef sires to artificially inseminate their cows. Also, some producers have made a concerted effort to identify differences between the muscling properties of cows in their herds. The MMB has assisted by publishing guide figures for assessing beefing qualities on a 1–5 conformation scale. The higher the beef-shape score, the better the beef conformation of their heifer progeny. Friesian-shape scores are illustrated in Fig. 4.2.

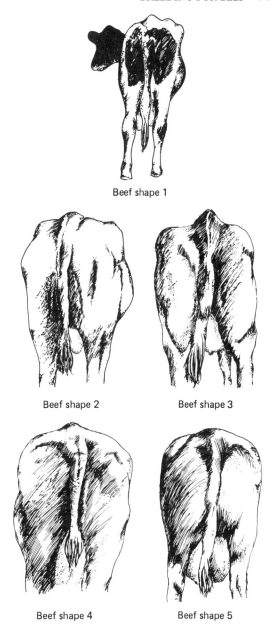

Beef shape 1

Beef shape 2

Beef shape 3

Beef shape 4

Beef shape 5

Fig. 4.2 Friesian shape scores (source: MMB).

5

Breeding for Lamb and Wool

The annual output from a sheep flock kept for fat lamb production is basically assessed by the number and quality of lamb carcasses sold; cull ewes and wool sales also make a contribution to output.

Such output is the end result of several interacting factors.

OUTPUT

Prolificacy

Rearing percentage measures the number of lambs reared per hundred ewes mated; the number is the net result of lambs which have survived birth from live, fertile ewes (see Fig. 13.10).

Prolificacy is mainly affected by breed, age, size, body weight, time of tupping and whether tupping occurs more than once per year. The body weight of a ewe increases with age and it has been shown that the incidence of twinning is largely dependent on the body weight of the ewe.

It is generally recognized that the practice of flushing prior to tupping increases twinning rate since its effect is to induce a temporary increase in body weight. Condition-scoring carried out six to eight weeks prior to tupping enables lean ewes to be batched and flushed to improve ovulation (see p. 182).

Lamb losses mainly occur during birth and shortly afterwards; exposure and starvation are the main causes of loss. Shelter to protect them from wind and rain and careful watch to ensure that they feed before they are six hours old are important. Injections to immunize them against lamb dysentery, pulpy kidney and other clostridial diseases are also highly relevant.

A breed such as the Finn is genetically very prolific and under trial conditions it has been crossed with the Dorset Horn breed to produce ewes capable of giving five lamb crops in three years, i.e. a lambing interval of 7 months on a flock basis using artificial daylight to induce oestrus and hormones to synchronize oestrus resulting in an annual production of 3.5 lambs per ewe; such trials indicate that there is no biological limitation for the development of intensive sheep systems.

Milk Capacity and Weaning Weight

Within a breed or a specific cross, lamb weight up to weaning is conditioned by the milk production of the ewe; the correlation between lamb weight and milking capacity is greatest up to eight weeks of age when the lamb is largely dependent on the dam's milk. The milking capacity of the dam is mainly affected by the level of feeding she receives coupled with her age and size. The sex of the lamb and whether it is a single or a twin will also affect the weaning weight attained.

There is a marked difference in the milking capacities of different breeds of ewes; hill and upland breeds are prolific milkers compared with down breeds under lowland conditions of feeding.

Growth Rate After Weaning

Birthweight coupled with the milking ability of the ewe will have a profound influence on the overall growth rate of lambs up to time of slaughter; growth rate after weaning, however, depends mainly on the availability of grass or creep and the worm burden.

Liveweight gain is directly related to the mature weight of the ewe so that heavier breeds of sheep grow faster than lighter breeds; the use of the correct breed of sire is thus important for inducing rapid lamb growth.

Carcass Quality

MLC Classification

The Meat and Livestock Commission have designed a carcass classification scheme which could be used by buyers as a basis for carcass grading. The scheme describes carcasses by four characteristics:

1. *Weight:* Cold carcass weight after dressing.
2. *Category:* Lamb, hogget, sheep, ram or ewe.
3. *Fat Class:* The fat beneath the skin is assessed on a five point scale where 1 is very lean and 5 is very fat; classes 2, 3 and 4 describe the majority of acceptable carcasses.
4. *Conformation Class:* This is the overall shape of the carcass as represented by the thickness of lean meat and fat in relation to the size of the skeleton. There is a wide average class, an E class for exceptional conformation and C + Z classes for poor conformation.

Fig. 5.1 illustrates the various fat and conformation classes. Fig. 5.2 shows the joints obtained from a lamb carcass.

Carcass Classification

The carcass classification of a lamb resulting from any production system depends on three factors:

i) rate of liveweight gain, which determines the live weight of the lamb at any period during its development;
ii) rate of maturity, which determines the shape and relative composition of bone, meat and fat tissue within the body;
iii) age and finish at which the farmer decides to select lamb for sale and subsequent slaughter.

As the lamb increases in weight the rate of tissue development is in the order bone, muscle and fat. Since fat is the latest developing tissue,

heavier carcasses tend to be fatter ones; Fig. 5.3 shows this relationship for Southdown, Romney and Southdown–Romney cross sheep as studied by Fourie *et al.* under New Zealand conditions; this basic pattern of development applies to all breeds of sheep.

Since breeds differ in the rate at which they grow and mature, it is important for any producer to choose a breed or cross which will produce a carcass of the desired conformation, level of fatness and weight for a given market.

Fast growth, early maturing at a light carcass weight is required for early lamb production when concentrates are fed to meet an early, high priced market; early maturing breeds of rams such as the Dorset Down mated to milky crossbred ewes match this requirement. The genetic growth potential within such breeds of sheep is highly variable so that selection of fast growing rams within the breed is desirable.

With grassland flocks, good lamb growth-rate is required but there is flexibility concerning time of finishing. Late maturing, rapid growing breeds such as Suffolk can supply rams for crossing with milky pure or cross-bred ewes for this purpose. The ram's genetic qualities can confer fast growth for finished carcasses in early or mid-season, and where restricted feeding slows down growth the heavier carcasses produced later in the season do not become excessively fat. The Texel breed is emerging as a new competitor to the Suffolk; although there is a slower growth rate the resulting carcass contains less fat and bone and a higher proportion of lean meat; it would seem that the voluntary food intake of the Texel is such that its relative intake above maintenance requirement supports muscle growth with only limited additional energy available for fat deposition.

The market trend is for leaner carcasses of lamb but the financial incentives to the producer appear to be insufficient for him to breed and produce such quality lamb. The variable premium paid under the existing EEC Sheep Meat Regime is only affecting extreme lambs and consequently does not encourage a concerted policy within the industry to improve lamb quality.

Market requirements for lamb carcasses can be broadly summarized as follows:

Weight:

Britain	15–22 kg
Belgium, France, Germany	16–19 kg
Middle East	12–15 kg
Mediterranean countries	11–13 kg

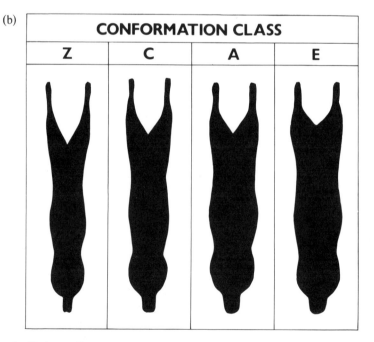

Fig. 5.1 Carcasses classified according to Meat & Livestock Commission. (a) Fatness classes described according to fat cover. (b) Conformation classes; Z = very poor, C = poor, A = average and E = extra.

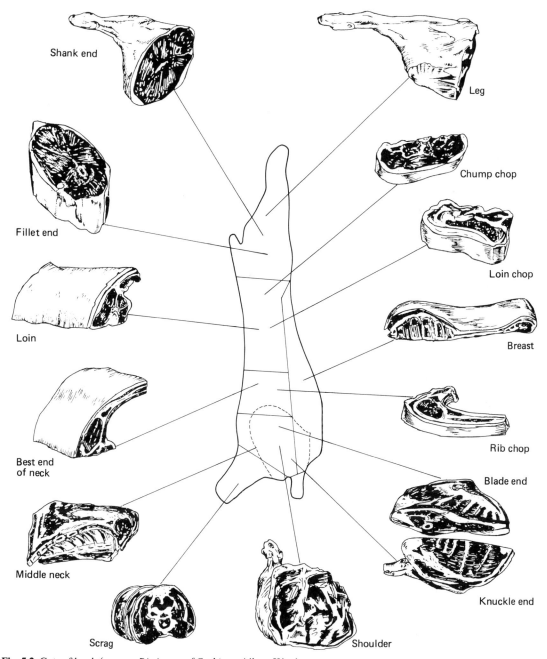

Shank end

Leg

Chump chop

Loin chop

Fillet end

Loin

Breast

Best end
of neck

Rib chop

Blade end

Middle neck

Knuckle end

Scrag

Shoulder

Fig. 5.2 Cuts of lamb (source: *Dictionary of Cooking* – Aileen King).

Fatness:	*Fat class*
Middle East	1
Europe	2
Others	2 + 3L
Some domestic trade	3H

Conformation:	Average and E

The enlightened producer requires to know the classification of the lambs which his system produces. Information feedback of this kind can enable him to alter breed or management to produce as high a proportion as possible of quality lambs for his proposed market. The overriding consideration for the industry is to increase the falling demand for lamb by providing the leaner carcasses which the consumer wants.

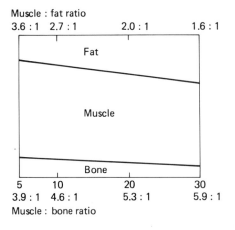

Muscle : fat ratio

3.6 : 1   2.7 : 1   2.0 : 1   1.6 : 1

5   10   20   30

3.9 : 1   4.6 : 1   5.3 : 1   5.9 : 1

Muscle : bone ratio

Fig. 5.3 Percentage composition of the carcass.

Fleece Weight and Quality

The prime function of the fleece is to keep the sheep warm and dry during the winter. A good fleece must be of fair weight and have fine fibres of uniform length. It must also be free from kemp, hairiness and coloured fibres. Selection can greatly improve the quality of the fleece. Care must be taken, however, against the selection of fleeces which do not protect the ewe properly during the winter.

With hill breeds, however, it is important that the fleece contains a limited quantity of kemp. Ewes with such fleeces produce hairy coated lambs which are able to stand and suckle immediately. Such inborn strength is important under rigorous hill conditions.

GENETIC CONSIDERATIONS

Breeds

Sheep are kept under hill, upland and lowland conditions and as a consequence there is a stratification of breeds which results nationally in a planned system of cross-breeding as follows:

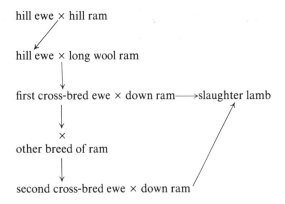

hill ewe × hill ram

hill ewe × long wool ram

first cross-bred ewe × down ram──→slaughter lamb

×
other breed of ram

second cross-bred ewe × down ram

Sheep breeds can be conveniently classified as follows (Table 5.1):

(a) *Hill, mountain or moorland flocks* able to survive in adverse climatic conditions and exploit poor grazing. The ewe is small in size, hardy, and able to suckle one, late-born lamb. Most female lambs are used as replacements and male store lambs, draft cast ewes and wool are the main sources of income.

(b) *Upland flocks* produce pure-bred ewe lambs, two-tooth ewes or draft ewes and first-cross ewe lambs for lowland flocks and the majority of male lambs are castrated and sold as stores.

(c) *Pure-bred longwool flocks* are mainly kept to produce sires for crossing with hill and upland ewes; female lambs not used for replacements are sold as store or finished lambs. The genetic qualities of such breeds are prolificacy, milking capacity and growth rate. The first-cross ewes produced combine these qualities with the high milking capacity of the hill or upland ewe. Such cross-breds are intermediate in size between the two breeds used.

(d) *Pure-bred down flocks producing finished lamb sires.* These are kept to breed sires for crossing with first and second cross ewes; female lambs not used for replacements are sold as finished lambs. The meat ram is required to sire lambs which grow rapidly to the right level of maturity and the desired weight, thus producing a quality carcass.

Under the same feeding levels, breeds of sheep can be graded according to rate of growth and earliness of maturity. This is important in longwool and down breeds where rams are used to confer these qualities on their lamb offspring. With a few exceptions, the rate of growth and earliness of maturity are closely related to the mature size of the breed; as rate of growth increases the rate of maturity decreases. Thus lambs from heavy, late-maturing breeds are able to grow to much heavier weights without becoming excessively fat; as shown in Table 5.2 there was a 4.2 kg difference in carcass weight between the Southdown and the Wensleydale when slaughtered at a fat level equivalent to 3L class.

Table 5.1. Classification* of breeds of sheep

Category	Important characteristics	Breeds
(a) Hill flocks	1. Hardiness 2. Ability to rear 100% lamb crop 3. Satisfactory quality and weight of fleece	Blackface† Black Welsh Cheviot South† Dales-Bred Dartmoor Derbyshire Gritstone Exmoor Horn Herdwick Hill Radnor Lonk North Country Cheviot† Rough Fell Scottish Blackface Shetland South Welsh Mountain Swaledale† Welsh Mountain† Whiteface Dartmoor
(b) Upland flocks	1. Hardiness 2. Milking capacity 3. Twinning rate 4. Lambing regularity	Clun Forest† Hardy Speckleface North Country Cheviot† South Country Cheviot
(c) Longwool flocks producing the sires of crossbred ewes	1. Prolificacy 2. Milking capacity 3. Growth rate	Blue Faced Leicester Border Leicester British Oldenburg Colbred Cotswold English Leicester Finnish Landrace Lincoln Longwool Teeswater Wensleydale
(d) Down flocks producing fat lamb sires	1. Growth rate 2. Carcass quality	Charolais Cotswold Dorset Down† Hampshire Down Ille de France Leicester Lincoln Longwool Oxford Down Ryeland Shropshire Southdown Suffolk† Texel Wiltshire Horn
(e) Self-contained flocks producing their own replacements, females for sale and fat lambs	1. Prolificacy 2. Milking capacity 3. Growth rate 4. Carcass quality 5. Weight and quality of wool	Beulah Speckled Face Cambridge Charmoise Cornwall Longwool Devon Close Wool Devon Long Wool Jacob Kent or Romney Marsh† Kerry Hill Llanwenog Lleyn Meatline South Devon
(f) Lowland flocks being developed for lambing out of season and more frequently than once a year	1. Above-average lambing frequency 2. Reasonable prolificacy 3. Milking capacity	Dorset Horn Polled Dorset Horn

* Classification although based on the Report of the Sheep Panel to the National Livestock Breeding Conference, Harrogate 1962, has been modified.
† The most numerically important breeds.

Table 5.2. Means of lamb carcass weight and lean meat percentages in ram breed comparison (11.7% subcutaneous fat content) (source: Croston, Jones and Kempster, 1979)

	Carcass weight (kg)	Carcass lean meat (%)
Southdown	16.2	56.3
Dorset Down	17.5	55.8
Hampshire Down	17.6	55.6
North Country Cheviot	18.4	56.3
Ille de France	18.5	56.7*
Border Leicester	19.7	55.9
Suffolk	19.7	56.1
Oxford Down	20.3	55.8
Wensleydale	20.4	56.6†

* High lean reflects low bone percentage.
† High lean reflects low intermuscular fat percentage.

Heritability

The heritability of characters of major importance in sheep are summarized in Table 5.3. It can be seen that they divide themselves into two main categories.

1. Lamb survival as measured by prolificacy and to a lesser extent by milk yield. The factors responsible have low heritability values; within breeds, flushing can be a major management tool but little improvement can be obtained by selection. There are breed differences and crossing results in a high degree of heterosis which probably accounts for extensive cross-breeding within the sheep regime; the factors are also sensitive to inbreeding depression.

2. Carcass quality and the yield and quality of wool which have medium to high heritability values. This implies that selection for these characters within breeds can result in effective improvement particularly in meat sire breeds.

Performance and Progeny Testing

Performance testing of individual animals, particularly rams, is effective as a selection technique for highly heritable characters such as fleece weight and quality. With traits of (a) low heritability such as prolificacy, milking capacity and growth rate, and (b) traits which can only be assessed in slaughtered animals, e.g. carcass quality, progeny testing needs to be undertaken.

The extent to which these forms of testing have been applied can be appreciated by reference to the examples quoted on pp. 60–62.

Selection of Replacements

Whatever the form and nature of performance records which are used for the selection of replacement rams and ewes, it is essential that

Table 5.3. The heritability of characters of major importance in sheep (source: MLC)

Objective characters of the ewe	Component character	Probable heritability
Breeding frequency	Age of puberty	
Weaning percentage	Date of first oestrus	0.25–0.35
	Barrenness – proportion of ewes lambing put to ram	0.00–0.10
	Litter size at birth	0.10–0.20
	Lamb mortality before weaning	0.00–0.05
Easy lambing	Frequency of assisted lambing	Not known
Efficiency of feed conversion in the ewe	Annual feed intake	Not known
Dairy characters	Yield of milk	0.10–0.20
	Milk quality	0.40–0.50
	Corrected lamb weight to 50 days	0.10–0.30
Wool	Wool weight	0.30–0.45
	Fineness of staple (quality of fleece)	0.40–0.70
Character of the lamb		
Food conversion efficiency	Efficiency on test	Not known
Carcass quality	Fat content of carcass (composition and conformation)	0.25–0.35
Rate of gain	Gain to 100 days	0.10–0.30

their phenotypic appearance and condition satisfy certain basic requirements. They can be summed up as follows.

The Ewe

1. Appearance: she must conform to breed type. She must also be of an alert type, because alertness is an important factor in the survival of twins at birth.

2. Feet must be good and sound and free from foot-rot, otherwise she will not be able to walk and forage for her food properly; this will certainly lower her performance.

3. The udder must have two good quarters with sound teats, and no sign of mastitis.

4. Freedom from diseases such as foot-rot, liver fluke, or heavy worm infestation. Neither must she be susceptible to milk fever, twin-lamb disease or hypomagnesaemia.

5. Good mothering qualities. Besides having ample milk, the ewe must look after her lambs properly for maximum performance.

6. Easy lambing, i.e. she must lamb quickly and with the minimum of assistance.

7. Thriftiness, i.e. the ability to forage for food and thrive on limited food supply.

8. Docile temperament. Although the ewe must be alert, she must not be troublesome, e.g. always going through hedges, etc.

The Ram

1. Appearance – alert and conform to breed type.

2. Feet – sound and free from foot-rot. The activity of the ram must not be hampered because of bad feet.

3. Active and fertile – the ram must seek out and serve all the ewes on heat quickly and effectively.

4. Freedom from disease of any sort.

5. Docile temperament.

Cross-Breeding

Cross-breeding is widely practised in sheep breeding. With the exception of self-contained lowland flocks, cross-breeding is the rule. The hybrid offspring roughly average the performance of the parent breeds, particularly in respect of growth rate, rate of maturity, carcass quality together with fleece weight and quality.

There is evidence of heterosis in cross-bred stock in respect of lambing percentage, birth and weaning weights; this may be one reason why cross-breeding is so widely practised in sheep.

The evidence concerning the effects of cross-breeding on growth rate is rather inconclusive. Some experiments indicate that cross-bred rams do sometimes, but not always, sire progeny with a growth rate better than rams of the two pure breeds from which the cross-bred rams were produced; the most favourable cross increases growth rate by some 8–9%. Most cross-bred rams, however, do show growth rate improvement resulting from hybrid vigour.

Cross-breeding as a means of producing an entirely new breed of sheep has already been described (see p. 34).

Examples of some well known half-breeds are:

Rams	Ewes	Half-breeds
Teeswater	× Dales	Masham
Blue Faced		
Border Leicester	× Swaledale	Mule
Border Leicester	× Blackface	Scottish Greyface
Border Leicester	× Cheviot	Scottish Half-bred
Border Leicester	× Welsh Mountain	Welsh Half-bred

THE BREEDING SITUATION

Numbers and Production

Fat lambs emerge from pure and cross-bred flocks (Table 5.4). Roughly 60% of fat lambs slaughtered originate from pure-bred hill ewes, pure-bred lowland ewes crossed with down rams and hill/longwool ewes crossed with down rams; the remaining 40% are produced from pure-bred longwool, down, upland and lowland breeds together with other cross-bred combinations. Cross-bred flocks depend on a constant flow of cast ewes from the hill breeds; the latter thus act

as an important 'bank' of sheep from which the lowland farm can draw.

Breed Structure

Genetically, improvement by selection can only be achieved within pure breeds of sheep. Within each breed of sheep there exists a pyramidal structure of breeding. Flocks within a breed can be classified into three broad categories:

i) Registered pedigree breeders' flocks which

Table 5.4. Probable contribution of various groups of ewes to total output of lamb carcass meat from the 1972 lamb crop in Great Britain (excluding Shetland) (source: MLC sheep breed survey 1972)

	No. of ewes (000)	Lambs reared per ewe	No. of lambs reared (000)	No. of lambs retained (000)	No. of lambs slaughtered (000)	Lamb carcass wt. (kg)	Total carcass wt (000 tons)
Hill ewes purebred	4601	0.75	3450	1200	2250	14.5	32.1
Hill ewes × Longwool rams	1151	1.00	1151	390	760	17.2	12.9
Hill ewes × Upland rams	76	0.90	70	30	40	16.3	0.6
Hill ewes × Down rams	1068	0.95	1010	30	980	16.3	15.8
(L × H) ewes × Down rams	1941	1.30	2530	130	2400	20.4	48.2
(U × H) ewes × Down rams	300	1.20	360	–	360	20.0	7.0
(D × H) ewes × Down rams	154	1.20	190	–	190	20.0	3.7
Second cross ewes	632	1.25	790	10	780	20.4	16.1
Other cross ewes	502	1.25	630	–	630	20.4	12.7
Longwool ram breeds	24	1.30	30	10	20	21.8	0.5
Down ram breeds	243	1.20	290	80	210	21.4	4.4
Other purebred ewes*	503	1.10	550	260	290	20.0	5.7
Other purebred ewes* × Down	877	1.20	1100	90	1010	20.4	20.3
	12 072	–	12 151	2230	9920	18.4	179.7

L = Longwool; H = Hill; U = Upland; D = Down.
* Upland, Devon, Romney and Lowland breeds.

buy or interchange stock rams amongst themselves. (They comprise about 2–5% of the total of the breed);

ii) Multiplier flocks: registered or non-registered flocks which buy stock rams from the breeders' flocks and act as propagators of the breeders' stock;

iii) Commercial flocks: non-registered flocks in which sheep are used for commercial lamb production.

The direction of gene flow is thus from the breeders' flocks downwards throughout the entire breed. If genetic improvement is to be realized, then any ideal breeding scheme should involve all of the breeder and multiplier flocks in the breed. They would then form the genetic nucleus from which improved replacement rams could be purchased and used on commercial flocks. Culling and selection of replacement ewes and rams in commercial flocks is mainly a tool of management rather than a means of fostering genetic improvement.

Successful breeders are improving the qualities of a breed by limiting their objectives; in addition they select for such traits in a given order of priority.

Practical Difficulties

The task of the individual breeder is made difficult because of several factors:

1. Flocks are usually small in size.
2. Flock-life of ewes is short.
3. Rams are limited in number.
4. Many lambs are sold alive and their carcass quality cannot be assessed.

This situation limits the extent to which progeny and/or sib testing can be applied. In other words, the 'population' of progeny is too small to evaluate the breeding qualities of even a small number of rams, let alone the large number of rams which would be required to bring about marked improvement in the breed as a whole. With few rams the dangers of too intense in-breeding within flocks and breed are always present.

Examples of schemes which enable breeders to overcome these inherent difficulties can be quoted:

1. *Performance testing of Welsh Mountain rams*
Fig. 5.4 summarizes the procedures involved. The objective is to test the ability of ram lambs to hand on growth rate to their progeny; weighing them at 14 months old is a performance test adopted for measuring their ability to hand on this genetic character to their offspring. Since the ram inherits its characteristics from its dam as well as its sire, care is taken to select a nucleus of potential mothers on type and conformation before progeny testing them via their lamb offspring. This procedure can confer genotypic improvement within a flock on a given farm.

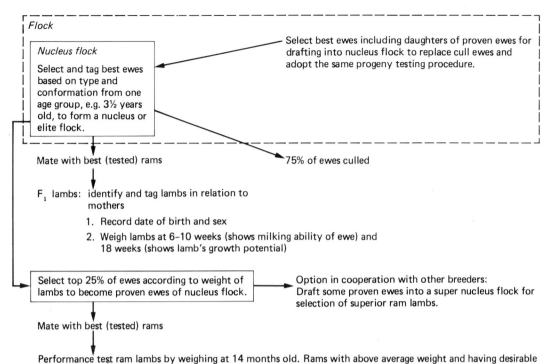

Fig. 5.4 Performance testing of Welsh mountain rams.

2. Group breeding scheme with Welsh Mountain sheep

Fig. 5.5 summarizes a scheme of Camdacynwyd Limited which has been established in collaboration with the Animal Breeding Research Organization (ABRO), the Agricultural Development and Advisory Service and the Meat and Livestock Commission.

The nucleus flock is kept at Rhydylafer Farm,

which is run by ABRO. The breeding objective is to improve commercial performance by breeding sheep that wean heavier lambs under hill conditions. The ten members of the group record the performance of the flock under the MLC scheme and the ewes recording the highest performance, as measured mainly by the weaning weight of lambs produced over three lamb crops, are transferred to the nucleus flock.

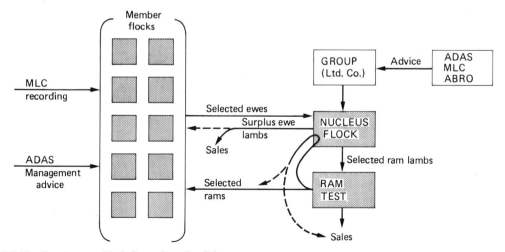

Fig. 5.5 The Camdacynwyd Ltd. Group Breeding Scheme.

The nucleus flock rears its own ewe replacements and the best ram lambs are sent to the Ram Performance Testing Unit at Talybont; rams are selected for use in the nucleus flock from among these tested rams. Since the object of the scheme is to provide sires for the members, the latter can choose them as ram lambs, as performance tested lambs or as rams no longer required by the nucleus flock.

Such a scheme is an attempt to overcome the disadvantage of selection of superior genotypes within a limited single flock population of sheep.

3. Progeny testing of Welsh Mountain rams

Welsh Mountain ram lambs from about 90 flocks have been performance tested at University College of North Wales, Bangor for 17 years. The test is conducted on pasture between October and May and rams are assessed on final weight, fleece characteristics and conformation. Rams of above (4+) and below average (5−) are then progeny tested for carcass characteristics and at the same time the lifetime breeding performance of the female progeny is studied. Results of the 1977 Progeny Test are shown in Table 5.5. The April born, single lambs were tagged, weighed at birth and pedigrees recorded. The ram lambs were kept with their dams on the hills until weaning in August and then brought down to the lowland for finishing at 34 kg. Lean percentages were similar in both groups but there was a tendency for the progeny of minus sires to be fatter at this weight; the progeny of plus rams reached slaughter weight 22 days earlier than those of minus rams.

Because carcass characteristics are highly heritable, this procedure is effective for the selection of superior rams for further breeding and improvement of flock performance.

Table 5.5. 1977 progeny testing of performance tested Welsh mountain rams

A: Details of performance tested rams used in 1977 Progeny Test (mean ± S.E.)

Ram no.		Initial wt. (kg) 16.10.75	Final wt. (kg) 7.5.76
Top	1	32.7	54.5
25%	2	40.9	52.7
	3	40.0	53.6
	4	36.4	54.5
Mean		37.5 ± 1.85	53.8 ± 0.45
Bottom	6	28.2	40.0
25%	7	28.6	39.1
	8	25.5	38.2
	9	27.3	41.8
	10	32.7	40.9
Mean		28.5 ± 1.20	40.0 ± 0.63
Overall test ave.		32.4 ± 0.27	46.5 ± 0.30

B: Slaughter characteristics (means ± S.E.) of progeny from groups of plus and minus rams 1977

	4+ sires	5− sires
Slaughter age (days)	249 ± 7.14	271 ± 7.91*
Slaughter wt (kg)	33.8 ± 0.06	33.8 ± 0.05
C.C.W. (kg)	15.8 ± 0.13	16.0 ± 0.11
Dressing %	46.6 ± 0.36	47.3 ± 0.32
% estimated lean	55.1 ± 0.29	54.9 ± 0.22
% estimated fat	22.5 ± 0.34	22.9 ± 0.35
% estimated bone	19.1 ± 0.30	18.6 ± 0.32

* $p \leq 0.01$

4. Breeding of new prolific lowland sheep breeds

The Cambridge is an example of a new prolific breed which has been bred in recent years. The crossing followed by the selective procedures involved have been described (p. 34).

6

Breeding for Pig Meat

The annual output of a sow used solely for pig-meat production is assessed by the number and grades of carcasses processed from her offspring; cull sows also make a contribution. This output is the end result of several interacting factors.

OUTPUT

Number of Pigs Reared

This depends on:

(a) *Number of pigs born per litter*. Whilst many of the twenty or so eggs released by the sow during ovulation may be fertilized, several of the resulting foetuses or embryos die and wither away before farrowing occurs. Other embryos may be still-born; such still-borns are usually more frequent in small litters.

Litter size is influenced by the care, particularly the feeding, of the sow during the post-weaning period and pregnancy; at birth she should be neither too thin nor too fat. The genetic control of litter size is very limited (see Heritability, Table 6.2).

(b) *Number of litters born per year*. If young piglets are weaned at 6 weeks of age and the sow is served again within a week, then the 115 day gestation period of the sow allows for 2.5 litters to be born and reared per year. In practice this is not always achieved; 2 litters per year is average. Early weaning of pigs at five or three weeks can, with good management, further increase the number of litters per sow per year.

Management of the sow at weaning is a key factor and time can be lost if the sow's first heat period after weaning is missed (see p. 12); breeding records are essential to determine which sows to watch and when.

(c) *Pig losses between birth and weaning*. Some 14% of pigs born do not survive to weaning. This large wastage is mainly caused by poor management; disease, chills and overlying are the main causes of deaths. The death of genetically weak pigs also contributes to a limited extent to this percentage mortality figure.

Economy of Production

This depends on:

(a) *Growth rate*. The daily weight increase of a pig is a measurement of its speed or rate of growth. This speed of growth is greatly influenced by feeding. A well-fed pig will grow faster than one which is poorly fed. This rate of growth, however, does vary between breeds and between strains within single breeds. Genes determine the maximum rates of growth.

(b) *Food conversion ratio*. Closely associated with growth rate is the ability of the pig to convert food into muscle (meat) and fat. This capacity to digest and assimilate food is measured by dividing the liveweight increase of the pig into the weight of food eaten by the pig. The numerical result of this simple division is known as the food conversion ratio or factor, and is defined as the weight of food required to put on one unit liveweight, e.g.

Liveweight increase of pig = 90 kg
Food consumed by pig = 270kg
Food conversion ratio $= \dfrac{270}{90} = 3$ kg food per kg liveweight gain

Factors affecting this ratio are:

i) *Age of pig*: The ratio increases with age. For a 6 week old piglet only 2 kg of creep food are normally required to produce 1 kg liveweight gain. For a bacon pig approaching slaughter weight it could take over 5 kg of meal.

Over the period from weaning to slaughter the following are average performances:

Porker	Baconer
2.8	3.0

ii) *Quality of feed and feeding system*: Food nutritionally unbalanced will not give good food conversion rates. Wasteful feeding also leads to poor results.

iii) *Insulation of buildings*: Cold, draughty buildings with poor insulation do not provide the ideal conditions for efficient food conversion. Under these circumstances pigs need extra food to maintain body weight and temperature.

iv) *Genetic variation*: Marked genetic variation exists between and within breeds and improvement can be realized by selection of breeding stock with low food conversion factors;

(c) *Killing out percentage*. The killing out percentage is calculated as follows:

$$\frac{\text{Cold carcass weight} \times 100}{\text{Last liveweight}}$$

The cold carcass weight is equal to the weight of hot head and chine plus twice the weight of the cold left side (including flare fat, kidney, feet and fillet).

Pigs with high killing out percentages are obviously desirable. Since killing out percentage is controlled genetically to a large extent, selection can bring about a measure of improvement.

Carcass Quality

Carcasses of bacon are graded on weight, length and the thickness of fat (Table 6.1); length is not so important in pork and heavy cutter carcasses. Grading standards that were previously devised by the Ministry of Agriculture have been abandoned; quality standards are now determined by buyers catering for a given consumer market. All buyers are seeking a carcass which is as lean as possible irrespective of the weight of the carcass required. The joints obtainable from a pork carcass are shown in Fig. 6.1.

Table 6.1. Bacon pigs – specification (for clean pigs weighing 59–77 kg dead weight) (source: F.M.C. (Meat) Ltd.)

Grade	Weight (kg)	Length (minimum)	Backfat shoulder loin (maximum)	P_2 probe (maximum)
AA1	59–72.5	775 mm	42/22 mm	16 mm
B1	59–77	None	None	20 mm
C1	59–77	None	None	None

The quality of the carcass is the end result of a growing process which not only involves the pig's overall growth rate but the comparative rates at which its bone, muscle and fat tissues develop; this latter process is called its rate of maturing.

As the pig increases in weight, changes occur in the shape or conformation of its body. When born the head is large and the legs are long; the body is short in length and shallow in depth. The next stage of development is a lengthening of the body. The body then becomes deeper so that the pig's legs appear shorter; development of the muscles on the upper bone of the leg also occurs so that the thighs become convex in shape. The last stage is the development of a deep, rounded, fat body.

Weight increase is due to the growth of fat, muscle and bone. These tissues grow at differing rates. In the early stages of life, bone makes most growth, followed by muscle. Fat attains its maximum rate of growth in the later stages of development. The rapid growth of fat in the later stages creates the deep, fat-bodied stage of development.

Genetic selection within breeds has basically produced strains of pigs suitable for market requirements. All markets require minimum fat and maximum lean tissue development.

1. *Pork and bacon strains*. These mature at a rate which enables them to grow into:

(a) Porkers 35 – 63 kg live-weight.
(b) Cutters 64–81 kg live-weight.
(c) Baconers 82–90 kg live-weight.

2. *Heavy hog strains*. These mature slowly so that fat is not laid down in any quantity until heavy body weights have been reached. They are often capable of building up their body tissues on cheaper meal containing less protein than is contained in meal fed to porkers and baconers.

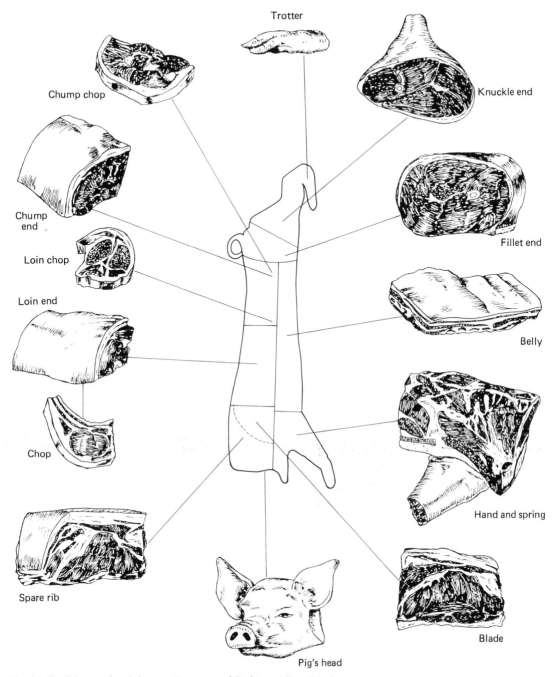

Trotter

Chump chop

Knuckle end

Chump end

Fillet end

Loin chop

Loin end

Belly

Chop

Hand and spring

Spare rib

Blade

Pig's head

Fig. 6.1 English cuts of pork (source: *Dictionary of Cooking* – Aileen King).

GENETIC CONSIDERATIONS

From a breeding point of view improvement of economic traits has to originate by selective procedures within breeds of pigs. Any cross-breeding which may be made subsequently will thus ensure that the superior genetic qualities of both parent breeds are incorporated in first cross pigs.

Breeds

Since genetic improvement occurs within pure breeds of pigs, a few comments on some important breeds of pigs are relevant.

1. *Welsh.* An all-white, long, lop-eared pig with good hams. It has been called the British Landrace because of its similarity to the Danish breed. The lop ears facilitate good grazing habits and its colour and conformation meet the requirements for bacon.

2. *Large White or Yorkshire.* Numerically it is the most popular breed in Britain. Its colour should be all white. The ears are long, thin, slightly inclined forward and fringed with hair; head moderately long, face slightly dished, snout broad, not too much turned up, jowl light and wide between the ears. It is the most widely distributed breed in the world. Pure-bred pigs are used for producing Wiltshire bacon carcasses; when crossed with other long breeds good commercial baconers are produced.

3. *British Landrace.* It was imported as the Swedish Landrace in 1949 and 1953. It is an all-white pig with semi-lop ears; it has a particularly long body and large well-rounded hams. It was originally developed for producing Wiltshire baconers, but is widely used for crossing with other breeds for bacon production.

Heritability

The heritability estimates for economic traits in pigs are shown in Table 6.2.

Because most carcass characteristics are highly heritable, selection of superior parents can effect immediate significant improvement of carcass quality in their offspring. Subsequent selection from first generation pigs can yet again ensure further improvement. In other words, the quality of carcasses produced in a breed of pigs can be effectively improved in a comparatively short period of time by continued rigorous selection of parents used for breeding in successive generations.

The medium heritability values of growth rate and food conversion efficiently imply that improvement by selection can also be effective; the time taken to reach a given performance standard will, however, be longer than that for highly heritable characters.

The low heritability value for prolificacy shows that this character is determined mainly by factors other than genetic factors. Improvement by selection within breeds of pigs will have little immediate effect and does not present a

Table 6.2. Heritabilities (source: based on MLC Testing Station Data, and *The Genetic Aspects of Litter Productivity in British Pigs*, G. S. Strang, 1970)

Low heritability
Number of pigs born alive
Number of pigs at 8 weeks
Litter weight at 8 weeks
Mortality from birth to 8 weeks

Medium heritability
Boar daily gain
Killing out percentage
Trimming percentage
Ham and rump back as percentage of side
Average sib daily gain of a pair

High heritability
Boar feed conversion
Boar echo sounding
Caliper fat depths
Percentage lean rump back
Percentage lean in side
Hindquarters as percentage of side
Eye muscle area
Average sib feed conversion of a pair

practical answer for bettering the number of pigs born and reared per litter.

Performance and Progeny Testing

When performance recording was initially adopted to estimate the breeding value of pedigree boars, progeny testing was widely used. The boar was mated to four sows and from one litter produced from each sow, two boars, one castrated and one gilt pig were sent after weaning to a pig progeny testing centre. Recordings were made on liveweight growth, feed conversion ratio and carcass quality of each pig and average figures for the group of four pigs compiled.

Similar recordings of the progeny of other boars of the same breed under test at the same time were also made. It was thus possible to calculate average figures for all the progeny of the same breed under test at the station, i.e. to calculate contemporary average figures. The relative breeding value of a particular boar could then be assessed by comparing the performance figures of his offspring with contemporary average figures (see 'contemporary comparison', p. 28).

The Meat and Livestock Commission has abandoned progeny testing of boars and replaced it with performance testing. There were three main reasons for this decision.

1. The service was expensive and it restricted the number of boars which could be tested.

2. Many boars were 2 years old before their breeding value had been assessed and by that time an important part of their breeding life was over.

3. The heritability values of the traits recorded are so high that performance testing can be an effective means of boar selection. Although less accurate than progeny testing, it does ensure a larger throughput of genetically superior boars.

Performance testing is currently carried out at three testing stations and is designed to assess the potential of a young boar for siring profitable progeny. A group of four pigs from the same litter, each comprising two boars, one castrate and one gilt, are sent to the testing station. The pigs are weighed on arrival and their individual weights should be between 18 and 25 kg; the test commences when each boar weighs 27 kg, and the sibs (the castrate and gilt) weigh 54 kg in total. The test is completed when each boar weighs 91 kg and the sibs' collective weight is 165 kg.

Each pair of boars is housed in a kennel-type building. They are allowed to lie together but are fed separately in order to record accurately their individual feed consumption. The sibs are housed in a fully enclosed building and fed as a pair.

The records kept enable assessments to be made concerning economy of production and carcass quality. The purpose of testing the castrate and gilt is to obtain detailed carcass information. When their combined weights total 165 kg they are slaughtered and detailed carcass measurements taken and sample joints dissected into lean, fat and bone. Additionally, feed consumption, liveweight gain and ultrasonically measured fat depths are recorded for each boar. This information in combination with feed consumption and growth records from the sibs, together with their carcass measurements, is expressed in a selection index as a points score for each boar. An example of an MLC test result is shown in Table 6.3.

Table 6.3. Report of combined tests (source: Meat and Livestock Commission)

Report of combined 9799/3 test   Born 7th April 1980   Tested at Selby   Report issued 2nd October 1980

Breed: Large White

Tested on behalf of
J. B. & J. C. Evans
Meteor Pigs Ltd.,
Coolmoor Farm,
Shawbury
Nr Shrewsbury, Salop
Tel: Shawbury 250233
Herd Prefix COOLMOOR

Sire of Group: Coolmoor Field Marshal 44th
Dam of Group: Coolmoor Champion Lady 101st

Ear No.	Herd Book No.	Test Report
7489	451311	196 PTS
7608	335008	

Points Score

Ear No. of Boar	8529	8530	Average of both Boars	Contemporary Average
Economy of Production	64	63	64	50
Carcase Quality	92	85	88	50
Total	156	148	152	100

Av. Sib Length = 795 mm.

Estimated genetic superiority of individual characters

Character	Ear No. of Boar 8529	8530
Daily Gain (g)	2B	7B
Food Conversion	0.057B	0.071B
Killing Out %	0.06W	0.29W
Trimming %	0.07B	0.02B
% Lean in Side	1.45B	1.24B
Eye Muscle Area (cm²)	0.65B	0.49B

B. Better
AVE. Average
W. Worse

The score for economy of production reflects the boar's value for daily gain, feed conversion, and killing out percentage. The score for carcass quality is a reflection of its value for trimming percentage, percentage lean in side and eye muscle area. The average points score for each breed for economy of production and for carcass quality is 50 each, giving a total score of 100. Boars scoring below 90 points are slaughtered and those scoring above this figure are offered back to their breeders.

The Estimated Genetic Superiority section is an estimate of the genetic value of each boar for a number of economically important characters and is expressed as a deviation better (B) or worse (W) than contemporaries of the same breed at the same test station.

Since the boars tested are selected from above-average herds, ones with scores above 90 will bring about improvements in most commercial herds.

Carcass Evaluation

MLC carcass evaluations are carried out on carcasses dressed to nationally recommended standards and split into two by sawing down the centre of the vertebral column. The head is removed by a cut at right angles to the back between the atlas and the skull. A number of measurements and subjective assessments are carried out on the left side of each carcass. The most important are fat depths at P_2 (over eye muscle at last rib), at shoulder and loin positions, the length of side and the width of the eye muscle (Fig. 6.2).

On-farm Testing

Tests on some boars but mainly gilts are carried out on farms by MLC staff. Regular visits are made in order to measure the fat depths on live pigs using an ultrasonic machine. Potential breeding pigs of 68 to 113 kg liveweight are tested.

The fat measurements are taken at fixed points P_1 and P_3 (Fig. 6.2) over the eye muscle at the last rib, at shoulder and at loin. The P_1 and P_3 figures together with figures of weight for age are combined to give a simple index score for each pig. Index scores are based on a rolling herd average and this overcomes factors other than genetic differences which can influence weight for age and fatness under farm conditions. These factors include prevailing weather conditions, type of ration, housing and health. The average

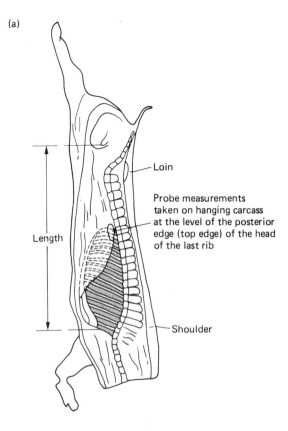

(a)

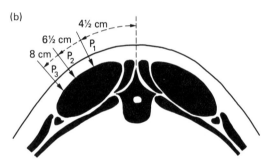

(b)

Fig. 6.2 Measurements taken on a bacon carcass. (a) Length and back fat measurements (source: Ministry of Agriculture); (b) Position of measurements taken with an optical probe (intrascope) at the level of the head of the last rib. P_1 and P_3 apply to split or unsplit carcasses (method 1) and P_2 to split carcasses (method 2) (source: MLC).

figure is calculated only within the same breed and sex and is always 10 points. The range is usually from -20 to $+40$ and the higher the score the better the pig.

Selection of Replacement Gilts

A sow must be highly fertile, capable of enduring repeated pregnancies and of suckling her litters for some 8 weeks. A replacement gilt is selected (a) on appearance and condition; and (b) on the performance records of her mother.

Appearance and Condition

A good sow should possess:

1. The appearance and conformation of her breed.
2. A long, deep body: this indicates the sow's capacity to utilize food efficiently and to carry successive litters without undue strain.
3. Good feet: since the sow lives on her feet, any defect of the feet will hinder her in performing her task.
4. Twelve teats: a minimum of twelve functioning teats is necessary for rearing a large litter of pigs.
5. Freedom from disease: this indicates that the sow is healthy and vigorous.
6. No noticeable defects: hernias and other physical defects can only hinder the sow's work.
7. Easy farrowing ability: this is extremely important as a sow may lose all or most of her litter if difficulties arise during farrowing.
8. Docile temperament: a good mothering sow is invaluable.

Performance Records

In recorded herds, replacement gilts are chosen from mother sows which have shown consistency of performance. The MLC on-farm testing scheme (p. 68) gives priority to nucleus and reserve nucleus herds but other breeders who breed their own female replacements are eligible to apply for the service. A selection index score for each gilt is calculated as follows:

$$\text{Index} = (101.4 \times \text{DG}) - (0.892 \times P_1 + P_3) + (0.02W) + 2.6$$

W = weight in kg when P_1 & P_3 measured
DG = daily liveweight gain in kg.

Selection of Boars

A boar must be highly fertile and capable of consistently handing on commercial qualities to his offspring. A boar is selected (a) on appearance and condition; (b) on performance records.

Appearance and Condition

The boar must possess the following characters:

1. Conform to breed type.
2. Long, deep body.
3. Good feet.
4. Freedom from disease.
5. No notable defects.
6. Docile temperament.

Performance Records

Boars are invariably selected from mothering sows showing consistency of breeding performance. Pedigree boars are usually selected on the results of a performance test. The best policy as far as the commercial producer is concerned is either to purchase an above-average performance-tested boar or one of its relatives.

Cross-Breeding

Approximately 75% of the national herd is made up of cross-bred females. Records indicate that such females on average produce and rear more pigs than pure-bred females (Table 6.4) due to the effects of hybrid vigour.

With cross-breeding it is important to ensure that the genetic qualities of the two or more parent breeds used to produce the hybrids are of the highest quality, particularly in respect of growth rate and carcass quality. With these two traits, the performance of the hybrid offspring will roughly average the performance of the parent breeds, i.e. their system of inheritance is mainly additive (see p. 20).

Table 6.4. Comparison of pure and cross-bred pigs (source: MLC Feed Recording Service analysis).

	Pure-bred	First Cross
Number of herds	120	120
Average herd size	62.4	64.6
Average number of litters per sow and gilt per annum	1.7	1.8
Average number of pigs born alive per litter	9.9	10.3
Average number of pigs reared per litter	8.3	8.8
% mortality	15.8	15.0
Average number weaners per sow per annum	14.2	15.9

THE BREEDING SITUATION

Structure of the Industry

With each breed of pigs there exists a pyramidal structure of breeding (Fig. 6.3).

This description is a simplification of the real situation but it does show how the genetic influence of top-quality stock, particularly boars, is spread throughout the entire national herd.

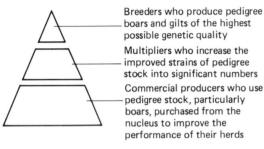

Breeders who produce pedigree boars and gilts of the highest possible genetic quality

Multipliers who increase the improved strains of pedigree stock into significant numbers

Commercial producers who use pedigree stock, particularly boars, purchased from the nucleus to improve the performance of their herds

Fig. 6.3 Pig breeding pyramid.

Meat and Livestock Commission

This nationally constituted commission aids the pig industry to improve its efficiency. Its main functions are:

1. *To assist the pedigree breeder*
In order that pedigree breeders can improve their herds a Pig Improvement Scheme is available and is based on the performance testing of young boars (p. 66). The scheme incorporates nucleus and reserve nucleus herds.

The nucleus herds are selected from pure-bred populations and are intensively tested. Young boars are regularly performance tested at testing stations and the performance of gilts is tested on the farm.

The reserve nucleus herds are those which aspire to nucleus classification and these aim to select and test on-farm with the same intensity as the nucleus herds. Both nucleus and reserve nucleus herds must be members of the Government Pig Health Scheme.

2. *To provide artificial insemination*
This service has been described under artificial insemination (p. 12) and it enables genetic traits from a comparatively small number of high-quality boars to be spread over a large pig population. Selecting replacement stock from these boars will improve both economy of production and carcass quality. It is also one of the safest ways of introducing new blood lines into the herd since all boars have to be approved by Ministry of Agriculture's Animal Health Division and are regularly checked for brucellosis, TB and Aujesky's disease.

3. *To produce recording schemes for commercial producers*
Farm records are essential for efficient pig management and Pig Plan offers a recording and consultancy service to producers. The scheme helps to monitor standards of management achieved; weaknesses are exposed which can be corrected with advice. The use of computer facilities ensure a swift turn around of information, enabling problems to be highlighted at an early stage. Results are published in such a way that current figures can be compared with the previous year for the herd and also with the top-third herds. Both physical and financial information is provided and projected. Cash-flows and production forecasts can also be made available within the scheme.

4. *To evaluate cross-bred stock produced by breeders and breeding companies*
Since cross-bred animals are an important part of pig production an evaluation of their merit is clearly required by the Industry. The Commercial Pig Evaluation Scheme is a test on gilts and boars put up for sale by pig breeding companies. Each year stock from a number of companies are purchased for testing. Individual companies provide seven boars and at least 24 gilts randomly selected. Information on numbers of pigs born and reared and weaning weights is collated for the breeding stock. Feed conversion ratios, daily liveweight gain and carcass measurements are recorded for the feeding pigs and a proportion of the carcasses are fully dissected. The company pigs are compared with each other (Table 6.5).

Co-operation amongst Pedigree Breeders

Within the industry, the process of breeding and supplying high-quality pure-bred and cross-bred pigs is becoming highly rationalized. Large pedigree pig breeders are grouping together to form consortia or companies. This pooling of resources enables genetic breeding to be undertaken on a considerable scale. Companies often employ professional geneticists and veterinary officers to assist them. Selection is based on recorded information which is processed and analysed by computers. The whole operation becomes highly skilled and specialized, thus ensuring a steady stream of high-quality stock to the commercial producer of pig meat (Table 6.5).

Table 6.5. Relative company performance: the three-year average.

	Company									
Sow productivity	*FM*	*EH*	*NP*	*PI*	*PP*	*QL*	*UP*	*Ac*	*WL*	*MP*
Number of pigs born alive per litter	104	102	98	104	99	100	101	94	98	101
Number of pigs alive per litter at 5 weeks	101	102	96	104	98	102	101	95	99	102
Average piglet weight at 5 weeks	99	103	98	99	99	97	103	105	99	99
Feed per kg weaner	100	104	94	101	98	98	104	100	101	100
Performance to 86 kg										
Feed conversion ratio	99	100	104	101	98	99	100	100	99	100
Daily gain:										
restricted	99	102	104	101	97	99	99	101	99	100
ad lib	101	102	92	102	101	98	99	101	104	100
Killing out %										
restricted	100	98	101	99	101	101	99	100	101	100
ad lib	100	101	100	99	100	100	100	99	101	102
P_2	97	102	116	108	92	94	105	101	86	101
Lean in carcass	98	98	106	100	99	99	102	99	99	100
Lean tissue feed conversion ratio	97	98	113	100	96	99	102	97	99	101

The overall average for each characteristic is 100. The performance for each company is expressed as a percentage of this average; ratings above 100 are better than average, ratings below 100 are worse than average.

Companies included in the test report include Accredicross Pigs Ltd (Ac), Elite Hybrids Ltd (EH), Farm Mark Ltd (FM), Meteor Pigs Ltd (MP), Northern Pig Development Co Ltd (NP), Pig Improvement Co Ltd (PI), Premier Pig Testing Co (Sales) Ltd (PP), Q-Lean Ltd (QL), United Pig Breeders Ltd (UP), Walls Livestock Ltd (WL), Cotswold Pig Development Co Ltd (Cw) and Peninsular Pigs (South West) Ltd (PE).

SECTION B

Feeding and Management of Farm Livestock

7

Animal Structure and Function

The farmer has to feed animals, keep them healthy and breed from them during their lifetime on the farm. A knowledge of the internal structure of farm animals and how they perform their living functions is necessary for understanding sound husbandry practices.

GENERAL STRUCTURE

When an animal is slaughtered, the chest and abdominal walls are opened and all the entrails or internal organs removed; the animal is then skinned to reveal a carcass consisting of meat or muscle, bone or fat. The carcass with its covering of skin is known as the *body-wall*.

If the muscles and fat are removed from this carcass the skeleton of the animal can be clearly seen (Fig. 7.1). The backbone is the basal foundation of the skeleton and consists of small bones called vertebrae arranged end to end; small sliding movements between consecutive vertebrae enable the animal to bend its back. All the other parts of the skeleton virtually hinge on the backbone and consist of the following:

i) a skull made up of the cranium and the jaw bone;

ii) long and short bones separated by joints which form the framework of fore and hind limbs;

iii) paired ribs forming a hooped box; each rib articulates with a vertebra at one end and fuses with the breast bone at the other end.

A typical long bone consists of a shaft, which is hollow for part of its length and which is

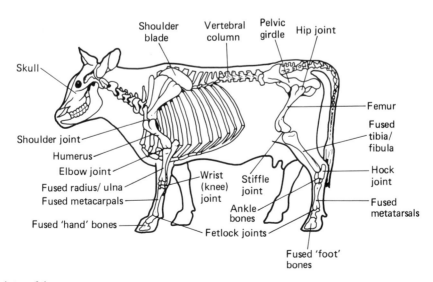

Fig. 7.1 Skeleton of the cow.

swollen out at the ends (Fig. 7.2(a)). The cavity in the shaft is filled by blood vessels and soft fatty tissue, the marrow. The dense bone consists of a matrix of white organic fibres impregnated and strengthened with mineral salts, chiefly calcium phosphates; scattered throughout this porous matrix are cells which are kept alive by a capillary blood supply (Fig. 7.2(c)).

The functions of the skeletal system are many:

1. Protection of vital organs; the central nervous system is protected by the skull and vertebral column, the heart and lungs by the rib-cage and the urino-genital system by the pelvis.

2. The skeleton gives the animal its shape.

3. Movement; it is the particular way in which muscles are attached to bones which enables the animal to move. The action of muscles to facilitate movement can be readily appreciated by referring to Fig. 7.3. This shows the attachment of muscles which enable to and fro movements of the hind leg. Muscles always work in pairs because each muscle is only capable of a pulling action, i.e. it cannot push. Contraction of muscles marked A pulls the femur bone forward; contraction of muscles marked B pulls the femur back into its original position. Movement is also made easier because joints placed between bones enable each limb to bend in several places (Fig. 7.4). To reduce friction and wear the ends of the long bones are coated with very smooth gristle or cartilage; the joint is lubricated by fluid secreted by the synovial membrane within the walls of the joint.

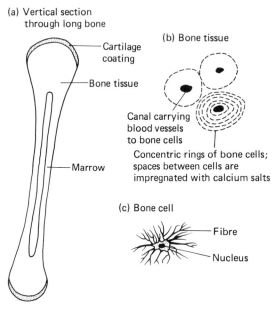

Fig. 7.2 Bone structure.

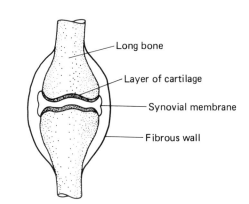

Fig. 7.4 Typical joint.

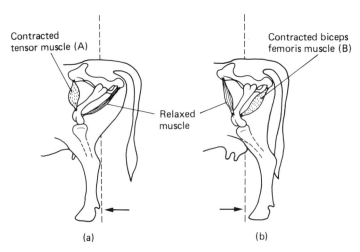

Fig. 7.3 Hind leg movement.
(a) Forward; (b) backward.

4. The entire skeleton serves as a storage area for minerals, particularly calcium and phosphorus. These minerals may then be withdrawn into the bloodstream when needed, as is the case during pregnancy.

5. Red blood corpuscles are made in the marrow of bones.

The muscular structure embracing the skeleton is usually coated with a covering layer of fat and can be readily seen on a carcass of lamb, beef or bacon. This is the layer of fat lying underneath the skin of the animal and it acts as an insulator. Globules of fat are often deposited in between muscle fibres; it is this deposition that gives the 'marbled' effect in certain meat cuts.

The internal organs are neatly compacted inside the box-like frame of the body wall. On examining these internal organs it becomes apparent that they are grouped together into unified systems; each system is adapted to carry out special functions.

DIGESTIVE SYSTEM

The function of this system is to digest food mechanically and chemically. Before proceeding to describe the system, firstly consider the nature and composition of foods.

Foods and Foodstuffs

Foods for feeding to livestock can be conveniently classified as follows:

1. *Succulent foods:* contain a high percentage of water, e.g. swedes contain 88.5%.

i) Green leaf crops, e.g. grass, silage, kale, cabbage, rape.
ii) Roots, e.g. turnips, swedes, mangolds, potatoes.
   2. *Dry foods:*
i) Roughages: contain a fairly high percentage of lignin fibres and cellulose, e.g. hay and straw.
ii) Concentrates: contain only very small quantities of water (about 10%) and fibre (about 0.5%):
   (a) farm grown, e.g. barley, oats, peas and bean seeds,
   (b) farm imported, e.g. either simple products such as maize meal, ground-nut cake and palm kernel cake or as ready-mixed proprietary products for milk production, calf rearing, egg laying and bacon production.

On examining thin slices of some crops under the microscope, grains of starch, crystals of sugar or bubbles of fat can be seen (Fig. 7.5). These products are called *foodstuffs* (often referred to as *nutrients*). Some other foodstuffs cannot be seen by the aid of a microscope but can be detected by chemically analysing the crops in the laboratory. If, for example, a small portion of swede is heated in a suitable container, drops of water condense on the sides of the container. On continued heating, the crop material burns until all that remains is a small amount of ash. This shows that the crop contains water and a mixture of mineral salts which make up the ash.

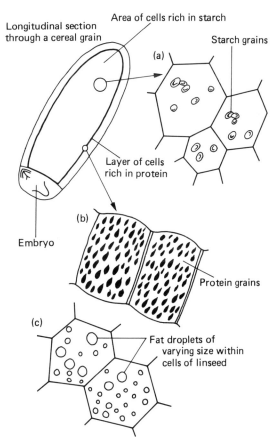

Fig. 7.5 Foodstuffs in the cells of farm crops. Approximate magnifications: (a) × 65; (b) × 400; (c) × 300.

Table 7.1. Sources and functions of foodstuffs

Foodstuffs	Source of supply	Functions within the animal body
SUGARS	Found as crystals in sugarbeet, mangolds, turnips, swedes, carrots and in all sweet-tasting crops	Oxidized to produce energy or heat Converted into fat
STARCHES	Found as grains in almost all crops particularly potatoes, cereals, herbage and concentrates	Oxidized to produce energy or heat Converted into fat
FATS	Found as solid fat or liquid oil within linseed, cotton seed, palm kernals, coconuts and soya beans, i.e. most of the foods which compose imported concentrates	Oxidized to produce energy or heat Little is essential to prevent loss of appetite
PROTEINS	Found generally in kale, clovers, oats, good silage, good hay, good dry grass and particularly in medium and high protein concentrates	Enable the animal to build up muscle or meat, i.e. body building foodstuffs
MINERAL SALTS Calcium and phosphorus	Good grassland herbage, especially legumes. Cereal grains rich in phosphorus and poor in calcium	For the production of strong bones and teeth For the production of blood which clots well For the formation of milk To prevent rickets (weak and brittle bones which are pulled out of shape) in young animals, e.g. pigs, young calves To prevent milk fever (muscular spasms, paralysis and coma at the commencement of the lactation)
Chlorine	Found in any mixed vegetable diet	Prevents retarded growth and indigestion (excess salt may cause oedema in pigs and poultry who consume kitchen wastes only)
Magnesium	Magnesium salts. Green herbage	To prevent tetany, a condition sometimes occurring in dairy cows, breeding ewes and other cattle (acute excitability, tremors and convulsions)
TRACE ELEMENTS Copper	Pulse crops, cereals, greens. Copper sulphate in mineral mixtures (usually fed to pregnant ewes)	Forms a part of the blood Prevents sway-back in lambs (the animal finds difficulty in rising, the hind-quarters sway, are dragged along and the lamb may stagger and collapse)
Cobalt	Cobalt salts fed in licks or spread on pastures	Prevents 'pining' (loss of appetite, listlessness, dry wool and eventually dwindling to skin and bone)
VITAMINS A	Cod and halibut oils, green vegetables, dried grass, well-made yellow-green or olive-green silage	Promotes healthy, vigorous, normal growth and increases the body resistance to disease Prevents inflammation of the eyes in cattle and poultry
D	Cod and halibut oils (usually supplements the diet of calves and poultry). Exposure of the animal to the sun	Prevents rickets
B	Outer coating of seeds, yeast and all green crops. Rice polishings	Prevents polyneuritis (convulsions and inability to stand) in poultry

Foodstuffs are classified as:

1. *Carbohydrates*: i.e. compounds which contain carbon (carbo-) and water (hydrates). Examples of these are sugar and starches.
2. *Fats*: e.g. linseed oil, butter.
3. *Proteins*: e.g. white of egg.
4. *Water*.
5. *Mineral salts*: of phosphorus, calcium, sulphur, magnesium, copper, etc.
6. *Vitamins*: e.g. A, B complex, C, D, E and many others.

The source of supply of the main foodstuffs and their functions within the animal's body are summarized in Table 7.1.

Digestive System of the Pig

The food (or alimentary) canal consists of a long tube of varying thickness passing from the mouth to the anus; it includes the food pipe (oesophagus), stomach, small intestine and large intestine (Fig. 7.6(c)). Two other organs, the liver and pancreas, are attached by ducts to the small intestine. Food eaten by the animal is conveyed along this tube by wave-like contractions of its muscular walls.

As food passes along the food canal, juices are secreted from the abomasum wall, liver, pancreas and intestinal wall. These juices are thoroughly mixed with the food by churning actions of muscular walls. Chemical compounds called *enzymes* are contained in these juices. The enzymes are able to convert insoluble foodstuffs such as starch, protein and fat into soluble foodstuffs. This process is known as *digestion*. Some of us have had the experience of chewing a cereal grain and discovering that it becomes sweet to the taste after thorough chewing. Ptyalin, an enzyme in saliva, changes the starch in the grain into sugar.

When starch is added to cold water and shaken, the water becomes cloudy due to the presence of starch grains suspended in water, i.e. the starch grains do not dissolve. On boiling such a solution, a jelly is formed. Similarly the white of egg becomes a resilient solid on boiling. Foodstuffs such as these are insoluble. Sugar, on the other hand, will dissolve in water and is described therefore as being soluble in water. Digestion can be represented by the following equation:

insoluble
foodstuff + enzyme = soluble foodstuff
e.g. starch + enzyme = sugars
protein + enzyme = amino acids
fat + enzyme = glycerine and
fatty acids

These soluble foodstuffs are then absorbed into the bloodstream.

Digestive System of the Ruminant

A sheep or cow has a 'four-compartmented stomach' which enables it to deal with large quantities of fibre in such foods as silage, hay or straw (Fig. 7.6(a)). Since the pig has only a

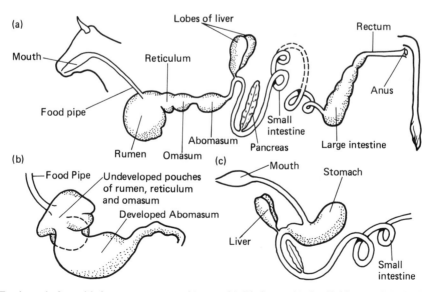

Fig. 7.6 (a) Food canal of ox with four-compartmented 'stomach'. (b) 'Stomach' of calf. (c) Part of the food canal of a pig (non-ruminant).

simple stomach, it cannot break down bulky fibrous foods and is thus fed on concentrated food. During the first three weeks of a calf's life only the abomasum or true stomach is formed. When the calf begins to eat dry foods, the pouches at the lower end of the food tube enlarge to form the rumen, reticulum and omasum (Fig. 7.6(b)).

Cows and sheep ruminate or chew their cuds. When grazing, the cow embraces a tuft of grass with its tongue, tears it and draws it into its mouth. The grass is ground in between the teeth by strong lateral movements of the jaws and moistened with spit or saliva. The food is swallowed down the food-tube into the 'first compartment' or *rumen*. Bacteria present in the rumen partly break down the cellulose and fibre of the food, which is then regurgitated back along the food-tube into the mouth. Further chewing of the food or cud occurs before it is reswallowed into the rumen. This to-and-fro action between mouth and rumen continues until the food is sufficiently broken down to pass into the *reticulum*. Further breakdown occurs here, before the food is passed into the *omasum*. Here the mixture is strained, the 'gruel-like' portion being allowed to pass into the *abomasum* and the more solid portion retained and later returned to the rumen for further 'breakdown'.

Part of the protein in the diet is broken down by bacteria into ammonia; such protein is known as rumen degradable protein (RDP). The remainder of the protein, which passes through the rumen unchanged, is called undegradable dietary protein (UDP).

The degree of protein degrading which occurs varies with the food source and the time it remains in the rumen.

The ammonia formed is re-synthesized by bacteria into protein and the extent to which this occurs depends on the presence of mineral elements, especially sulphur, but primarily on the energy available in the rumen; about 8 g of protein can be synthesized per megajoule (MJ) of metabolizable energy (ME) available in the rumen (p. 92). Bacteria-synthesized protein and undegraded protein then pass into the abomasum and the small intestine, where they are digested into amino acids; about 50% of the total available amino acids are eventually assimilated into meat and other proteins (see p. 84).

Bacteria responsible for breaking down lignin fibre in hay and straw are different from the bacteria capable of breaking down the mainly cellulose thickening in green grass and silage. Beef cattle wintered on hay usually suffer a check in growth rate when turned out to spring grass. The explanation for this is based on the varying proportions of the two different kinds of bacteria present in the rumen. On turn-out the bacteria in the rumen responsible for lignin breakdown are plentiful but they are incapable of acting on the cellulose of fresh grass. Over a period of time the second type of bacteria multiply until they are sufficiently numerous to handle the amount of fresh, cellulose-containing grass eaten by the animal. The only way to overcome such a setback is to allow calves and older cattle to have limited access to early grass when they are still being fed on a mainly indoor diet of hay; this form of management synchronizes with the growth behaviour of the two types of bacterial colonies in the rumen. Cattle that have been wintered on silage suffer little or no check when turned out to fresh grass; in this case only one type of bacteria is required and the bacterial population is already at a high level when the cattle are turned out.

Upsets in the normal rumination process are described on pp. 217 and 229.

Functions of the Liver

The liver is an extremely important organ and performs many functions.

1. It breaks down worn out red corpuscles to form bile. This substance is essential for the emulsification of fats in the small intestine.
2. It converts nitrogenous waste products into urea. The kidneys extract this urea together with salts to form urine.
3. It stores sugars and oxidizes fat.

If this latter process is upset, it may result in the disease acetonaemia. Fat is oxidized with the help of sugar in the liver. Normal oxidation results in the release of large quantities of heat or energy and the formation of carbon dioxide and water. When sugars in the liver are scarce, such fats are not oxidized completely and substances called ketones are produced instead of carbon dioxide and water. Such sweet-smelling ketones are released into the bloodstream, extracted by the kidneys and expelled with the urine. Sweet-smelling urine is a symptom of the disease.

Absorption and Utilization of Foodstuffs

The soluble foodstuffs resulting from digestion are absorbed into the bloodstream in the small intestine. The walls of the intestine are similar in texture to a velvet cloth because of minute

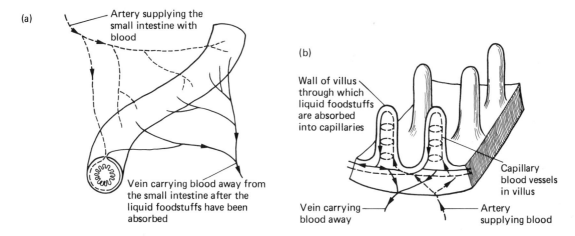

Fig. 7.7 (a) Blood supply to small intestine. (b) Part of internal wall of small intestine showing blood supply to villi.

hair-like structures, *villi*, projecting from and covering the whole of its internal surface (Fig. 7.7). The foodstuffs are absorbed by the villi. The foodstuffs pass through the wall of each villus into the capillary network of blood contained in its centre.*

* The absorption of glycerine and fatty acids into the lacteal canal and lymphatic system has been left out to simplify description.

These foodstuffs are carried in the bloodstream to different parts of the body where they are utilized by the animal to produce body heat, body tissues and body secretions.

All food material which is not absorbed into the bloodstream in the small intestine is passed into the large intestine. Here, most of the water contained in the undigested food is absorbed into the blood. The semi-solid faeces are then ejected through the anus.

RESPIRATORY SYSTEM

This system enables oxygen from the air breathed in through the nose and mouth to pass into the lungs, where it is absorbed into the blood; the carbon dioxide and water vapour which pass out from the blood through the walls of the lungs are exhaled through the nose and mouth (Fig. 7.8a).

Each lung consists of pink spongy tissue divided into lobes; although the lungs are bounded by a smooth pleural skin, their structure is broadly similar to that of a sponge. Large air spaces are made possible because the tissue is arranged microscopically into innumerable air sacs; each sac consists of many balloon-like alveoli whose walls are extremely thin.

Air passes from the mouth to the lungs through a stiff-walled wind-pipe which divides into two bronchial tubes, one entering each lung; this passage of air is facilitated by movements of the chest wall and diaphragm, i.e. normal breathing movements. Inside the lung, each bronchial tube divides repeatedly into smaller tubes or bron-

chioles like the branches of a tree; the thin tips of such branches form the openings of air sacs (Fig. 7.8b).

The lungs are supplied with blood by the pulmonary artery emerging from the right ventricle of the heart. Inside the lung this artery divides into smaller and smaller branches, each branch ending up as a network of fine hair-like capillaries contained within the thin wall of an alveolus. Oxygen diffuses across these thin walls into the blood carried in the capillaries; carbon dioxide and water also diffuse from the capillary blood into the cavity of the alveolus. Capillaries re-group into fewer but larger branches which eventually emerge from the lung as the pulmonary vein; the veins from both lungs return blood to the heart. Thus venous blood returning from the lungs contains oxygen, whilst arterial blood passing into the lungs contains carbon dioxide and water vapour.

The rate of breathing can be measured by

(a) General view

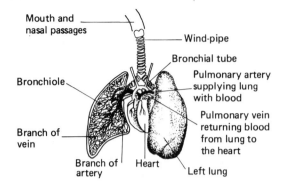

(b) Microscopic portion of lung showing bronchioles leading into air sacs; also blood supply to air sacs

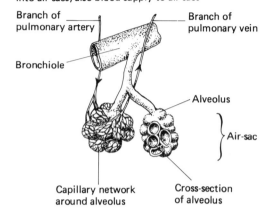

Fig. 7.8 Respiratory system. (a) General view; (b) microscopic portion of lung showing bronchioles leading into air-sacs; also blood supply to air-sacs.

counting the number of times that the chest expands in a minute. Normal rates of breathing are as follows:

12–16 inhalations per minute in cattle
15–20 inhalations per minute in sheep
10–20 inhalations per minute in pigs.

When cattle and sheep are chewing their cuds the breathing rate increases to 60–80 in cattle and up to 100 in sheep. Rate of breathing also increases considerably when it is too hot, when the animal is excited or frightened or after any exertion such as running or giving birth.

BLOOD SYSTEM

Blood is pumped around the animal's body by the heart. When the heart is opened it is seen to be divided by a longitudinal wall into a left and a right side. On each side of the division there are two cavities, an *auricle*, resting above a *ventricle* (Fig. 7.9).

At each heart-beat blood is pumped out from both left and right ventricles into blood vessels called *arteries*. These vessels are thick-walled and carry blood under pressure to all parts of the body.

The pulsing of the blood through an artery can be felt by pressing a finger on the underside of the tail a few inches from the body. The rate of heart beat and pulse is usually four times faster than the breathing rate. Normal rates per minute are as follows:

cow: 45–50
sheep: 70–90
pig: 70–80

Within the body tissues each artery divides to form a branching system of minute blood vessels similar to the branching system of a tree; the smallest branches are no thicker than a hair from one's head. The hair-like vessels are called *capillaries*, and form a dense network through all tissues of the body. They are sometimes defined as the endings of arteries and the beginnings of veins. Veins are blood vessels which return blood from the body to the heart.

There are two distinct circulations of blood.

(a)

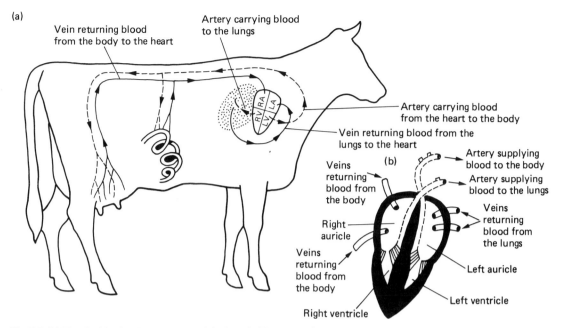

Vein returning blood from the body to the heart

Artery carrying blood to the lungs

Artery carrying blood from the heart to the body

Vein returning blood from the lungs to the heart

Veins returning blood from the body

(b)

Artery supplying blood to the body

Artery supplying blood to the lungs

Veins returning blood from the lungs

Right auricle

Left auricle

Veins returning blood from the body

Left ventricle

Right ventricle

Fig. 7.9 (a) The double circulatory system of the blood. (b) Longitudinal section through the heart.

The pulmonary artery, arising from the right ventricle, carries blood to the lungs where it absorbs oxygen; this oxygenated blood is then conveyed to the left auricle by the pulmonary vein. A flap-like valve controls the movement of blood from the left auricle into the left ventricle. The oxygenated blood from the left ventricle then begins its second circulation in the aorta artery which branches to all parts of the body, e.g. brain, skin, muscles, bones, stomach, small intestine, liver, pancreas, kidney, udder, etc. The venae cavae return the blood from the body parts to the right auricle; the blood is now deoxygenated because the oxygen has been absorbed by the cells of the body. Another valve controls movement of blood from the right auricle into the right ventricle. The double circulation of the blood is now complete. Note that it is the longitudinal division of the heart which ensures that oxygenated blood is separated from deoxygenated blood.

The hepatic portal system (Fig. 7.10) is an important exception to the usual arrangement of blood vessels in the circulatory system whereby an artery breaks up into capillaries that then recombine to form a vein; a portal system begins in capillaries and ends in capillaries. Capillary blood from the stomach, spleen, intestines and pancreas drains into the portal vein which carries the blood to the liver. In this large organ the portal vein breaks up into capillaries; this arrangement enables blood to filter through the liver before it enters the venae cavae. The significance of this 'filtering' process becomes apparent when the functions of the liver are studied (p. 80).

Blood consists of red and white corpuscles, microscopic in size, suspended in liquid plasma. Red corpuscles are spongy discs which absorb haemoglobin, a chemical rich in iron. When iron is deficient, insufficient haemoglobin is synthesized and the animal suffers from anaemia. Young piglets are highly susceptible to anaemia and this is why iron salts are injected into them soon after birth. Haemoglobin is capable of loosely combining with oxygen to form oxyhaemoglobin and on reaching the cells of the body the oxygen is released into them and the original haemoglobin restored. Each white corpuscle

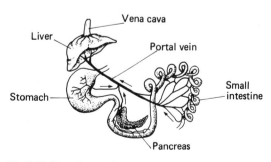

Vena cava

Liver

Portal vein

Stomach

Small intestine

Pancreas

Fig. 7.10 Hepatic portal system.

consists of a large nucleus embedded in cytoplasm (Fig. 7.11). When foreign bacteria invade the body, these corpuscles are capable of ingesting them; pus formed on an open wound consists of dead white corpuscles that have ingested such bacteria. Plasma consists of two liquids – serum and fibrinogen. When the skin is cut and fibrinogen is exposed to the air it changes from a liquid into thin threads of fibrin; a blood clot consists of white corpuscles enmeshed in a weave of such fibrin threads. The clear, straw-coloured liquid which oozes from the sides of a blood clot is serum. Serum is used for prevention and treatment of diseases because it contains the antibody fractions of the blood.

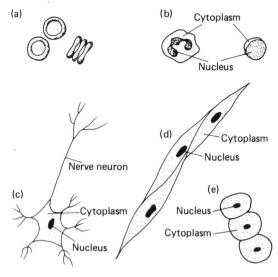

Fig. 7.11 Cells: (a) red corpuscles; (b) white corpuscles; (c) nerve cell; (d) muscle cells; (e) cells lining the stomach wall.

CELLULAR ACTIVITY

Every tissue and organ in the body is made up of microscopic units called cells. An example of a simple cell is a white corpuscle (Fig. 7.11). It consists of a nucleus embedded in a mass of jelly-like substance, cytoplasm. Every cell is basically constructed in this way; cells from different tissues differ, however, in shape and in the specialized function that they perform. For example, muscle cells are spindle-shaped and are able to contract in size; certain cells in the villi are columnar and are able to absorb liquid foodstuffs from the small intestine; cells in the salivary glands are able to secrete saliva containing ptyalin. Cells are able to absorb from blood contained in capillaries, the oxygen and liquid foodstuffs they require. They are also able to pass into the blood any waste or excretory products produced as a result of cell activity. Broadly speaking the functions performed by cells can be described under three headings.

Production of Energy and Body Heat

So as to remain healthy and active, the animal must maintain a constant body temperature. It must also be supplied with sufficient energy for growing, walking, grazing, chewing and digesting its food, breathing, pumping blood around its body and all other essential activities.

Body heat and energy for 'body work' are obtained by chemically burning or oxidizing foodstuffs within the living cells; this process is called internal cell respiration. It is essentially a process in which foodstuff molecules are broken down to release energy. Enzymes enact the oxidation process. When carbohydrates and fats are oxidized, heat is formed together with carbon dioxide and water as waste products. Sugar respiration can be expressed equationally thus:

$$C_6H_{12}O_6 + 6O_2 = 6CO_2 + 6H_2O + \text{heat}$$

When proteins are oxidized, nitrogenous waste products and salts are formed in addition to carbon dioxide and water. The waste products are passed into the bloodstream for eventual removal by the excretory organs.

The body temperature of a farm animal is usually recorded by inserting a clinical thermometer in the rectum and leaving it there for one minute; care is taken that the thermometer is shaken before using.

Normal body temperatures:
cattle   38.0–38.2°C
sheep   38.8–39.1°C
pigs   38.3–40.5°C

Synthesis of Body Tissues

The growth of a young animal into a mature beast implies building up of tissues such as bone, meat and fat. Since bone is composed mainly of calcium and phosphorus salts, an adequate supply of these mineral salts is necessary, particularly to rapidly growing young animals.

Meat or muscle is composed almost entirely of proteins. The 'liquid proteins' or amino acids absorbed in the small intestine are conveyed to muscle cells, where they are linked together in chains to form proteins and muscle. This process of building up proteins and protein tissues is very complicated and is called *assimilation*. Proteins are known as body-building foodstuffs, since they are the basic compounds required for assimilation.

Fat is usually formed late in the animal's development. Any fat not utilized by the animal for energy production is laid down in masses under the skin and around the internal organs.

Synthesis of Body Secretions

Fluids of different kinds are constantly being produced in the animal's body. The most vital fluid found is blood. We have already referred to the production of digestive juices from glands in the mouth, stomach wall, small intestine wall, pancreas and liver. Other fluids known as *hormones* are produced in other glands in the body and play an important role in certain bodily processes. To synthesize these fluids the animal requires digested foodstuffs as basic materials.

Milk secretion. The secretion of most interest to the farmer is milk. It is interesting to note that for every 5 litres of milk taken from the cow, 4.7 g of chlorine, 7.1 g of calcium oxide and 14.2 g of phosphate are lost to the cow; these losses emphasize the importance of minerals in a cow's diet. To appreciate how milk is formed it is necessary to study the structure of the udder (Figs. 7.12 and 7.13).

Internally the udder of the cow is divided into four distinct and separate quarters. Each quarter consists of a mass of spongy tissue throughout its upper portion. The tissue consists of millions of minute, balloon-like spheres of cells called *alveoli*. From the alveoli little ductlets or tubules pass downwards into the lower portion of the quarter, where they join together to form a hollow milk cistern above the teat. A narrow sinus or tube passes through the length of the teat connecting the milk cistern to the outside of the udder. A circular band of muscle protects the opening of the teat sinus.

The udder is supplied with blood from a branch of the body's main artery, the aorta. The artery sub-divides and breaks up into capillaries which surround the alveoli. The capillaries rejoin and leave the udder as a milk vein.

The soluble foodstuffs diffuse from the capillary blood into each alveolus by two distinct processes:

1. Water and vitamins pass unchanged from the blood through secretory cells into the alveolus cavity.

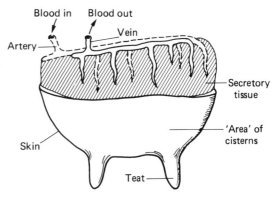

Fig. 7.12 A longitudinal section through the upper part of an udder.

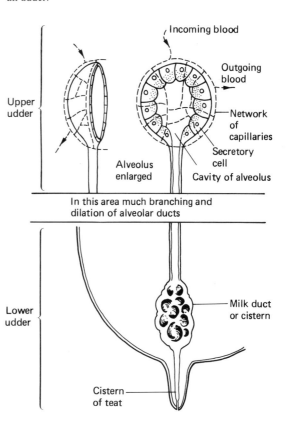

Fig. 7.13 Secretory and milk storage systems.

2. Amino acids, fats and glucose sugar pass from the blood into the secretory cells. Here they are changed into milk protein, butterfat and milk sugar, respectively. These changed products then pass into the alveolar cavity. This mixture of foodstuffs contained in the alveolus is milk.

The blood, drained of its foodstuffs, passes back through the capillaries into the milk vein.

EXCRETORY SYSTEM

The waste or excretory products formed as a result of cell activity are carbon dioxide, water, salts and nitrogen waste products; the latter are converted into urea in the liver (p. 80). The waste products are conveyed in the blood stream to the lungs, skin and kidneys where they are extracted from the blood.

Lungs

Carbon dioxide and some water diffuse from the blood via the walls of the capillaries and alveoli (p. 81).

Skin (Fig. 7.14)

The skin contains countless sweat glands. Each gland consists of a single tube with one blind end; the other end opens as the pore on the surface of the skin. The tube is twisted about itself near the blind end and is surrounded by a network of capillaries. Some water and mineral salts diffuse out from the blood through the thin walls of the capillaries and sweat tube. The tube fills with this saline solution (known as sweat) and passes out on to the surface of the skin through the pore.

Urine Excretory System (Fig. 7.15)

The kidneys are the main excretory organs. Water, mineral salts and urea are extracted from the blood stream in these two organs; this mixture of excretory products known as urine is conveyed from each kidney through a narrow tube (ureter) to the thin-walled bladder where it is stored. When the bladder is full, urine is passed out from the body via a urethral tube running through the penis in the male animal and through the wall of the vagina in the female animal.

The kidney itself is a bean-shaped organ, darkish-red in colour. When examined microscopically the kidney tissue is seen to consist of millions of urine-collecting tubules arranged radially; a cup-like structure, called a Bowman's capsule, forms the terminal end of each tubule; the open end of each tubule opens into the funnel-like openings of the upper end of the ureter.

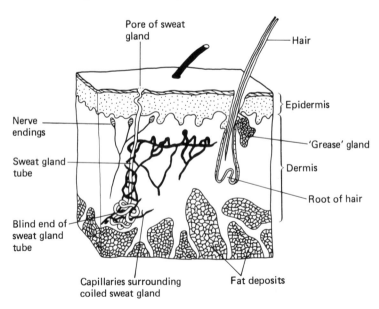

Fig. 7.14 Microscopic section of skin.

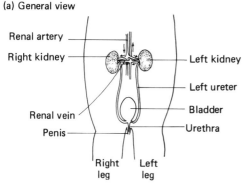

(a) General view

Renal artery
Right kidney
Renal vein
Penis
Right leg
Left leg
Left kidney
Left ureter
Bladder
Urethra

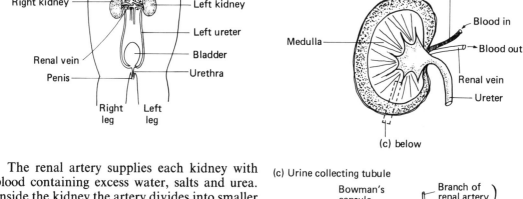

(b) Section through the length of a kidney

Cortex
Renal artery
Blood in
Medulla
Blood out
Renal vein
Ureter

(c) below

The renal artery supplies each kidney with blood containing excess water, salts and urea. Inside the kidney the artery divides into smaller and smaller branches, each branch ending up as a small bunch of capillaries inside the Bowman's capsule. The waste products in the blood diffuse through the thin walls of the capillaries into the capsule and the resulting urine passes down the tubule into the collecting funnel of the ureter.* The capillaries from each capsule rejoin into fewer but larger veins which finally emerge from the kidney as a single renal vein; the blood in this vein is free of excess water, salts and urea.

* To simplify description, the maintenance of homoeostasis by the kidneys has been omitted.

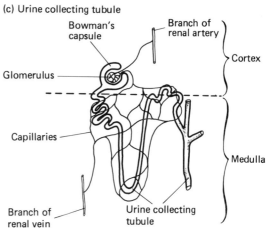

(c) Urine collecting tubule

Bowman's capsule
Branch of renal artery
Cortex
Glomerulus
Capillaries
Medulla
Branch of renal vein
Urine collecting tubule

Fig. 7.15 Urine excretory system.

CONTROL OF CONSTANT BODY TEMPERATURE

In normal healthy animals, the body temperature remains remarkably constant because the balance between heating itself and cooling itself is so well maintained.

The animal cools itself by getting rid of heat through its breath and urine and by evaporation of sweat from its skin. Under hot, moist atmospheric conditions the rate of breathing and sweating greatly increases; this is accompanied by a faster heart-beat so that a larger blood supply reaches the lungs and skin.

The animal heats itself by internal cell respiration. Under cold conditions this rate of respiration increases and heat loss from the skin is reduced by contraction of arteries in the skin which reduces the supply of blood and consequently of heat loss; this may result in shivering. The animal's hairy coat and layer of fat under its skin act as insulators.

METABOLISM

The twin processes of internal cell respiration and assimilation are often referred to as metabolic processes; Table 7.2 summarizes these processes and how they are maintained in the body. Further details concerning failures in the proper functioning of metabolic processes are described under 'Metabolic Diseases' (p. 216).

The metabolic energy relationships of ruminants are described in greater detail in Chapter 8.

Table 7.2. A summary of the animal's metabolic processes

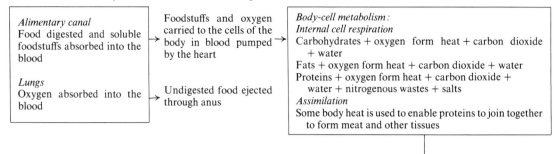

| *Alimentary canal*
Food digested and soluble foodstuffs absorbed into the blood

Lungs
Oxygen absorbed into the blood | → Foodstuffs and oxygen carried to the cells of the body in blood pumped by the heart

→ Undigested food ejected through anus | → *Body-cell metabolism:*
Internal cell respiration
Carbohydrates + oxygen form heat + carbon dioxide + water
Fats + oxygen form heat + carbon dioxide + water
Proteins + oxygen form heat + carbon dioxide + water + nitrogenous wastes + salts
Assimilation
Some body heat is used to enable proteins to join together to form meat and other tissues |

Waste products and waste heat are absorbed by blood from the body cells. These are returned to the lungs, kidneys and sweat glands (Nitrogenous wastes are converted into urea in the liver)

| *Symptoms of normal metabolism:*
Body temperature
Cattle   38.0–38.2°C
Sheep   38.8–39.1°C
Pigs   38.3–40.5°C

Rate of respiration
Cattle   12–16 breaths per min.
Sheep   15–20   ,,   ,,   ,,
Pigs   10–20   ,,   ,,   ,,

Rate of pulse and heart beats
Respiration rate × 4 | *Lungs:* Carbon dioxide, water vapour and heat are removed from the blood and passed out as exhaled air

Kidneys: Urea, salts, water and heat are removed from blood and passed out as urine

Sweat glands: Salts and water are removed from blood and passed out as sweat which evaporates and removes heat from the animal body |

CO-ORDINATION

Most bodily processes are co-ordinated by the nervous system; it is this system which enables the animal to act as a unified individual.

The nervous system consists of the brain, the spinal cord and thread-like, white nerves which radiate to all parts of the body (Fig. 7.17).

The co-ordinating function of this system can be appreciated if a simple reflex action is considered. If a cow is irritated by warble flies, it automatically switches its tail to remove the source of irritation; the irritation is called a stimulus, and the tail switching a response. How is it possible for the animal to react in this way to such an environmental change? The stimulus induces electrical impulses, or messages, to be conveyed along the nerve running from the skin on the back of the animal to the spinal cord (Fig. 7.16). The impulses are then carried across the cells of the spinal cord to another nerve which transmits the impulses to the muscles in the tail of the cow. The impulses stimulate the muscles to contract resulting in a switching movement of the tail.

The eyes and ears are highly developed sensory organs adapted to receive the stimuli of light and sound from the animal's external environment. The stimuli received by these organs induce electrical impulses in the nerves which connect these organs to the brain; when the impulses are received by the brain, sensations of sight and sound are experienced. Such sensations may induce simple responses such as blinking of the eye when stimulated by intense light or more complicated responses, as when a sheep runs away from the sight and sound of a dog. Stimuli from sensory organs located in the nose, tongue

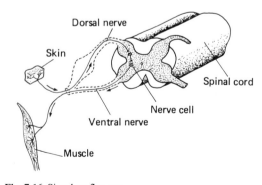

Fig. 7.16 Simple reflex arc.

and skin also convey impulses to the brain, resulting in the sensations of smell, taste and touch respectively.

The nervous system also controls responses resulting from stimuli received from changes in the internal environment of the body. For example the presence of food in an animal's stomach stimulates the glands in the stomach wall to secrete gastric juices; similar responses are induced by the presence of food in any part of the alimentary canal. Many responses induced by the nervous system are not only automatic but continuous, as is the case with the control exercised over rate of breathing and heart beat.

Hormonal Control

Endocrine glands situated in a distinct part of the body secrete, directly into the blood stream, chemical liquids known as hormones. Some of these hormones often produce an immediate response in a given organ. For example, oxytocin is produced in the pituitary gland and is conveyed to the udder where it immediately induces milk let-down. Other hormones such as adrenaline do not produce a response in just one organ but affect the general metabolic rate of the entire body; the effects produced, however, are just as immediate. Generally speaking, however, hormones are usually slower and more sustained in their action. The importance of hormones can be appreciated by referring to Table 7.3.

With some reflex actions both nerves and hormones are involved. This is the case with milk let-down.

Milk Let-Down

Some milk passes from the upper udder down to the main ducts, milk cisterns and teat sinuses during the period between milkings, but most of it remains in the alveoli and ductlets. Udder and teats become turgid with milk shortly after milking commences; the cow is said to have *let down* her milk into the lower udder.

A combination of external stimuli, such as sound of milking plant, feeding of dairy cake, or application of teat cups to teats, stimulates the cow to let down her milk. Nervous impulses are conveyed along the nerves and spinal cord to the

Table 7.3. Some endocrine glands and the effects of selected hormones produced by them

Gland	Situation in the body	Hormones	Effects of hormones
Thyroid	Near the larynx (voice-box)	Thyroxine	Accelerates metabolic rate; deficiency induces dwarfism in cattle
Adrenals	Close to kidneys	Adrenaline	Produced when an animal is frightened; increases rate of heart-beat breathing, cellular respiration and energy supply for an emergency; interferes with the effects of oxytocin
Pituitary	Base of the brain	Somatotropin	Stimulates growth
		Luteinizing hormone	Maintains yellow bodies in the ovaries and stimulates lactation
		Oxytocin	Stimulates uterine contractions during birth and causes milk let-down
Pancreas	Duodenal loop of small intestine	Insulin	Regulates sugar metabolism, i.e. prevents diabetes
Ovaries	Dorsal wall of abdomen	Oestrogen	Regulates female secondary sexual characters, e.g. development of udder, slower growth rate than male, laying down of fat deposits during finishing
		Progesterone	Prevents heat periods and ovulation
Testes	Between hind legs	Androgen	Regulates male characteristics such as high growth rate, little fat deposition during finishing and distinct flavour to meat; castration eliminates such characteristics
Placenta	Attached to uterus during pregnancy	Oestrogen etc.	Maintains normal pregnancy and prevents heat periods and ovulation

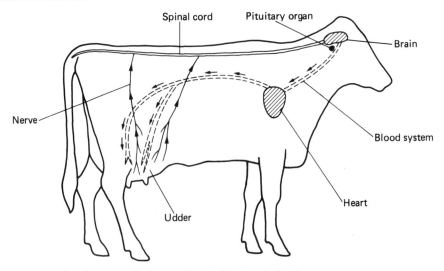

Fig. 7.17 Diagram showing the 'mechanism' controlling the 'let-down' of milk.

brain (Fig. 7.17). These impulses excite the *pituitary gland* at the base of the brain to secrete a hormone, *oxytocin*, into the bloodstream. The circulating blood carries the hormones to the udder where it causes the alveoli to contract. The pressure set up inside the alveoli and ductlets forces the milk down into the cisterns of the lower udder. The effect of oxytocin lasts about 7 to 10 minutes. This fact implies that the milking operation must be quick and methodical.

A nervous cow often fails to let down her milk because adrenaline has been released into the bloodstream. This hormone interferes with the effects of oxytocin.

The nervous and hormonal systems are thus complementary in the sense that they jointly co-ordinate the many diverse processes which constitute a living animal.

Hormones can now be chemically synthesized and used as aids in husbandry. Two notable examples are synthetic progesterone, which is used to control heat onset in ewes (p. 9), and hexoestrol, which is implanted to speed up growth-rate in beef cattle (p. 160).

8

Metabolic Energy Relationships

The sun's kinetic energy is the main source of energy for plants and animals. The sun's rays are trapped by the leaves of green plants and converted by photosynthesis into foodstuffs such as sugars, starch, fats, proteins; the latter are assimilated to form the tissues of the plants themselves. Green crop-plants are the foods on which all animals and humans depend and can be thought of as 'store houses' of potential energy. Farm animals ingest the plant foods, digest them, absorb from them the foodstuffs they require, and convert them into heat for warming their bodies, and into their own tissues (e.g. bone, fat and muscle) and secretions (e.g. milk). Thus animals and their products are a second source of potential energy for human needs.

FORMS OF ENERGY

Unit of Energy

A given quantity of food can be encased in a metal container, known as a bomb calorimeter, ignited by means of an electrical spark and the heat generated by its oxidation measured by immersing the 'bomb' in a jar containing a given quantity of water. The kinetic heat released warms the water and raises its temperature. The heat required to raise one gram of water one degree celsius is called a calorie. The calorific or energy value of a food is the number of calories released by a gram of that food.

The calorie as a unit of energy has now been replaced by the joule (J), one calorie being equivalent to 4.184 joules. Since the joule is a very small unit of energy the energy values of food are measured in megajoules (MJ), where 1 megajoule = 1 000 000 joules.

Gross Energy (Energy Value)

The main foodstuff contained in crops is water. In the subsequent discussions on energy this foodstuff is assumed to have no energy value but is considered as the substrate in which all energy changes occur; protoplasm itself consists mainly of water, and the essential processes of life can only occur in this liquid medium.

The gross energy of a food released as heat from a bomb calorimeter is measured as the number of megajoules per kilogram of the dry matter contained in the food. This energy value is directly related to relative amounts of carbohydrates, fats and proteins contained in the dry matter. Pure carbohydrate has an energy value of 17.5 MJ/kg, fats 44 MJ/kg and proteins about 26 MJ/kg. Since carbohydrates are the main foodstuffs in most foods, energy values are usually 18 MJ/kg of dry matter.

It needs to be appreciated that whilst the energy values of two foods may not differ greatly, the quantities of actual food required to supply the same amount of energy can differ considerably; the following example illustrates the point.

Equivalent weights of foods required to give the same quantity of gross energy:

	MJ/kg DM	Dry matter (%)
Barley (grain)	13.7	86
Kale	11.0	14

100 kg barley gives $13.7 \times 86 = 1178.2$
MJ gross energy

100 kg kale gives $11.0 \times 14 = 154.0$
MJ gross energy

In gross energy terms
  1 kg barley = $1178.2 \div 154.0 = 7.7$ kg kale.

91

Digestible Energy

After food has been eaten by the ruminant its fibrous matrix is firstly broken down by rumination and digestion by rumen bacteria; subsequently, digestion occurs in the abomasum and the small intestines; the digested foodstuffs are absorbed into the blood stream by the villi and conveyed to the cells of the body. The undigested food is passed out as faeces. If the faecal energy loss is subtracted from the gross energy of the food the resultant energy is known as digestible energy.

Digestibility and consequently digestible energy available is reduced for a food if:

i) its crude fibre content increases;
ii) its crude protein content decreases because this limits the activity of the bacteria in the rumen; a 12% crude protein requirement is minimal;
iii) high level of feeding is adopted; this induces faster passage of food through the alimentary canal thus reducing the rate of digestion as is the case with young succulent grass;
iv) grains are not rolled or milled.

Metabolizable Energy (ME)

Bacterial activity in the intestines will result in some methane gas being formed and passed out via the anus; the energy content of this gas is a loss to the animal.

The liquid foodstuffs which are absorbed from the blood into the cells are internally respired to form heat energy and excretory products such as carbon dioxide, water, salts and urea; the three latter products are passed out as urine which can be easily collected and its energy loss to the animal measured. Thus, when the energy losses from methane and urine are subtracted from the digestible energy value, this gives a metabolizable energy value. This is the quantity of heat energy resulting from the process of internal cell respiration and which is available to the animal for the:

i) maintenance of body temperature as heat losses occur from the skin surface of the animal;
ii) maintenance of body weight and essential living functions such as respiration, excretion, nutrition, movement, co-ordination and blood circulation;
iii) the synthesis of:
   (a) bone, fat and meat, i.e. growth resulting in liveweight gain,
   (b) milk and other secretions.

The energy and protein values of feeds together with the energy allowances and protein

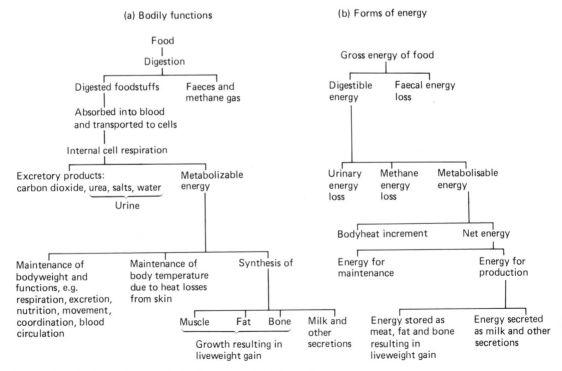

Fig. 8.1 Relationships between (a) bodily functions and (b) forms of energy.

needs of ruminants are listed in the appendix to this chapter and need to be referred to when mentioned in the text.

Net Energy

This is the energy available for the functions described under (ii) and (iii) in the previous paragraph. Equationally it is represented thus:

$$\text{Net energy} = \text{Metabolizable energy} - \text{Body heat gain.}$$

The inter-relationships between these forms of energy resulting from the animal's varied metabolic processes are shown in Fig. 8.1.

ENERGY RELATIONSHIPS IN THE DAIRY COW

Daily, during her productive cycle, the dairy cow is:
  i) producing a given quantity of milk except when she is dry;
 ii) gaining or losing body weight.

The energy required for these processes can only come from the cow's daily intake of food, and the quantity of the latter she can eat varies throughout the productive cycle. Fig. 8.2 shows part of the productive cycle of a 565 kg Friesian cow in her third lactation, giving 5000 litres of milk in total; this figure should be referred to when reading the following account of the basic principles involved.

Lactation

In the first three or four days of lactation colostrum is produced which is essential to the new born calf. The lactation period varies considerably but normally lasts about 300–320 days (official milk records are taken over a period of 305 days). This gives a dry period of six to eight weeks to allow for udder repair, preparation for calving and the next lactation. The lactation can be divided thus:

1. Early lactation period from calving to peak yield, which normally takes between eight and ten weeks. It is important that bulky fodders are restricted during this period (if silage – 7 kg DM per cow per day) to allow for the lead feeding of extra concentrates, e.g. 0.5 kg per litre instead of 0.4 kg per litre. Proper feeding during this period has a major influence on the cow's performance during the remainder of the lactation. This ensures that she will achieve her potential peak yield and also maintain it for a longer period. Failure to maintain adequate feeding at this time can result in loss of peak yield, acetonaemia, delayed oestrus and conception and low s.n.f. in milk.
2. Mid-lactation period from about the 10th to the 30th week of lactation. During this period concentrates are fed according to yield and bulky fodder can be increased slightly (if silage – 8 kg DM per cow per day).
3. Late lactation – during this period the cow's needs should be satisfied from forage whenever possible.

A cow in her 5th to 6th month of pregnancy will show a distinct decline in milk yield. On average about two-thirds of the total yield will occur in the first half of the lactation and the rate of decline will be about 2.5% per week once the post-peak decline has started.

A predicted lactation curve can be drawn for any cow based on the following assumptions.

1. Expected peak yield is:

either (a) actual milk yield at 14 days multiplied by a factor of 1.1, e.g. yield at 14 days = 18 litres
Expected peak yield = 18 × 1.1 = 20 litres
or (b) estimated total milk yield divided by a factor of 200, e.g. estimated yield = 5000 litres
Expected peak yield = 5000 ÷ 200 = 25 litres.

2. After peak yield, milk production decreases by 2.5% per week. What is the expected milk yield in week 25 of a lactation with a decrease from peak yield commencing in week 15?

$$\text{weeks of drop} = 10$$
$$\text{peak yield} = 25 \text{ litres}$$
$$\text{Drop in quantity} = 25 \times 10 \times \frac{2.5}{100}$$
$$= 6.25 \text{ litres,}$$
$$\text{Expected yield in week 25} = 25 - 6.25$$
$$= 18.75.$$

Seasonality of Production

Dairy cows tend to increase their daily yield in Spring irrespective of when they calve; spring calvers do not have this advantage, so they tend to give less milk in a lactation, e.g. a March calver will give about 95% of her potential yield;

a September calver will give about 104% and a November calver 108%.

Reproductive Performance

Most herds do not on average achieve more than one calf in 370 days, and for many one in 390 days; cows tend to slip about one month per year; first-calvers in November tend to have their fourth calves in February. The ideal 305 day lactation, 56 day dry-period, and 82 day interval between calving and mating is seldom achieved. This is because, even at best, conception rate is seldom better than 75% over the 50–

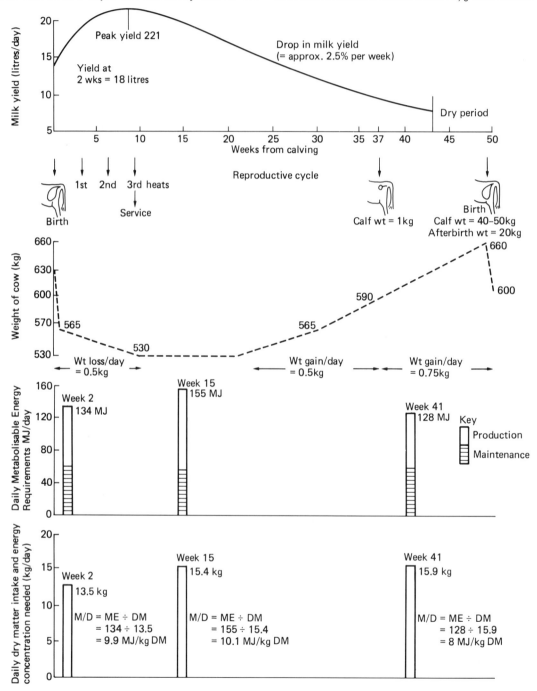

Fig. 8.2 Relationship between milk yield, calving, weight changes, energy needs, dry matter intake and energy concentrations needed in rations; 565 kg cow yielding 5000 litres of milk.

82 day period after calving, which is the critical period to maintain a 365 day calving index.

Reproductive Cycle

The fertilized egg takes approximately 40 weeks to grow into a fully developed calf. During the last 12 weeks of pregnancy rapid growth of the calf occurs and some 40–50 kg of foetal tissue is formed, as well as some 20 kg of placental (afterbirth) tissue. This means an increase in the cow's weight of some 65 kg over 84 days, i.e. a weight gain of 0.75 kg/day.

After the birth of the calf the cow continues to lose some of her body weight for approximately 10 weeks. In the main her body fat store of tissue is oxidized to form energy which is used for milk production. Lead feeding, i.e. feeding above level of milk produced, is thus necessary so that her body weight losses do not amount to more than 0.5 kg per day.

During the period of peak milk production there is no loss in body weight. During the period of falling milk production she tends to put on body weight by 0.5 kg per day and feed input must be adequate for this to occur. This daily rate of weight gain continues until the cow enters her last 12 weeks of pregnancy when the gain increases to 0.75 kg per day.

A Friesian cow properly fed should increase in body weight per lactation by about 35–40 kg up to her fourth lactation. In the example shown in Fig. 8.2 the cow has increased from 565 kg at the start of her lactation to 600 kg at the end. This could be the possible description of a Friesian cow in her third lactation having started as a down-calving heifer of 460 kg. Thus:

$$460 + (3 \times 35) = 565 \text{ kg.}$$

Metabolizable Energy Requirements

In the dairy cow the total energy requirements can be simply calculated by adding (or subtracting) the energy components required for:

1. Maintenance; this is related to body weight and values are shown in Table 8.2. It can be calculated by using the following formula:

$$8.3 + (0.091 \times \text{body weight}).$$

2. Milk production; values are shown in Table 8.3 for milk of varying composition. In Fig. 8.2 it has been assumed that fat content is 34 g/kg and s.n.f. content is 89 g/kg, giving an energy requirement of 4.9 MJ per litre.

3. Body weight changes; when a cow is losing weight by oxidizing her fat reserves, it has been calculated that 28 MJ of heat are released per kg of body tissue. On the other hand when a cow gains weight she is using energy to assimilate liquid foodstuffs into meat and fat, and a higher energy need of 34 MJ/kg of body tissue is required.

The energy requirement at any point in a cow's productive cycle can be illustrated by reference to three separate weeks:

e.g. What is the daily energy requirement of the cow in week 2?

		MJ
Maintenance: $8.3 + (560 \times 0.091)$	=	60
Milk: lead feed to 20 litres @ 4.9 MJ/litre	=	98
		158
less Body weight loss: 0.5 kg @ 28 MJ/kg	=	−14
		134

e.g. What is the daily energy requirement of the cow in week 15?

		MJ
Maintenance: $8.3 + (530 \times 0.091)$	=	57
Milk: 20 litres @ 4.9 MJ/litre	=	98
Body weight gain or loss	=	0
		155

e.g. What is the daily energy requirement of the cow in week 41?

		MJ
Maintenance: $8.3 + (605 \times 0.091)$	=	63
Milk: 8 litres @ 4.9 MJ/litre	=	39
Body weight gain: 0.75 kg @ 34 MJ/kg	=	26
		128

Energy Input

The productive capacity of the cow is determined mainly by the quantity of food and in particular the dry matter which she can eat in a day. This quantity varies according to her body weight and the quantity of milk she produces. Table 8.4 shows the probable dry matter intake in mid and late lactation and is based on the following equation:

Dry matter intake = 0.025 body weight + 0.1 litre milk yield.

Thus dry matter intake (DMI) in weeks 15 and 41 could be as follows:

Week 15
DMI = $(0.025 \times 530) + (0.1 \times 20)$
= 13.38 + 2.0 = 15.4 kg

Week 41
DMI = $(0.025 \times 605) + (0.1 \times 8)$
15.1 + 0.8 = 15.9 kg.

The dry matter intake of a cow is much reduced in the first ten weeks of her lactation and her appetite is probably 2–3 kg below the value in Table 8.4. Thus in:

Week 2
DMI = (0.025 × 560) + (0.1 × 20) = 16.0
less correction for early lactation   −2.5
                                    ‾‾‾‾‾‾
                                    13.5 kg

Digestibility, processing and method of conservation of forage, nature of feeding systems and timing of feeds are all factors that affect the dry matter intake and the experience and judgement of the stockman are invaluable in this respect.

Energy Concentration of Ration

It can now be appreciated that in any week during her productive cycle:

i) the cow requires a given quantity of metabolizable energy, and
ii) the amount of dry matter she can eat is limited.

Thus for each week the cow requires a ration of food whose dry matter contains sufficient energy per kilogram to meet her energy needs. This is known as the energy concentration of a ration's dry matter (M/D), i.e. metabolizable energy per kg of food dry matter. Examine the concentrations required in the different weeks under review:

e.g. What energy concentration (M/D) is required in the ration during week 15?
Metabolizable energy required = 155 MJ
Dry matter food intake   = 15.4 kg
M/D = 155 ÷ 15.4 = 10.1 MJ/kg DM.

e.g. What M/D is required in the ration during week 41?
Metabolizable energy required = 128 MJ
Dry matter food intake   = 15.9 kg
M/D = 128 ÷ 15.9 = 8.0 MJ/kg DM.

e.g. What M/D is required in the ration during week 2?
Metabolizable energy required = 134
Dry matter food intake   = 13.5 kg
M/D = 134 ÷ 13.5 = 9.9 MJ/kg DM.

Devising a Ration using Two Foods

Now that the necessary information concerning the cow's energy relationship has been processed, it is simple to devise a ration provided only two foods are fed. Assume that silage (9 MJ/kg DM) and dairy cake (12.5 MJ/kg DM) are available. A ration can be devised by using the following equation:

Forage dry matter intake in kg
$$= \frac{\text{Dry matter intake} \times (\text{M/D of cake} - \text{M/D of ration})}{\text{M/D of cake} - \text{M/D of silage}}$$

e.g. For week 15
Forage dry matter intake
$$= \frac{15.4 \times (12.5-10.1)}{12.5-9}$$
$$= \frac{15.4 \times 2.4}{3.5}$$
= 10.6 kg silage dry matter
Dairy cake dry matter intake
= total DMI − Silage DMI
= 15.4 − 10.6 = 4.8 kg

The ration proper can now be calculated because the dry matter content of the silage (20%) and the dairy cake (90%) is known:
20 kg silage DM contained in 100 kg silage
10.6 kg silage DM contained in
$\frac{100}{20} \times 10.6 = 53$ kg silage
90 kg dairy cake DM contained in 100 kg dairy cake
4.8 kg dairy cake DM contained in
$\frac{100}{90} \times 4.8 = 5.3$ kg dairy cake;
e.g. for week 2,
Forage dry matter intake
$$= \frac{13.5 \times (12.5 - 9.9)}{12.5 - 9}$$
$$= \frac{13.5 \times 2.6}{3.5} = 10 \text{ kg silage dry matter};$$
Dairy cake dry matter intake
= 13.5 − 10 = 3.5 kg
20 kg silage dry matter contained in 100 kg silage
10 kg silage dry matter contained in
$\frac{100}{20} \times 10 = 50$ kg silage
90 kg dairy cake dry matter contained in 100 kg dairy cake
3.5 kg dairy cake dry matter contained in
$\frac{100}{90} \times 3.5 = 3.8$ kg dairy cake

e.g. for week 41, the metabolizable energy for silage alone (9 MJ/kg) is greater than the M/D requirement of the ration (8.0 MJ/kg). In this situation the cow is allowed to eat silage to satisfy her appetite.

Checking the Protein Content of the Rations

It has been previously stated in the paragraph on digestible energy that a minimum of 12% protein is required in the ration. It needs to be remembered that it is the assimilation of amino acids into proteins that determines the weight gain of meat (see Synthesis of Body Tissues, chapter 7); also, protein is lost in the milk secreted by the cow.

Tables 8.5 and 8.6 show the cow's protein needs for maintenance and milk production respectively. Table 8.1 shows the digestible crude protein per cent in the dry matter of foods consumed. The protein content of the ration for week 15 can now be checked:

Protein requirements of cow		*kg*
Maintenance	=	0.32
Milk production 20 litres @ 0.05 kg/litre	=	1.00
Total		1.32

100 kg moderate silage dry matter supplies 10.2 kg protein

10.6 kg silage dry matter supplies $\dfrac{10.2}{100} \times 10.6 = 1.08$

100 kg dairy cake dry matter supplies 12.5 kg protein

4.8 kg dairy cake dry matter supplies $\dfrac{12.5}{100} \times 4.8 = 0.60$

$$\underline{1.68}$$

Excess protein   0.36

Adequate protein is thus being supplied. The excess protein could be reduced by substituting barley grain for dairy cake.

Devising a Ration where Known Quantities of Home Grown Foods are Available

Often in practice a given quantity of either summer grass or winter food supplies are available on a daily basis. In this situation the energy supplied by these foods is calculated and the additional energy requirements of the cow satisfied by feeding concentrates. The method of calculation for this approach is shown in Example 8.1 (overleaf).

Computing Rations for High-Yielding Cows

A point is reached where cows which are capable of giving high quantities of milk are unable to consume their nutrient requirement if there is too much bulky food in their daily diet.

If the normal method of rationing were used, the following ration for a Friesian giving 32 litres daily could be devised:

Food	Dry matter content (kg)
7.0 kg hay	6.00
25.0 kg kale	3.50
1.8 kg barley	1.55
9.1 kg balanced concentrate	8.19
	19.24

This total of 19.3 kg of dry matter is well outside the cow's capacity, even for a large 560 kg animal.

In order to get all the required nutrients inside a high-yielding cow the amount of bulky food is drastically reduced and replaced by concentrates. The potential of many high-yielding cows is not reached because they are allowed to eat too much bulky fibrous food. It is usual practice for all the nutrients required for production to be supplied by balanced concentrate at 0.3 or 0.35 kg per litre and also part of the maintenance requirement is supplied by other concentrates, e.g. oats, barley or dried sugar-beet pulp. About 4.5–5.5 kg of hay or straw must be fed daily to ensure that the rumen has sufficient fibre to function properly. A daily ration for the above Friesian cow producing 32 litres could be:

Food	kg dry matter
4.5 kg hay ⎱ Maintenance	3.83
3.2 kg barley ⎰	2.75
11.0 kg balanced concentrates –	
Production	9.90
	16.48

The cow would be able to cope with this amount.

The feeding of high-yielding cows demands a high standard of cowmanship. A good stockman will realize that the dry matter capacity of these cows differs markedly one from the other, and each cow should be treated as an individual. Cows can be induced to eat more by feeding them small amounts frequently during the day, using high quality hay and concentrates fed at 0.3 kg per litre.

Steaming-Up

Steaming-up means feeding a concentrated ration over and above the cow's maintenance ration, so as to bring her into a fit condition for calving. Three factors must be considered when estimating such a ration.

1. *Condition of the cow or heifer.* An animal in poor, thin condition will obviously require more steaming-up than an animal in good condition. Fitness and not fatness is aimed at, so the ration of food must be rich in protein.

2. *Expected yield of milk in the next lactation.* The expected peak yield of milk will, to a large extent, determine the maximum amount of concentrates which are fed to the cow just prior to calving.

3. *Time of year.* A cow or heifer calving during the winter period and feeding on hay or silage

Example 8.1†

A 600 kg dairy cow in mid-lactation gives 25 kg of milk (s.n.f. 88 g/kg: b.f. 36 g/kg) per day: the cow's weight remains constant. The following home-grown foods are available per day throughout the winter period:

45 kg grass silage (high D)
3.5 kg barley grain

What quantity of 'dairy cake' needs to be fed?

1. Dry matter supplied by home-grown foods.

	DM (kg)
1 kg grass silage supplies 0.25[a] kg dry matter (DM)	
45 kg grass silage supplies 0.25 × 45	11.25
1 kg barley supplies 0.86[d] kg DM	
3.5 kg barley supplies 0.86 × 3.5	3.0
Total ration supplies	14.25

   [a] in Table 8.1, section 4; [d] in Table 8.1, section 8

2. Metabolizable Energy (ME) and Digestible Crude Protein (DCP) supplied by the dry matter of the home-grown foods.

	ME (MJ)	*DCP (kg)*	
1 kg of grass silage dry matter supplies	9.3[b]	0.11	(10.7[c] ÷ 100, to two places of decimals)
11.25 kg of grass silage dry matter supplies	9.3 × 11.25 = 104.6	0.11 × 11.25 = 1.23	
1 kg of barley dry matter supplies	13.7[e]	0.08	(8.2[f] ÷ 100, to two places of decimals)
3.0 kg of barley dry matter supplies	13.7 × 3.0 = 41.1	0.08 × 3.0 = 0.24	
	Total 145.7	0.47	

   [b] in Table 8.1, section 4; [c] in Table 8.1, section 4; [e] in Table 8.1, section 8; [f] in Table 8.1, section 8

3. Metabolizable Energy (ME) an Digestible Crude Protein (DCP) requirements of the cow.

	ME (MJ)	*DCP (kg)*	
Maintenance	63[g]		0.32[i]
1 kg milk requires 5.01 MJ[h]		0.05 kg[j]	
25 kg milk requires 5.01 × 25 =	125.25	0.05 × 25 =	1.25
Total	188.25		1.57

   [g] in Table 8.2; [i] in Table 8.5; [h] in Table 8.3; [j] in Table 8.6

4. Balancing of the energy requirement.

	MJ
Cow's requirement	188.25
Home-grown ration supplies	145.70
Energy needed	42.55

5. Dairy cake requirement.
   12.5 MJ of metabolizable energy supplied by 1.0 kg of cake dry matter (see p. 129)
   1 MJ of metabolizable energy supplied by 1.0/12.5 kg of cake dry matter
   42.55 MJ of metabolizable energy supplied by (1 × 42.55 kg)/12.5 of cake dry matter = 3.4 kg
   0.9 kg DM supplied by 1.0 kg cake (see p. 129)
   3.4 kg DM supplied by (1.0 × 3.4)/0.9 = 3.8 kg cake

6. Checking the ration.

	DM (kg)	*ME (MJ)*	*DCP (kg)*
45 kg grass silage	11.25	104.6	1.23
3.5 kg barley	3.00	41.1	0.24
3.8 kg 'dairy cake'	3.40	42.55	0.43 (0.125 × 3.4) (see p. 129)
Total supply	17.65	188.25	1.90
Cow's needs	17.50[k]	188.25	1.57
Excess protein			0.33

   [k] in Table 8.4

† The superior letters indicated on this page refer the reader to the tabular extracts on the page opposite. The complete tables will be found in the appendix to this chapter.

Extracts from tables to supplement Example 8.1

Extract from Table 8.1

Feed	Dry matter content (%)	Nutritive value on dry matter basis	
		Metabolizable energy (MJ/kg)	Digestible crude protein (%)
⋮	⋮	⋮	⋮
4. *Silage – clamp*			
Grass, very high D	25	10.2	11.6
Grass, high D	25[a]	9.3[b]	10.7[c]
Grass, moderate D	25	8.8	10.2
Grass, low D	25	7.6	9.8
⋮	⋮	⋮	⋮
8. *Cereal grains*			
Barley	86[d]	13.7[e]	8.2[f]
Maize	86	14.2	7.8
Oats	86	11.5	8.4
Wheat	86	14.0	10.5
⋮	⋮	⋮	⋮

Extract from Table 8.2

Body weight			
kg	... 500	550	600
MJ/head	... 54	59	63[g]

Extract from Table 8.3

Solids – not-fat content (g/kg)	Fat content of milk (g/kg)							
	30	32	34	36	38	40	42	44 ...
⋮	⋮	⋮	⋮	⋮	⋮	⋮	⋮	⋮
87	4.58	4.71	4.84	4.98	5.10	5.24	5.37	5.50 ...
88	4.62	4.75	4.88	5.01[h]	5.14	5.27	5.40	5.53 ...
89	4.65	4.78	4.91	5.04	5.17	5.31	5.44	5.57 ...
90	4.69	4.82	4.95	5.08	5.21	5.34	5.47	5.60 ...
⋮	⋮	⋮	⋮	⋮	⋮	⋮	⋮	⋮

Table 8.5

Breed	Ave. live wt (kg)	Maintenance requirements (kg protein)
Friesian, Shorthorn	560	0.32[i]
Welsh Black, Red Poll	500	0.32
Ayrshire, Guernsey	450	0.27
Jersey	380	0.23

Table 8.6

Butterfat (g/kg)	per litre (kg protein)
35–39	0.05[j]
40–44	0.05
45–49	0.06
50–53	0.06

Extract from Table 8.4

Live weight, W (kg)	Milk yield, Y (kg/day)							
	5	10	15	20	25	30	35	40
⋮	⋮	⋮	⋮	⋮	⋮	DL	⋮	⋮
550	14.3	14.8	15.3	15.8	16.3	16.8	17.3	17.8
600	15.5	16.0	16.5	17.0	17.5[k]	18.0	18.5	19.0
650	16.8	17.3	17.8	18.3	18.8	19.3	19.8	20.3
700	18.0	18.5	19.0	19.5	20.0	20.5	21.0	21.5

Example 8.2: Predict the liveweight gain of a steer weighing 250 kg and receiving the following daily rations:

	DMI* (kg)	ME (MJ)
4.0 kg hay (0.85 kg DM/kg hay at 9 MJ/kg DM) =	3.4 (4 × 0.85)	30.6 (3.4 × 9)
1.5 kg barley (0.86 kg DM/kg barley at 13.7 MJ/kg DM) =	1.3 (1.5 × 0.86)	17.8 (1.3 × 13.7)
	4.7	48.4

M/D of ration = 48.4 ÷ 4.7	= 10 MJ/kg[a]
ME for maintenance	= 31 MJ[c]
Therefore ME for production = 48.4 − 31	= 17.4 MJ[b]
MJ of net energy (E_g) available for production	= 8 MJ
Liveweight gain = 0.55 kg[d]	

[a] in Table 8.7; [c] in Table 8.2; [b] in Table 8.7; [d] in Table 8.8

* DMI = dry matter intake.

Example 8.3: A 250 kg steer is required to gain 0.75 kg/day. There is sufficient hay to feed 6 kg/day. How much barley needs to be fed?

DM intake/day	= 6.6 kg[e]
Net energy required/day	= 33.2 MJ[f]

∴ Minimum net energy concentration required in ration = 33.2 ÷ 6.6 = 5.11 MJ/kg DM.

Foods available:

	M/D	%DM
Hay (moderate)	8.4 MJ/kg	85
Barley	13 MJ/kg	86

At 250 kg liveweight and gain of 0.75 kg/day the APL is 1.5[a]. At an APL of 1.5, net energy available from

Hay = 4.7 MJ[h]
Barley = 8.6 MJ[i]

$$\text{Forage DM intake} = \frac{\text{DM intake (net energy barley − net energy ration)}}{\text{Net energy barley − Net energy forage}}$$

$$= \frac{6.6 (8.6 − 5.11)}{8.6 − 4.7} = 5.9 \text{ kg}$$

Barley DM intake = Total DM intake − Forage DM intake
= 6.6 − 5.9 = 0.7 kg

85 kg forage DM supplied by 100 kg forage

∴ 5.9 kg forage DM supplied by $\frac{100}{85}$ × 5.9 = 6.9 kg

86 kg barley DM supplied by 100 kg barley

∴ 0.7 kg barley DM supplied by $\frac{100}{86}$ × 0.7 = 0.8 kg

Ration reads: 7 kg hay
0.8 kg barley

[a] in Table 8.11; [e] in Table 8.9; [f] in Table 8.10; [g] in Table 8.11; [h] in Table 8.12; [i] in Table 8.12

Extracts from tables to supplement Example 8.2.

Extract from Table 8.2

Body weight (kg)	100	150	200	250	300	350	...
MJ/head	17	22	27	31[c]	36	40	...

Extract from Table 8.7

Energy concentration M/D (MJ/kg DM)

MEP (MJ)	7	8	9	10[a]	11	
5	1.4	1.7	1.9	2.1	2.3	...
10	2.9	3.3	3.7	4.1	4.6	...
15	4.3	5.0	5.6	6.2	6.8	...
				b		
20	5.8	6.6	7.5	8.3	9.1	...
⋮	⋮	⋮	⋮	⋮	⋮	

Extract from Table 8.8

E_g (MJ)   Liveweight, W (kg)

E_g (MJ)	100	150	200	250	300	350	
2	0.23	0.21	0.19	0.17	0.16	0.15	...
4	0.43	0.39	0.36	0.33	0.30	0.28	...
6	0.60	0.55	0.51	0.47	0.44	0.41	...
				d			
8	0.76	0.70	0.64	0.60	0.56	0.52	...
10	0.90	0.83	0.77	0.72	0.67	0.63	...
⋮	⋮	⋮	⋮	⋮	⋮	⋮	

Extracts from tables to supplement Example 8.3.

Table 8.9

Live weight W (kg)	100	150	200	250	300	350	400	450	500	550	600
DMI (kg)	2.94	4.26	5.48	6.60[e]	7.62	8.54	9.36	10.08	10.70	11.22	11.65

Extract from Table 8.10

Gain (kg)	Liveweight, W (kg)						
	100	150	200	250	300	350	
⋮	⋮	⋮	⋮	⋮	⋮	⋮	
0.6	18.7	22.6	26.5	30.4	34.4	38.3	...
0.7	20.0	24.2	28.1	32.2	36.3	40.4	...
				f			
0.8	21.4	25.7	29.9	34.1	38.4	42.6	...
0.9	23.0	27.4	31.8	36.2	40.6	45.0	...
1.0	24.6	29.3	33.9	38.5	43.1	47.7	...
⋮	⋮	⋮	⋮	⋮	⋮	⋮	

Extract from Table 8.11

Liveweight W (kg)	Liveweight gain LWG. (kg/day)					
	0.25	0.50	0.75	1.00	1.25	1.50
100	1.19	1.40	1.66	1.98		
150	1.16	1.36	1.59	1.87		
200	1.15	1.33	1.54	1.79	2.11	
250	1.14	1.30	1.50[g]	1.74	2.03	
300	1.13	1.29	1.47	1.70	2.97	2.33
⋮	⋮	⋮	⋮	⋮	⋮	⋮

Extract from Table 8.12

APL	ME of food, MEF (MJ/kg DM)						
	8	9	10	11	12	13	14
⋮	⋮	⋮	⋮	⋮	⋮	⋮	⋮
1.30	4.6	5.4	6.3	7.1	7.9	8.8	9.7
1.35	4.5	5.3	6.2	7.0	7.8	8.7	9.6
1.40	4.4	5.2	6.1	6.9	7.8	8.7	9.6
1.45	4.3	5.1	6.0	6.8	7.7	8.6	9.5
1.50	4.2 [h]	5.1	5.9	6.8	7.7	8.6[i]	9.5
⋮	⋮	⋮	⋮	⋮	⋮	⋮	⋮

will need a considerable quantity of concentrates. A spring calver, however, feeding on lush grass, will require far less concentrates.

Winter calvers in a lean condition are normally given their maximum ration of concentrates 7–10 days before calving. This maximum quantity is calculated as 50% of the daily concentrates which would be fed to the cow at her expected daily peak milk yield. Thus if the expected daily peak yield of milk was 20 litres, then 4 kg of dairy concentrates would be fed, i.e. half of 8 kg fed at peak yield. This amount of concentrate is then decreased, working backwards to the sixth week before calving, by 0.5 kg a week. To avoid flushing of the cow's milk, it is advisable to reduce the cow's concentrates some three days before calving.

When a cow or heifer is in good condition, then the amount of concentrates fed can be reduced. This form of feeding is illustrated in the following example.

Example 1. The steaming-up rations for a winter-calving cow, expected to yield 20 litres at her peak period of milking.

Weeks before calving	Max. daily concentrates (kg)
6	1.5
5	2
4	2.5
3	3
2	3.5
1	4*

The amount of steaming-up must ultimately depend on the stockman's judgement.

* Three days before calving, this amount is reduced to 2.5 or 3 kg.

ENERGY RELATIONSHIPS IN GROWING CATTLE

When cattle grow they increase in weight daily usually at a given rate, e.g. 0.5 or 0.75 kg per day. Thus the amount of energy they require for maintenance is constantly increasing. They are able to consume a given quantity of dry matter daily so that the amount of weight gain is related to the concentration of energy contained in the dry matter of any diet.

There are two ways in which the metabolizable energy system can be used in practice:

i) to predict the daily liveweight gain from a given ration, and
ii) to formulate a daily ration of food for a given liveweight gain per day.

Prediction of Daily Liveweight Gain

Example 8.2 (p. 100) shows a simple method which can be used. The basic assumptions which are made and quantified in the tables given are as follows:

1. Table 8.2 shows that as the cow's body-weight increases the quantity of energy required for maintenance increases.

2. Table 8.7 shows that the amount of net energy (E_g) available for productive liveweight gain depends on the metabolizable energy available for production and the energy concentration (M/D) of the ration. As the latter increases the quantity of net energy available increases.

3. Table 8.8 shows that

(a) at a given net energy level the amount of energy available for production decreases as the live-weight of the animal increases, e.g. at an energy level of 2 MJ the energy available for production in an animal weighing 100 kg is 0.23 MJ which decreases to 0.11 MJ when the animal weighs 600 kg;

(b) at a given live-weight the net energy available for production is directly related to the net energy made available from the food intake.

Formulating Rations for Given Levels of Performance

Example 8.3 (p. 100) shows a simple method which can be used. The basic assumptions which are made and quantified in the tables given are as follows:

1. Table 8.10 shows that

(a) at a given live-weight the net energy requirement varies directly according to the live-weight gain expected, e.g. at 100 kg live-weight approximately 1.1 MJ of net energy is required for every 0.1 kg daily increase in weight;

(b) at a given daily weight gain the net energy requirement varies directly according to the animal live-weight, e.g. at a daily weight gain of 0.2 kg the net energy requirement increases by approximately 3.4 MJ for every 50 kg of live-weight.

2. Table 8.11 shows the Animal Production Level (APL); this is the total net energy required as a multiple of the net energy required for maintenance only. For example, an animal weighing 100 kg and gaining 0.25 kg live weight per day requires 1.19 times as much energy for both production and maintenance as it requires for maintenance only; an animal weighing 600 kg and gaining 1.50 kg live-weight per day requires 2.13 times as much energy for both production and maintenance as it requires for maintenance only.

3. Table 8.12 shows that

(a) at a given APL the net energy from food available for maintenance and production varies directly according to metabolizable energy concentration of the food. For example, at an APL of 1.00, 0.7 MJ of net energy are available for every 1.0 MJ of metabolizable energy present in the food; at an APL of 2.25, 0.9 MJ of net energy are available for every 1.0 MJ of metabolizable energy present in the food;

(b) at a given metabolizable energy concentration of food the net energy from food available for maintenance and production decreases as the APL increases. For example, when 8 MJ of M.E. are available from food the net energy available for maintenance and production drops from 5.8 MJ at APL 1.00 to 3.6 MJ at APL 2.25.

Protein Check

The protein content in a given ration needs to be checked to ascertain whether it is sufficient to satisfy the protein requirements of the growing animal (Table 8.13). Minimum protein levels are essential but it is seldom possible to exactly balance protein intake and requirements. The method of checking is shown below for the two rations examples 8.2 and 8.3 described previously.

Example 8.2

Protein supplied by	kg	kg	
1 kg hay* DM =	0.04		(Table 8.1)
3.4 kg hay DM =		0.14	
1 kg barley DM =	0.08		(Table 8.1)
1.3 kg barley DM =		0.10	
ration =		0.24	
Protein required (250 kg steer with daily weight gain of 0.62 kg) =		0.40	(Table 8.13)
Protein deficiency		0.16	

Example 8.3

Protein supplied by	kg	kg	
1 kg hay* DM =	0.04		(Table 8.1)
5.9 kg hay DM =		0.24	
1 kg barley DM =	0.08		(Table 8.1)
0.7 kg barley DM =		0.06	
ration =		0.30	
Protein required (250 kg steer with daily weight gain of 0.75 kg) =		0.44	(Table 8.13)
Protein deficiency		0.14	

* Moderate digestibility

APPENDIX TO CHAPTER 8: COMPOSITION OF FOODS, ENERGY ALLOWANCES AND PROTEIN REQUIREMENTS TABLES

(Energy Allowances tables extracted from Technical Bulletin 33
Ministry of Agriculture, Fisheries and Food)

Table 8.1. Composition of some feeding stuffs

Feed	Dry matter content (%)	Nutritive value on dry matter basis		
		Metabolizable energy (MJ/kg)	Digestible crude protein (%)	D-value (%)
1. *Roots*				
Mangels	12	12.4	5.8	79
Swede/turnip	12	12.8	9.1	82
2. *Green feeds*				
Kale (thousand head)	16	11.1	10.6	71
Kale (marrow stem)	14	11.0	12.3	69
3. *Grasses*				
Pasture Grass:				
set stocking close grazing	20	12.1	22.5	75
Pasture grass:				
rotational grazing 3 week interval	20	12.1	18.5	75
Pasture grass:				
extensive grazing winter (free growth after June				
grazing)	20	9.7	10.1	63
4. Silage – clamp				
Grass, very high D	25	10.2	11.6	67
Grass, high D	25	9.3	10.7	61
Grass, moderate D	25	8.8	10.2	58
Grass, low D	25	7.6	9.8	52
5. *Silage – tower*				
Grass, very high D	40	10.4	12.1	68
Grass, high D	40	9.3	8.7	61
6. *Hay*				
Grass (very high digestibility)	85	10.1	9.0	67
Grass (moderate digestibility)	85	8.4	3.9	57
Grass (very low digestibility)	85	7.0	3.8	47
7. *Straw*				
Spring barley	86	7.3	0.9	49
Winter barley	86	5.8	0.8	39
Oats	86	6.7	1.0	46
8. *Cereal grains*				
Barley	86	13.7	8.2	86
Maize	86	14.2	7.8	87
Oats	86	11.5	8.4	68
Wheat	86	14.0	10.5	87
9. *Legume seeds*				
Winter beans	86	12.8	20.9	81
Peas	86	13.4	22.5	85
10. *Oil cakes/meals*				
Coconut cake	90	13.0	18.4	75
Cotton cake (decorticated)	90	12.3	39.3	70
Groundnut cake (decorticated)	90	12.9	44.9	76
Linseed cake	90	13.4	28.6	75
Palm kernel cake	90	12.8	19.6	76
Soya bean meal	90	12.3	45.3	79
11. *Animal origin*				
Fish meal	90	11.1	63.1	68
12. *By-products*				
Sugar beet molasses	75	12.5	3.1	79
Sugar cane molasses	75	12.7	1.4	80
Wheat feeds – middlings	88	11.9	12.9	72

Table 8.2. Daily maintenance allowance of ME for beef cattle and dairy cows

Body weight (kg)	100	150	200	250	300	350	400	450	500	550	600
MJ/head	17	22	27	31	36	40	45	49	54	59	63

(including safety margin). Based on $M_m = 8.3 + 0.091$ W.

Table 8.3. Metabolizable energy allowance to produce 1 kg milk of varying composition

Solids-not-fat content (g/kg)	Fat content of milk (g/kg)											
	30	32	34	36	38	40	42	44	46	48	50	52
84	4.48	4.61	4.74	4.87	5.00	5.13	5.26	5.39	5.52	5.65	5.79	5.92
85	4.51	4.64	4.77	4.90	5.04	5.17	5.30	5.43	5.56	5.69	5.82	5.95
86	4.55	4.68	4.81	4.94*	5.07	5.20	5.33	5.46	5.59	5.72	5.85	5.99
87	4.58	4.71	4.84	4.98	5.10	5.24	5.37	5.50	5.63	5.76	5.89	6.02
88	4.62	4.75	4.88	5.01	5.14	5.27	5.40	5.53	5.66	5.79	5.92	6.05
89	4.65	4.78	4.91	5.04	5.17	5.31†	5.44	5.57	5.70	5.83	5.96	6.09
90	4.69	4.82	4.95	5.08	5.21	5.34	5.47	5.60	5.73	5.86	5.99	6.12
91	4.72	4.85	4.98	5.11	5.24	5.37	5.51	5.64	5.77	5.90	6.03	6.16
92	4.76	4.89	5.02	5.15	5.28	5.41	5.54	5.67	5.80	5.93	6.06	6.19
93	4.79	4.92	5.05	5.18	5.31	5.44	5.57	5.71	5.84	5.97	6.10	6.23
94	4.82	4.96	5.09	5.22	5.35	5.48	5.61	5.74	5.87	6.00	6.13	6.26
95	4.86	4.99	5.12	5.25	5.38	5.51	5.64	5.77	5.91	6.04	6.17	6.30

(including safety margin)
* Milk of average composition   † Solids corrected milk (SCM)

Table 8.4. Probable dry matter intakes of cows in mid and late lactation (kg/day)

Liveweight W (kg)	Milk yield, Y (kg/day)							
	5	10	15	20	25	30	35	40
350	9.3	9.8	10.3	10.8	11.3	11.8		
400	10.5	11.0	11.5	12.0	12.5	13.0		
450	11.8	12.3	12.8	13.3	13.8	14.3	14.8	
500	13.0	13.5	14.0	14.5	15.0	15.5	16.0	
550	14.3	14.8	15.3	15.8	16.3	16.8	17.3	17.8
600	15.5	16.0	16.5	17.0	17.5	18.0	18.5	19.0
650	16.8	17.3	17.8	18.3	18.8	19.3	19.8	20.3
700	18.0	18.5	19.0	19.5	20.0	20.5	21.0	21.5

Based on DMI (kg/day) = 0.025 W + 0.1 Y.
N.B. In first 6 weeks of lactation, reduce values in this table by 2–3 kg DMI per day.

Table 8.5. Protein requirements of cattle

Breed	Ave. live wt (kg)	Maintenance requirements (kg protein)
Friesian, Shorthorn	560	0.32
Welsh Black, Red Poll	500	0.32
Ayrshire, Guernsey	450	0.27
Jersey	380	0.23

Table 8.6. Protein requirements for producing milk of varying quality

Butterfat (g/kg)	Per litre (kg protein)
35–39	0.05
40–44	0.05
45–49	0.06
50–53	0.06

Table 8.7. MJ net energy stored E_g from ME available for production MEP, at energy concentration M/D

MEP (MJ)	Energy concentration MD (MJ/kg DM)							
	7	8	9	10	11	12	13	14
5	1.4	1.7	1.9	2.1	2.3	2.5	2.7	2.9
10	2.9	3.3	3.7	4.1	4.6	5.0	5.4	5.8
15	4.3	5.0	5.6	6.2	6.8	7.5	8.1	8.7
20	5.8	6.6	7.5	8.3	9.1	9.9	10.8	11.6
25	7.2	8.3	9.3	10.4	11.4	12.4	13.5	14.5
30	8.7	9.9	11.2	12.4	13.7	14.9	16.1	17.4
35	10.1	11.6	13.0	14.5	15.9	17.4	18.8	20.3
40	11.6	13.2	14.9	16.6	18.2	19.9	21.5	23.2
45	13.0	14.9	16.8	18.6	20.5	22.4	24.2	26.1
50	14.5	16.6	18.6	20.7	22.8	24.8	26.9	29.0
55	15.9	18.2	20.5	22.8	25.0	27.3	29.6	31.9
60	17.4	19.9	22.4	24.8	27.3	29.8	32.3	34.8
65	18.8	21.5	24.2	26.9	29.6	32.3	35.0	37.7
70	20.3	23.2	26.1	29.0	31.9	34.8	37.7	40.6
75	21.7	24.8	27.9	31.1	34.2	37.3	40.4	43.5
80	23.2	26.5	29.8	33.1	36.4	39.8	43.1	46.4

Table 8.8. Liveweight gain in kg/day for MJ net energy stored E_g, in animals of live-weight W

E_g (MJ)	Liveweight, W (kg)										
	100	150	200	250	300	350	400	450	500	550	600
2	0.23	0.21	0.19	0.17	0.16	0.15	0.14	0.13	0.12	0.12	0.11
4	0.43	0.39	0.36	0.33	0.30	0.28	0.27	0.25	0.24	0.22	0.21
6	0.60	0.55	0.51	0.47	0.44	0.41	0.38	0.36	0.34	0.33	0.31
8	0.76	0.70	0.64	0.60	0.56	0.52	0.49	0.47	0.44	0.42	0.40
10	0.90	0.83	0.77	0.72	0.67	0.63	0.60	0.56	0.54	0.51	0.49
12	1.02	0.94	0.88	0.82	0.77	0.73	0.69	0.65	0.62	0.59	0.57
14		1.05	0.98	0.92	0.87	0.82	0.78	0.74	0.70	0.67	0.64
16			1.08	1.01	0.96	0.91	0.86	0.82	0.78	0.75	0.72
18			1.17	1.10	1.04	0.99	0.94	0.89	0.85	0.82	0.78
20				1.18	1.12	1.06	1.01	0.96	0.92	0.88	0.85
22				1.25	1.19	1.13	1.08	1.03	0.99	0.95	0.91
24					1.26	1.20	1.14	1.09	1.05	1.01	0.97
26					1.32	1.26	1.20	1.15	1.11	1.06	1.03
28						1.32	1.26	1.21	1.16	1.12	1.08
30						1.37	1.32	1.26	1.22	1.17	1.13
35							1.44	1.39	1.34	1.29	1.25
40								1.50	1.45	1.40	1.35
45									1.54	1.49	1.45
50										1.58	1.54

Based on $\text{LWG} = \dfrac{E_g}{(6.28 + 0.3\,E_g + 0.0188\,W)}$

Table 8.9. Daily dry matter intake (DMI) in growing cattle

Live-weight, W (kg)	100	150	200	250	300	350	400	450	500	550	600
DMI (kg)	2.94	4.26	5.48	6.60	7.62	8.54	9.36	10.08	10.70	11.22	11.65

Table 8.10. Net energy allowances (MJ/day) for maintenance and liveweight gain in growing and fattening animals

Gain (kg)	Liveweight, W (kg)										
	100	150	200	250	300	350	400	450	500	550	600
0	12.4	15.6	18.8	22.0	25.2	28.4	31.6	34.8	38.0	41.2	44.4
0.1	13.3	16.6	19.9	23.2	26.5	29.8	33.1	36.4	39.7	43.0	46.3
0.2	14.2	17.6	21.0	24.5	27.9	31.3	34.7	38.1	41.5	44.9	48.3
0.3	15.2	18.8	22.3	25.8	29.3	32.9	36.4	39.9	43.4	47.0	50.5
0.4	16.3	19.9	23.6	27.2	30.9	34.5	38.2	41.8	45.5	49.1	52.8
0.5	17.4	21.2	25.0	28.8	32.6	36.3	40.1	43.9	47.7	51.5	55.2
0.6	18.7	22.6	26.5	30.4	34.4	38.3	42.2	46.1	50.2	54.0	57.9
0.7	20.0	24.2	28.1	32.2	36.3	40.4	44.4	48.5	52.6	56.7	60.7
0.8	21.4	25.7	29.9	34.1	38.4	42.6	46.9	51.1	55.3	59.6	63.8
0.9	23.0	27.4	31.8	36.2	40.6	45.0	49.5	53.9	58.3	62.7	67.1
1.0	24.6	29.3	33.9	38.5	43.1	47.7	52.3	56.9	61.5	66.1	70.7
1.1		31.3	36.1	40.9	45.7	50.6	55.4	60.2	65.0	69.9	74.7
1.2		38.6	43.6	48.7	53.7	58.8	63.8	68.9	73.9	79.0
1.3			46.6	51.9	57.2	62.5	67.8	73.1	78.4	83.7
1.4				55.4	61.0	66.6	72.2	77.7	83.3	88.9
1.5					65.2	71.1	77.0	82.9	88.8	94.7

(including safety margin)
Based on $E_m = 1.05 [5.67 + 0.061 \text{ W}]$ and $E_g = 1.05 \left[\dfrac{\text{LWG} (6.28 + 0.0188 \text{ W})}{(1 - 0.3 \text{ LWG})} \right]$

Table 8.11. Animal production level

Liveweight W (kg)	Liveweight gain LWG (kg/day)						Liveweight W (kg)	Liveweight gain LWG (kg/day)					
	0.25	0.50	0.75	1.00	1.25	1.50		0.25	0.50	0.75	1.00	1.25	1.50
100	1.19	1.40	1.66	1.98			400	1.12	1.26	1.43	1.64	1.90	2.22
150	1.16	1.36	1.59	1.87			450	1.12	1.26	1.42	1.62	1.87	2.18
200	1.15	1.33	1.54	1.79	2.11		500	1.11	1.25	1.41	1.60	1.84	2.15
250	1.14	1.30	1.50	1.74	2.03		550	1.11	1.24	1.40	1.59	1.83	2.13
300	1.13	1.29	1.47	1.70	1.97	2.33	600	1.11	1.24	1.39	1.58	1.81	2.13
350	1.13	1.27	1.45	1.67	1.93	2.27							

Based on $\text{APL} = 1 + \left[\dfrac{\text{LWG} (6.28 + 0.0188\text{W})}{(1 - 0.3 \text{ LWG}) (5.67 + 0.061 \text{ W})} \right]$

Table 8.12. Net energy values for maintenance and production, NE_{mp} (MJ/kg DM)

APL	ME of food, MEF (MJ/kg DM)						
	8	9	10	11	12	13	14
1.00	5.8	6.5	7.2	7.9	8.6	9.4	10.1
1.10	5.2	6.0	6.8	7.6	8.3	9.1	9.9
1.15	5.1	5.8	6.6	7.4	8.2	9.0	9.8
1.20	4.9	5.7	6.5	7.3	8.1	8.9	9.8
1.25	4.7	5.5	6.4	7.2	8.0	8.9	9.7
1.30	4.6	5.4	6.3	7.1	7.9	8.8	9.7
1.35	4.5	5.3	6.2	7.0	7.8	8.7	9.6
1.40	4.4	5.2	6.1	6.9	7.8	8.7	9.6
1.45	4.3	5.1	6.0	6.8	7.7	8.6	9.5
1.50	4.2	5.1	5.9	6.8	7.7	8.6	9.5
1.55	4.2	5.0	5.8	6.7	7.6	8.5	9.5
1.65	4.1	4.9	5.7	6.6	7.5	8.4	9.4
1.75	3.9	4.8	5.6	6.5	7.4	8.4	9.3
2.00	3.8	4.6	5.4	6.3	7.3	8.2	9.2
2.25	3.6	4.4	5.3	6.2	7.1	8.1	9.1

Based on $NE_{mp} = \dfrac{(MEF)_2 \times APL}{1.39 \, MEF + 23 \, (APL - 1)}$

Table 8.13. Digestible crude protein requirements of growing cattle in g/day (source: Adapted from A.D.A.S. Advisory Leaflet No. 11)

Liveweight (kg)	Daily gain (kg)				
	0	0.5	0.75	1.0	1.25
100	130	240	295	350	405
150	170	295	360	425	485
200	195	335	405	475	540
250	215	365	440	515	585
300	230	390	470	545	620
350	245	410	490	575	650
400	260	430	515	600	680
450	270	445	530	620	705
500	280	460	545	635	720
550	285	470	560	655	740
600	290	480	575	670	755

9

Grassland Production

Grass, whether grazed or conserved, is the cheapest food that can be fed to ruminants at present prices of various input items. It is thus logical that as much high-quality grass as possible should be fed to ruminants. Grass grows for some six to seven months of the year; a ruminant has to be fed for twelve months. Any given areas of grass must thus be divided into a part for summer grazing, and a second part for growing grass which can be conserved as hay or silage for winter feeding.

GENERAL PRINCIPLES

Quantity and Quality

The total quantity of grass produced is primarily determined by weather, species, variety, management, and the amount of fertilizers applied, particularly nitrogen. The seasonal growth rate (quantity:time) is dependent on changes in seasonal temperature, rainfall and timely applications of nitrogenous fertilizers. The time at which growth commences and stops is largely determined by the geographical location and aspect of the farm.

If a pasture is allowed to grow unhindered, as is the case when it is closed for hay, it will undergo a series of developmental changes (Fig. 9.1). In spring primordial buds grow into vegetative tillers; later the flowering head appears, anthers emerge from it and after the flowers have been wind-pollinated, seeds are formed. Tissue changes accompany this development. Up until head emergence there is a limited growth of lignin fibre so that the grass is succulent because of high water content, it is highly digestible, and its energy concentration (M/D) is high. After ear emergence, lignin fibres are rapidly formed, reducing digestibility and energy concentration. Its quality is reflected in a single performance factor known as the D-value; this is a measure of the percentage digestible organic matter in the dry matter of the crop. The metabolizable energy value (ME) of a bulky food can be estimated from its D-value by using the following equation:

$$D\text{-value} \times 0.15 = ME(MJ/kg\,DM)$$

e.g. $\qquad 52 \times 0.15 = 7.8$

e.g. $\qquad 67 \times 0.15 = 10.1.$

It can be seen from Fig 9.1 that this value drops steadily as the grass matures and its quantity of dry matter increases. Harvesting of hay or silage is thus a compromise between quantity and quality.

When grass is grazed or mown as in zero grazing, this repeated defoliation prevents the grass from developing beyond the vegetative tillering stage so that its D-value remains high. Good grazing management attempts to provide an adequate daily quantity of grass of good quality; the grass growth curve has to be flattened by management involving the grazing animal and the mower. The key to grass management is to prevent overgrazing when rate of grass growth is low and undergrazing when rate of grass growth is high. It hinges on controlled grazing based on the principle of heavy grazing, followed by a rest period for replenishing the food reserves in the roots, thus enabling the growth of the buds into leafy shoots.

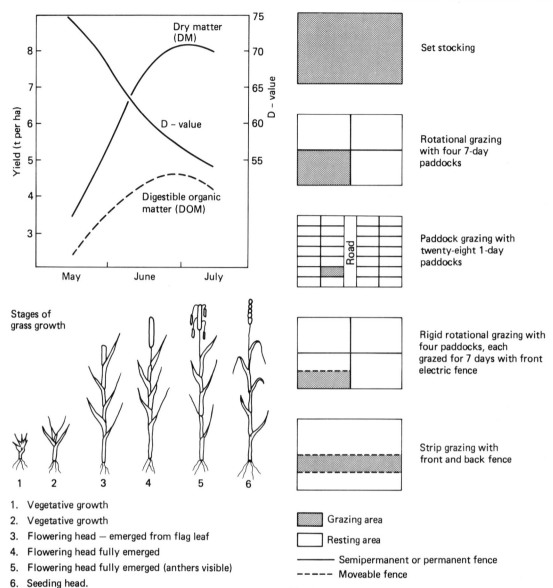

Stages of
grass growth

1. Vegetative growth
2. Vegetative growth
3. Flowering head — emerged from flag leaf
4. Flowering head fully emerged
5. Flowering head fully emerged (anthers visible)
6. Seeding head.

Fig. 9.1 D-value, yield of dry matter and digestible organic matter of an early perennial ryegrass (S24) during the first growth (from R. D. Harkess, West of Scotland Agricultural College, 1977).

Fig. 9.2 Systems of grazing.

GRAZING AND CONSERVATION

The growth rate of grass is highly seasonal. About 6 to 8 weeks after growth begins in spring, grass production is at its highest under a system of rotational grazing. If grass is not allowed to get into head the rate of production in June, July and August is at best 25% lower than it was in May. From August onwards there is a continuous decline in the rate of production because of the fall in sunlight energy at this time. Digestibility is the most important aspect of quality since protein is usually more than adequate for grazing animals. Although there is little difference in the digestibility levels of most grasses in the leafy stage, there are seasonal differences. The digestibility of re-growth grass falls less rapidly with time than that of first growth. In July, a rest period of two months gives a slightly lower digestibility than a rest of one month. There is less of a difference when such recordings are made in September.

Research has shown that a reduction of five units in D-value can have an adverse effect, e.g. between 0.25 to 0.35 kg liveweight growth per day on beef animals weighing between 200 and 400 kg. Good management is therefore essential if quality of grass is to be maintained.

Grazing animals select their food using their senses of touch, sight and smell. Sheep and young cattle are more selective than heavier beef cattle; growing cattle are more selective than dairy cows. Animals tend to avoid pasture fouled by or near to faeces of their own species. Lower quality material will be consumed if there is a shortage of herbage or if intervals between grazings are too long due to low stocking rates.

Cattle consume less herbage as pasture quality declines. It is difficult to identify the optimum height that will sustain either maximum liveweight gain or milk production, because consumption is not only based on height of sward but also on density. A set stocking system of grazing produces swards which are denser than from rotational systems; this results in closer grazing which maintains performance, unless dominated by stemmy species.

In order to equate grass requirement and availability, cattle and sheep are often bought and sold to match grass output. It is, however, the close integration of grazing and cutting which allows for the most efficient use of herbage produced. Cattle and sheep are often grazed together, ensuring better utilization of the pasture and reducing the risk of parasitism; sheep select a diet of higher quality than cattle during mixed grazing, and lambs often grow better when grazed with cattle.

With all systems the use of concentrates to supplement grazing at either end of the season is necessary.

Grazing Systems

Systems of grazing can be summarized as follows (Fig. 9.2):

1. *Continuous stocking*
Grazing animals have access to an area of pasture for the whole grazing season. This is the accepted system under extensive upland conditions, where stocking rate is relatively low.

2. *Rotational grazing in paddock systems*
Maximum advantage is obtained by this system,

which allows for the conservation of excess production, thus balancing stock numbers and grass production. Optimum yield and quality of grass is obtained in a 21 to 28 day grazing cycle, e.g. if eight paddocks are available with a 24 day rotation, three days will be available in each paddock; if this grazing period is too long then more paddocks can be added. Often, when two groups of cattle of different ages are being managed, a two layout system is adopted.

Usually a dairy herd is turned into a fresh paddock every day; each paddock is of the correct size to ensure:

i) that every cow has enough grass; and
ii) that all the grass is eaten – surplus grass is topped.

The size of each paddock is governed by the size of the herd and as a rough guide 0.2 hectares (ha) of good, well fertilized grassland should supply enough grass for a cow throughout the growing season. Hence a sixty-cow herd will need 12 ha of grassland. This grassland must be divided into equal-sized paddocks, sufficient for the cows to have a new paddock every day for say 21 days before starting to regraze. The size of each paddock can be determined thus:

12 ha ÷ 21 days (or paddocks)
        = 0.57 ha per paddock (Fig. 9.3)

Adequate nitrogenous fertilizer is also necessary to encourage quick, leafy growth. Between 50 and 62.5 kg per ha are applied to each paddock before each grazing, together with adequate P and K.

Given good weather and good grass growth,

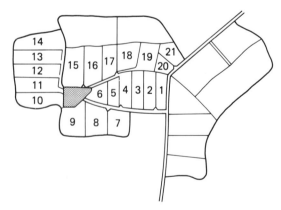

Fig. 9.3 A paddock layout for 60 cows. Each paddock = 0.57 ha. Total grazing area = 12 ha. Grazing cycle = 21 days. Remaining land used for conservation, young stock and cereal growing (after diagram in ICI booklet *Better Grassland*).

about six grazings can be obtained from each paddock during the season and this means that if the first grazing is begun in mid-April, the last will begin $6 \times 3 = 18$ weeks later, i.e. about late August. During this period each hectare will receive $62.5 \times 6 = 375$ kg of nitrogen together with about 100 kg each of P and K.

3. *The leader–follower system*
This has been designed for two age groups of cattle or sheep grazing in rotation around the same paddocks. The lambs or calves lead, selecting the best herbage, and the older stock follow, cleaning up the remaining herbage.

4. *The 1 . 2 . 3 system*
Under this system the growing season is divided into early, mid and late periods and the area of grassland utilized in accordance with the differential growth of grass as shown in Table 9.1.

Table 9.1. Grazing and cutting allocations in a 1.2.3. system

	Grazing allocation	Cutting allocation
Early season	$\frac{1}{3}$	$\frac{2}{3}$
Mid-season	$\frac{2}{3}$	$\frac{1}{3}$
Late season	All	Nil

5. *Zero grazing*
With this system the forage is carted and fed to housed cattle. It is well suited for use on heavy land, with very intensive grassland management, or where access by cattle to fields is not possible. The system relies heavily on machinery and may result in a slurry problem. It can result in a very high output per hectare but liveweight gain per animal is usually lower as compared with other systems.

Conservation

Since there is an excess of grass growth in the early season it is normal practice to cut between half and two-thirds of the grassland area during May and June. If half the area is conserved in May about 30% of total production is harvested. If two-thirds is conserved in May and the remaining third in July, about 45% of total production is conserved.

Hay and Silage Quality

Digestibility and feeding value of grass decreases with progressive stages of growth. The first essential in obtaining good silage and hay is to cut the grass at the correct stage of growth. Grass for silage should be cut in the leafy stage before ear emergence, and for hay as soon as possible after. The longer the delay in cutting after these stages, the lower will be the feeding value of the conserved product.

Silage should also be cut when dry in order to increase the dry matter in the finished product; nowadays, many farmers cut the grass and allow it to wilt for a day to help achieve this. This of course reduces the amount of water the cows have to consume in the silage, and consequently increases their dry matter intake.

After cutting at the right stage, the quality of the finished product will depend on how well it is made. In the case of silage it must be made quickly and a good fermentation obtained; in the case of hay, techniques must be used to dry it quickly with a minimum loss of leaf.

Good-quality hay or silage is of great importance for economic production; this is illustrated by the following examples.

Example 1: Hay

	Very high digestibility (D-value 67) $M/D = 10.1$ MJ/kg	Very low digestibility (D-value 47) $M/D = 7.0$ MJ/kg
ME energy supplied by 10 kg hay DM	101 MJ	70
Assume 63 MJ required for maintenance	63	63
ME available for production (a)	38	7
Equivalent litres of milk produced (a) ÷ 4.9	8	1.5

Example 2: Silage
Cows eating silage to appetite generally consume about 40 kg daily. Consequently, the quality of silage will largely determine the amount of nutrients they consume. Levels of production from silage estimated as follows can be:

	D-value 67	D-value 61	D-value 52
ME energy supplied by 10 kg silage DM	116	93	76
Assume 63 MJ required for maintenance	63	63	63
ME available for production	53	30	13
Litres of milk produced	11	6	2.7

Smaller quantities of concentrates will need to be fed as quality improves. The dry matter content of silage varies enormously, e.g. pit silage from 17 to 30% and tower silage from 35 to 55%. If dairy cows can eat 40 kg silage per day then the dry matter intake will depend on dry matter content; also as per cent dry matter increases, the quantity of energy supplied by forage increases with a consequential drop in concentrate intake. Thus with silage samples have a D-value of 67, and supplying $67 \times 0.15 = 10.1$ MJ/kg DM, the daily energy intake from them could be as follows:

Silage sample A: 25% DM

Silage consumed per day	= 40 kg
Dry matter consumed per day	= $\frac{40 \times 25}{100}$ = 10 kg
Energy supplied per day	= 10×10.1 = 101 MJ = 7.5 litres of milk

Silage sample B: 40% DM

Silage consumed per day	= 40 kg
Dry matter consumed per day	= $\frac{40 \times 40}{100}$ = 16 kg
Energy supplied per day	= 16×10.1 = 176 MJ = 22.5 litres of milk.

Silage should be sent for analysis so as to assist with proper rationing of silage and concentrates; Table 9.2 details an analysis report of a sample, the quality of which can be rated by comparing its components with the figures inserted for an average silage sample.

Table 9.2. Analysis of silage

For Mr. P. Farmer
Church Farm — Date of report: 15 Jan.
Sample number: 116 — Date received: 11 Jan.
Sample name: Clamp 1 — Cutting date: 20 May
Crop variety: Grass — Cut number: 1
Additive: None — Wilting time: 1 day
Fermentation: Good

		Average silage figures
% dry matter	24.2	25–30
% MAD fibre[1]	30.6	32
D-value	67	10
M.E. (MJ/kg DM)	10.62	
Ammonia nitrogen/Total nitrogen[2]	13	
pH value[3]	4.4	3.7–4.0
% crude protein[4]	17.7	
g/kg digestible crude protein[5]	121.1 (12.11%)	120 (12.0%)

[1] Percentage fibre as determined by the modified acid detergent method of chemical analysis.
[2] Nitrogen in the form of ammonia as a fraction of total nitrogen.
[3] Degree of acidity measured on a scale of 7 = neutral to 0 = very acid.
[4] Percentage of nitrogen-containing compounds including proteins, ammonia and others.
[5] Proportion of nitrogen-containing compounds which can be digested by a ruminant.

STOCKING DENSITY

Gross margin per forage ha is directly related to stocking density. An overall stocking density of say 2 livestock units per forage hectare or 0.5 forage hectares per cow $(1 \div 2)$ implies that 2 livestock units obtain all their summer grazing and winter roughage from one hectare. This is an overall annual picture which needs to be translated into areas of land for conservation shut off over say 3 months and areas of grazing land per month and per day for feeding the animal through its productive cycle.

Stocking density is an indicator of the level of grassland/forage production and utilization achieved in any given farm situation. Table 9.3 shows the general relationship between nitrogen application, grassland production and stocking density.

Table 9.3. Relationships between grassland productions (kg DM/ha), stocking density and nitrogen applications (source: Ministry of Agriculture, Fisheries and Food)

Stocking density		DM/ha	kg/N
(LU/ha)	(ha/LU)		
1.0	1.0	5 500	0
1.5	0.65	8 000	90
1.75	0.57	9 800	150
2.0	0.5	10 600	240
2.25	0.45	11 700	300
2.5	0.4	13 200	400

Stocking density is expressed as either grazing livestock units (GLUs) per adjusted forage hectare *or* adjusted forage hectares per grazing livestock unit. This figure expresses the level of stocking achieved on the hectares devoted to the production of forage crops. Grassland (including rough grazing) and other crops, e.g. kale, rape, swedes, specifically grown for grazing livestock are classified as forage crops. However, grain crops and pulses even when retained on the farm for feeding are not included in this category.

The procedure to follow in order to arrive at this figure in any given farm situation is as follows:

1. *Calculate the farm's adjusted forage hectares*
The farm's total forage area excludes land used by non-grazing livestock, i.e. pigs and poultry. This figure is then modified to give the adjusted forage area as follows:

(a) the area of equivalent rented keep is added and any land let is deducted;
(b) the area of land used for fodder sales and seed production is deducted;
(c) any areas of rough grazing are converted into the average grassland equivalent. If it is considered that 3 ha of rough grazing provides feed equivalent to 1 ha of the grassland area, then the rough grazing total area would be divided by 3, e.g. 21 ha rough grazing equals 7 ha of the average grassland.

2. *Calculate the total grazing livestock units for the farm*
The livestock unit system is based on an assessment of the dietary energy requirements of the various types of livestock. The energy requirements are based on the metabolizable energy (ME) system.

The standard unit is the average Friesian cow, which is given the figure of one livestock unit (1 LU), and other types of livestock are compared to this in terms of their dietary energy requirements. The average Friesian cow is taken as one weighing 600 kg and producing a 40 kg calf and 4500 litres of milk (36 g/kg butterfat (b.f.) and 86 g/kg solids-not-fat (s.n.f.) per year). Table 9.4 shows the livestock unit factors recommended by the Ministry of Agriculture. The figures quoted assume that the stock, with the exception of lambs, are on the farm for the full year.

The livestock units for each type of stock on the farm are calculated by multiplying the average number for the year with the appropriate factor. These figures are then added to give the farm's total livestock units. In order to provide accurate figures it is necessary to record livestock numbers on a monthly basis and to average these figures for the annual totals.

Table 9.4. Livestock unit coefficients

	Livestock unit factors
Cattle	
Dairy cows	1.00
Dairy bulls	0.65
Beef cows (excl. calf)	0.75
Beef bulls	0.65
Other cattle (excl. intensive beef systems)	
0–12 months	0.30
12–24 months	0.54
Over 24 months	0.80
Barley beef	0.41
Sheep:	
Ewes and ewe replacements (excl. suckling lambs)	
Light weight (40 kg)	0.07
Medium weight (60 kg)	0.09
Heavy weight (80 kg)	0.11
Rams	0.08
Lambs:	
Birth to store	0.04
Birth to fat	0.04
Birth to hogget	0.07
Purchased stores	0.04

3. *Calculate the stocking density*

$$\frac{\text{Total grazing livestock units}}{\text{Adjusted forage hectares}} = \text{Grazing livestock units per adjusted forage hectare}$$

or

$$\frac{\text{Adjusted forage hectares}}{\text{Total grazing livestock units}} = \text{Adjusted forage hectares per grazing livestock unit}$$

Example 1
In this example, we shall:
A: Calculate the overall stocking density of the farm;
B: Allocate the adjusted forage area to individual enterprises;
C: Consider the stocking implications of substituting one enterprise for another.

A: Calculate the overall stocking density of the farm
1. *Farm cropping*

(a) Farm information	ha
Temporary grass	75
Permanent grass	44
Barley	40
Rough grazing	12
Buildings, roads, woods, etc.	3
Total farm area	174

(b) Adjusted forage area

	Adjusted ha
Temporary grass	75
Permanent grass	44
Rough grazing $(12 \div 3)$	4
	123

2. Stocking

Type	Annual average through-put	Grazing livestock unit factor	Grazing livestock units	Enterprise GLUs
Dairy cows	91	1.00	91.00	} 91.65
Bulls for dairy herd	1	0.65	0.65	
Dairy replacements				
0 –12 mths	27	0.30	8.10	
12–24 mths	23	0.54	12.42	} 25.12
over 24 mths*	23	0.80	4.60	
Beef cattle				
0 –12 mths	42	0.30	12.60	} 23.13
12–24 mths†	39	0.54	10.53	
Sheep (heavy) –				
ewes	300	0.11	33.00	
rams	9	0.08	0.72	
Ewe replace-				
ments	90	0.11	9.90	
Lamb sold fat	90	0.04	3.60	} 61.63
Lambs sold				
store	194	0.04	7.76	
Birth to				
hoggets	95	0.07	6.65	
		Total	201.53	

* With average calving age of 2 yrs 3 mths (this group is kept for 3 months, i.e. 3/12 of a year) the calculation is as follows:

$$\frac{23}{1} \times \frac{0.8}{1} \times \frac{3}{12} = 4.60 \text{ LUs.}$$

† With an average age at selling of 1 yr 6 mths the calculation for this group is as follows:

$$\frac{39}{1} \times \frac{0.54}{1} \times \frac{6}{12} = 10.53 \text{ LUs.}$$

3. Stocking density

(a) Grazing livestock units per adjusted forage hectare

$$\frac{201.53}{123.00} = 1.64$$

(b) Adjusted forage hectares per grazing livestock unit

$$\frac{123.00}{201.53} = 0.61$$

These figures can be compared with standard or target figures and are useful efficiency measures for livestock farmers.

B : Allocate adjusted forage area to individual enterprises

	GLUs/ enterprise	adjusted × forage ha/GLU	ha/ = enter- prise
1. Dairy herd	91.65	×0.61	= 55.91
2. Dairy replace-ments	25.12	×0.61	= 15.32
3. Beef cattle	23.13	×0.61	= 14.11
4. Sheep	61.63	×0.61	= 37.60

This calculation assumes that the whole adjusted forage area receives the same treatment (e.g. fertilizer) and that all types of livestock are equally efficient in the use of this area.

C : Consider the stocking effects of, say, abandoning milk production and allocating the land released equally between the beef and sheep enterprises

1. *Land released*

	ha
Dairy cows	55.91
Dairy replacements	15.32
Total	71.23

2. (a) *Proposed beef enterprise on available land*

	ha
Present forage area	14.11
Additional land released for enterprise $(71.27 \text{ ha} \div 2)$	35.62
Total	49.73

Currently 14.11 adjusted forage hectares finish 39 fat cattle per year.
Following replanning 49.73 adjusted forage hectares could finish

$$\frac{39 \times 49.73}{14.12} = 137 \text{ fat cattle.}$$

(b) *Check on calculations*

Proposed stocking	LUs
Beef cattle	
0 –12 mths	$147 \times 0.30 = 44.10$
12–24 mths	$137 \times 0.27 = 36.99$
Total	81.09

At current stocking rate, i.e. 1.64 grazing LUs per adjusted forage hectare. 81.09 LUs will require

$$\frac{81.09}{1.64} = 49.45 \text{ ha.}$$

This figure agrees closely with the original allocation of land (49.75 ha).

3. (a) *Proposed sheep enterprise on available land*

	ha
Present forage area	37.60
Additional land released for enterprise $(71.27 \text{ ha} \div 2)$	35.62
Total	73.22

Currently 37.60 adjusted forage ha carry 300 ewes. Following replanning 73.22 ha could carry

$$\frac{300 \times 73.22}{37.60} = 584 \text{ ewes.}$$

(b) *Check on calculations**

		LUs
Ewes	$584 \times 0.11 =$	64.24
Rams	$18 \times 0.08 =$	1.44
Ewe replacements	$175 \times 0.11 =$	19.25
Lambs	$553 \times 0.04 =$	22.12
Birth to hoggets	$185 \times 0.07 =$	12.95
	Total	120.00

* Assumptions – 1: ewes/ram = 32.
   2: replacement rate = $\frac{1}{3}$ of flock.
   3: % lambing = 130.

At current stocking rate 120 LUs will require

$$\frac{12\,000}{1.64} = 73.17 \text{ ha.}$$

This figure agrees closely with the original allocation of land (73.22 ha).

Such substitution of enterprise calculations can be used as guidelines for a final solution, based on sound practical judgement, of the farm's resources.

Example 2: How to plan the stocking on a newly purchased farm
1. *The farm*
The land and buildings are suitable for dairying and the category of the land is such as to have a potential stock carrying capacity of 2 LUs per forage hectare. The total land available is 100 ha (adjusted). It is assumed that:

(a) the average number of lactations per cow will be 5;
(b) the average age at calving will be 2 years 3 mths;
(c) the herd replacements will be reared on the farm.

2. *Replacement requirements*
One replacement unit will be required for every five cows in the herd. With proposed calving at 2 years 3 mths each replacement unit will be made up as follows:

	LUs
0 –12 mths	0.30
12–24 mths	0.54
Over 24 mths (for 3 mths only)	0.20
Total	1.04

Thus for: Every 5 cows, 1 replacement unit totalling 1.04 LUs will be required; Every single cow, one replacement unit totalling 1.04/5 = 0.208 LUs.

3. *Total stocking of land in livestock units*

Total land available = 100 ha

Total livestock units possible = $100 \times 2 = 200$ LUs

4. *Maximum number of dairy cows possible*

	LUs
One dairy cow	= 1.000
Replacement units per cow	= 0.208
Total livestock units required per cow and replacement	= 1.208

With a potential of 200 LUs the maximum number of dairy cows will be:

$$\frac{200}{1.208} = 165$$

The stocking will be:

Dairy cows	165
Heifers 0 –12 mths	37
0 –24 mths	35
over 24 mths	33

The annual requirement will be 33 down-calving heifers and in order to achieve this, 37 heifer calves need to be retained every year. This higher figure will allow for mortality, failing to get heifers in-calf, and any other problems that may arise from time to time.

Check on calculations:

		LUs
Dairy cows	165×1.00	165.00
Heifers 0 –12 mths	37×0.30	11.00
12–24 mths	35×0.54	18.90
over 24 mths	33×0.20	6.60
(for 3 mths only)		201.50

Stocking density

$$\frac{201.50 \text{ LUs}}{100 \text{ ha}} = 2.01$$

per adjusted forage hectare. This figure agrees closely with the original figure of 2 LUs per adjusted forage hectare.

RELATIONSHIPS

Effective grassland management attempts to produce and utilize sufficient quantity and quality of grass. In a given farm situation the area of grass available has to be grazed and conserved on a periodic and daily basis. Relationships exist between total annual dry matter production, seasonal growth patterns of grass, relative areas of grazing and conservation, the quality of the grazed or conserved grass products and the levels of animal production which can be achieved; the latter hinges on the overall annual and seasonal stocking densities possible and the energy concentration (quality) of the grass ingested.

Table 9.3 shows the general annual relationship between nitrogen application, grassland production and stocking density. An attempt can be made to translate these annual production levels into monthly and daily requirements by means of theoretical models; in this way the farmer's managerial dilemma can be appreciated, at least in general terms.

Dairy Herd

Two production levels are adopted in the following examples. The standard of grassland management on any farm can lie below, between or above these levels; it needs to be appreciated that possible real answers in terms of grassland management are many and varied.

Example 1: High grass production

A: Theoretical model to show the relationship between the grass growth curve, stocking density, relative areas of grazing and silage, quality of grass and milk production for a 60-cow herd

Assumptions:

(a) total dry matter per hectare = 11 700 kg;
(b) average kg nitrogen per ha per year = 300;
(c) consumption of grass per day per grazing cow = 70 kg = 14 kg dry matter;
(d) consumption of silage per day per cow = 40 kg = 10 kg dry matter;
(e) percentage of grass growth per month as shown.

1. *Grazing*
The grass growth curve for grazing is shown below.

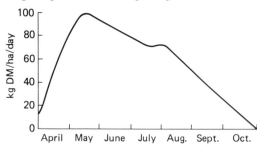

	April	*May*	*June*	*July*	*Aug.*	*Sept.*	
(a) % of total grass growth	13	25	21	19	14	9	
(b) DM/ha/month (kg) (11 700 × a)	1521	2925	2457	2223	1638	1053	
(c) DM/cow/month (kg) (14 × 30)			420				
(d) DM/60 cows/month (kg) (c × 60)			25 200				*Average*
(e) ha/60 cows/month (d ÷ b)*	16.6	8.6	10.3	11.3	15.4	23.9	14.4 ha/herd
(f) ha/60 cows/day (e ÷ 30)	0.55	0.29	0.34	0.38	0.51	0.79	0.48 ha/herd
(g) m²/day/cow (f ÷ 60)	92	48	57	63	85	100	80 m²/cow/day

* The figures of this line are represented in Fig. 9.4 (a).

2. *Winter silage conservation*

(a) Silage (25% DM) consumption per cow/day = 40 kg
(b) Silage dry matter consumption per cow/day; a × 25/100 = 10 kg
(c) Silage dry matter consumption for 60 cows/day: b × 60 = 600 kg
(d) Silage dry matter consumption for 60 cows/month: c × 30 = 18 000 kg
(e) Silage dry matter consumption for 60 cows/6 months: d × 6 = 108 000 kg
From Fig. 9.1 it can be seen that
(f) First cut of silage in mid-June would yield approximately 5650 kg DM/ha, and second cut at the end of July would yield say 3350 kg DM/ha, giving a total of 9000 kg
(g) Total ha required for herd: e ÷ f = 12 ha*
(h) ha/cow: g ÷ 60 = 0.2 ha

* The hectares shut off for silage are shown in Fig. 9.4(a).

3. *Total area required*

	Herd (ha)	Per cow (ha)
Grazing	14.4	0.24
Silage	12.0	0.20
Total	26.4	0.44

Overall stocking density of cows per ha = 1 ÷ 0.44 = 2.3.

B: Real cropping
In practice the grass growth curve for grazing can be flattened by avoiding over- or undergrazing and by using species and varieties which mature at different times of the year, i.e. they have different seasonal growth rhythms. Cropping could be as follows:

1. *Conservation*
12 ha for silage.

2. *Grazing*
Italian rye grass ley for early grazing during first 14 days of April:

Dry matter intake per cow	14 kg
Dry matter intake per cow for 14 days	196 kg
Dry matter intake per 60 cows for 14 days	1176 kg
Assume production of 5500 kg/DM/ha	
Area required = 11 760/5500 = 2 ha.	

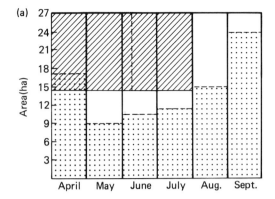

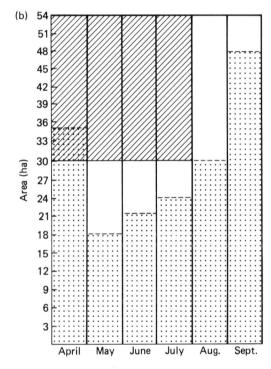

Silage area

Grazing area required

Spare area available

Fig. 9.4 Silage area, grazing area required and spare area available for a 60 cow herd at grass production levels of (a) 11 700 kg DM/ha; (b) 5500 kg DM/ha.

Grazing block for grazing between mid-April and mid-August re-seeded with perennial rye grass:

ha required/cow	= 0.2 ha
ha required 60 cows 0.2×60	= 12.0 ha
Area required per paddock if grazed every 21 days $= 12.0 \div 21$	= 0.57 ha

Five grazings could be obtained lasting $5 \times 21 = 105$ days $= 15$ weeks.
Grazing period = mid-April to mid-August.

During mid-August to late September or October the silage aftermath, Italian rye grass and perennial rye grass areas would be available. These could be managed by set stocking bringing in other stock or the mower if any undergrazing appears likely.

3. *Energy and milk production from grass*
Summer: Grass managed in the above way could have a D-value of 75 with an energy concentration of 12.0 MJ/kg.
The production expected from grass per day is calculated thus:

DM intake	14	kg
ME intake $= 14 \times 12.0$	168.0	MJ
ME required for maintenance	63.0	MJ
ME for production	105.4	MJ

At 4.9 MJ per litre, this is equivalent to $105.0 \div 4.9 = 21.5$ litres of milk/day.
Winter: Good quality silage could have a D-value of 67 and an energy concentration of 10.2 MJ/kg.
The production expected from silage per day is calculated thus:

DM intake	= 10 kg
ME required 10×10.2	= 102 MJ
Me required for maintenance	= 63 MJ
ME for production	= 39 MJ

At 4.9 MJ/litre this is equivalent to $39 \div 4.9 = 8$ litres of milk/day. The approximate daily energy intake per cow would appear as in Fig. 9.5(a).

4. *Gross margin/ha*
If we assume a gross margin per cow of £400 then gross margin/ha would be $400 \times 2.25^* = £900/ha$.
* $60 \div 26.4 = 2.25$ cows/ha.

Example 2: Low grass production

A: Theoretical model
A similar model can be designed using the same assumptions with the exception of assumptions (a) and (b) above

(a) Assumption: total dry matter/ha = 5500 kg
(b) Assumption: Ave. kg N/ha = 0

This would result in an overall stocking density of approximately one cow per ha and a total area requirement of 54 ha (30 ha for grazing and 24 ha for silage). The seasonal picture for silage area, grazing available and required would be as shown in Fig. 9.4 (b).

B: Real cropping
This level of grass production would usually be associated with extensive grazing. This would result in:

1. Overgrazing during March/April period with a possible reduction in dry matter intake.

ha required by herd (Fig. 9.4(b)) = 54 ha
ha available for grazing = 54 − 24 for silage = 30 ha

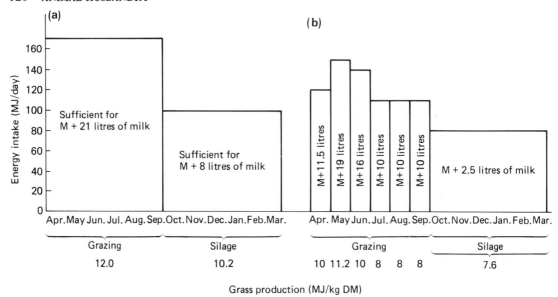

Fig. 9.5 Energy intake/cow/day during a twelve month period, with grass production levels at (a) 11 700 kg DM/ha; (b) 5500 kg DM/ha.

DM/ha/April = 5500 × 13/100 = 715 kg
DM/30 ha/April = 715 × 30 = 21 450 kg
DM/cow/April = 21 450 ÷ 60 = 357.5 kg
DM/cow/day = 357.5 ÷ 30 = 12 kg

If it assumed that this early grass had an M/D of 10 MJ/kg, then each cow would be supplied with 10 × 12 = 120 MJ of energy, i.e. sufficient for M + 11.5 litres of milk.

2. Undergrazing during the remainder of the year would probably result in the D-values and metabolizable energy concentrations of the grass and energy intake per cow declining as follows:

	D-value	ME (MJ/kg)	DM intake (cow/day)	ME intake (cow/day)
May	70	11.2	14	157
June	60	10.0	14	140
July	50	8.0	14	112
Aug.	46	8.0	14	112
Sept.	50	8.0	14	112

3. Poor quality silage may accompany this form of grassland management having say a D-value of 52 and M/D value of 7.8 MJ/kg DM.

	kg
DM intake	= 10
ME intake = 10 × 7.8	= 78
ME required for maintenance	= 63
ME for production	15

At 4.9 MJ/litre this is equivalent to 15 ÷ 4.9 = 3.1 litres.

The approximate daily energy intakes per cow would appear as in Fig. 9.5(b).

4. *Gross margin/ha*
If we assume gross margin/cow of £400 then gross margin per ha would be:

$$400 \times 1.0 = £400.$$

Growing Cattle

The daily intake of dry matter increases in direct proportion to the weight of the animal (Fig. 9.6);

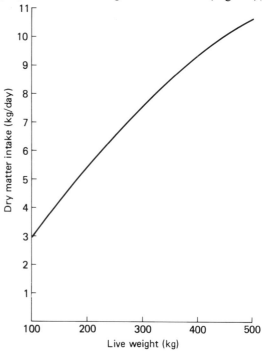

Fig. 9.6 Relationship between live weight and dry matter intake for beef cattle.

consequently there is a progressive increase of energy and protein intake. This enables the beast to satisfy its increasing maintenance requirement and sustain liveweight growth.

Since the dry matter production of the grass growth curve varies monthly, cattle numbers need to be adjusted so as to maintain their liveweight growth. In the following two examples, the monthly stocking levels possible are calculated; in practice the art is to match cattle numbers to the availability of grass.

Example 1: Theoretical model No. 1 – to show the relationship between the grass growth curve and stocking during the grazing season in growing cattle

Assumptions:
(a) Total dry matter utilized per hectare = 8000 kg
(b) Average kg nitrogen per hectare per year = 150 kg
(c) Weight at turnout = 180 kg
(d) Weight at yarding = 318 kg
(e) Average liveweight gain per day = 0.77 kg

Stocking density at grazing:

	April	*May*	*June*	*July*	*Aug.*	*Sept.*
(a) % of total growth	13	25	21	19	14	9
(b) DM/ha/month (kg)	1040	2000	1680	1520	1120	720
(c) Weight at beginning of month (kg)	180	203	226	249	272	295
(d) Weight at end of month (kg)	203	226	249	272	295	318
(e) Average weight for month (kg)	191.5	214.5	237.5	260.5	283.5	306.5
(f) DM intake/beast/day (kg) (Fig. 9.6)	5.24	5.87	6.27	6.87	7.2	7.78
(g) DM/beast/month (kg) [f × 30]	157	176	188	206	216	233
(h) Beasts/hectare [b ÷ g]	6.5	11.5	9	7.5	5	3

Example 2: Theoretical model – to show the relationship between the grass growth curve and stocking during the grazing season in older growing cattle

Assumptions:
(a) Total dry matter utilized per hectare = 8000 kg
(b) Average kg nitrogen per hectare per year = 150 kg
(c) Weight at turnout = 330 kg
(d) Weight at slaughter = 465 kg
(e) Average liveweight gain per day = 0.84 kg

Stocking density at grazing:

	April	*May*	*June*	*July*	*Aug.*	*Sept.*
(a) % of total growth	13	25	21	19	14	9
(b) DM/ha/month (kg)	1040	2000	1680	1520	1120	720
(c) Weight at beginning of month (kg)	330	355	377	402	427	452
(d) Weight at end of month (kg)	355	377	402	427	452	477
(e) Average weight for month (kg)	342.5	367.5	389.5	414.5	439.5	464.5
(f) DM intake/beast/day (kg) (Fig. 9.6)	8.3	8.7	9.1	9.5	9.8	10.2
(g) DM/beast/month (kg) [f × 30]	249	261	273	285	294	306
(h) Beasts/hectare [b ÷ g]	4	7.5	6	5.5	4	2.5

INITIAL PASTURE IMPROVEMENT

The composition and consequential productivity of any sward is determined by the interaction of many factors such as climate, topography, and soil conditions (including lime status and level of fertility), together with the timing, sequence, and extent of defoliation undertaken by the mower, the grazing animal or both.

In any farm situation the types of ruminants and the numbers of each which can be kept is determined by the area and quality of grassland available as determined by the above factors; it is the mix of upland, lowland, land aspect and slope, woodland, undrained land pockets which dictates the proportion of sheep, beef cattle and dairy stock which can be kept coupled with the overall stocking density.

Initial improvement of the existent grassland is possible with or without the plough. Areas of permanent pasture can be improved by judicious draining, liming, phosphating and/or surface seed broadcasting or sod seeding; fencing for controlled stock grazing can maintain the improved quality of such swards. Ploughing and re-seeding with species and varieties which match soil conditions and grazing/conservation objectives can dramatically change pastures for intensive grass production and utilization.

The grassland potential realized by such initial improvement is maintained in accordance with the underlying principles which have been described in the main part of this chapter.

10

Feeding and Management of the Dairy Herd

Any system of dairy herd management is concerned with four operations:

i) conveyance of milk from cows to container for farm collection;
ii) conveyance of (a) bulky forage and (b) concentrates from storage area to cows;
iii) conveyance of manure and other wastes from cows to fields usually via an intermediate storage area;
iv) providing winter bedding area for cows.

The gradual evolution in the systems used can be broadly appreciated by reference to Table 10.1. The trend has been away from individual cow feeding in the cowshed system, to herd or group feeding in yard and parlour systems. This trend has been mainly governed by economic pressure compelling the farmer to substitute capital in the form of buildings and equipment for labour. During the last fifteen years the dairy cow population has not changed appreciably, but the number of herds has halved. Thus the proportion of large herds has increased, with the effect that more cowmen are caring for greater numbers of cows.

Two rules have to be obeyed when feeding cows:

1. Food needs to be available at all times.
2. Concentrates cannot be fed in large quantities at any one time.

In the cowshed system a herd of cows can be fed and managed individually according to their stage in the productive cycle. In this way concentrate intake is directly linked to milk yield and stage of lactation and cows can respond according to their individual genetic potential. Recent results from Ministry of Agriculture, Fisheries and Food Experimental Farms confirm that cows of higher genetic potential are capable of greater response to any level of feeding,

particularly during early lactation lead-feeding, so that individual allocation of feed according to milk yield is desirable. The weakness of the cowshed system is the fact that only a limited number of cows can be managed in this way by a cowman.

The Self-Feed Silage System is an attempt to manage a herd of cows as one cow affording ease of handling. It is a less precise system of feeding in the sense that individual cows will eat different quantities of silage and the metabolic energy intake will depend on the quality of the silage stored. The forage intake may limit the quantity of concentrates which can be eaten, particularly by potentially high-yielding cows. This disadvantage has been partly overcome by dividing the herd into groups according to either stage in lactation or potential milk yield, and allowing them to feed on different silage faces according to the lowest common yield factor of the group, the silage of highest quality being offered to the high-yielding group. In addition, cows can be fed concentrates individually according to milk yield from parlour or out-of-parlour dispensers.

The Complete Diet System is one which does not accommodate individual cow rationing. Forage and concentrates are mixed with added minerals and different mixes fed to cows grouped according to milk yield. The weakness of group feeding, as with all group systems, is that low-yielding cows receive too high an energy food intake and high-yielding cows too low an energy food intake.

The latest automated tower silo systems are costly to erect but can supply a high-quality silage with a dry matter content of between 30 and 50%. Where weather conditions permit, maize and lucerne silages (the latter with a dry matter content of 50%) are being produced. Such silages can be automatically controlled by pressing a button.

Table 10.1. Systems of herd management

		Milking	Feeding	Bedding	Manure handling	Manure storing
(a)	Cowshed system	Within cowshed. From cow direct to *either* bucket *or* churn *or* bulk tank	Within cowshed. Hay fed in mangers. Concentrates to cow from *either* hand bucket *or* overhead hoppers and delivered either by hand-operated or electronically-operated dispensers.	Within cowshed. Tied by chains or yolks to stands.	Farmyard manure + urine cleaned out daily either by hand or by mechanical scraper.	Midden – carted out to fields as required.
(b)	Yard + parlour	Within parlour. From cow direct to bulk tank.	Cows self-fed on silage face. Concentrates to cows from overhead hoppers and either hand- or electronically-operated dispensers.	Yards with straw or kennels or cubicles or slatted floors to reduce straw usage.	Seepage from silage pit and loose faeces + urine forming slurry. Scraped out mechanically as required.	Either Lagoon or overground tanks. Pumped out and carted as required.
(c)	Yard + parlour with tower silo	As for (b)	Cows fed from mangers. Silage to cows from silo by conveyor belt and unloader. Automated control dispenses silage or silage/concentrates mix as required.	As for (b)	Drier slurry	As for (b)
(d)	Yard + parlour with complete feed	As for (b)	Cows fed from mangers. Forage and concentrates mixed in mechanical mixer and conveyed direct or by conveyor belt to mangers.	As for (b)	As for (c)	As for (b)

HERD NET MARGIN

Gross Margin

A gross margin for an average dairy herd of 80 cows with a given level of performance could be as shown in Table 10.2.

It can be seen that gross margin per herd or per cow is the difference between the output from milk, calves and cull cows *less* heifers purchased making up enterprise output *less* the variable costs of concentrates, miscellaneous items and fertilizers and seeds required on the forage area for grazing and conserved grass. It needs to be remembered that a gross margin reflects the performance of a herd over a period of one year.

A high gross margin per cow depends on a high milk yield per cow per year which in turn is determined by the following factors:

1. The genetic potential of the cow.
2. An adequate fibrous diet of hay or silage, supplemented by concentrates fed at the correct levels through the productive cycle. Steaming-up prior to calving and lead-feeding during early lactation ensures that she realizes her peak yield; feeding according to milk yield and condition required during the remainder of the lactation ensures economic use of concentrates (see p. 94).

3. The Calving Index. The target is a calf per 365 days. If a cow has a Calving Index of say 407 days then a 'gross margin' of £391 calculated over this period would become a gross margin per year of $\frac{391}{407} \times 365 = £391$. Adequate breeding records are thus necessary to detect, for each cow within the herd, heat periods, time of service and onset of birth (see p. 131).

4. Percentage dry cows. If cows have too long a dry period then this will be reflected as a lower gross margin per cow in the herd.

5. Replacement rate of cows. The higher the rate of replacement the higher the average depreciation cost per cow per year (see p. 38).

Gross margin per hectare hinges on the gross margin per cow and the number of cows kept per ha, i.e. stocking density.

Table 10.2. Physical and financial data for a herd of 80 dairy cows (autumn calving)

(a) *Gross margins*

	Herd			Per cow	
	Quantity	Price/unit	£	Quantity	£
Milk	400 000 litres	14.1 p/litre	56 400	5000 litres	705
Calves	67– 68	£45	3 040	0.84	38
			59 440		743
Replacement costs (depreciation)					
Cull cows	16 –17	£280	+4 640	0.21	+58
Purchase/transfer heifers	18–19	£460	−8 720	0.22	−109
Enterprise output			55 360		692
less Variable costs concentrates:					
Barley	36 t	£100	3 600	0.45 t	45
16% concentrates	84 t	£140	11 760	1.05 t	147
Vet & medicines			720		9
Sundries			1 440		18
Gross margin (before forage)			37 840		473
Forage costs			6 560		82
Gross margin (after forage)			31 280		391

Gross margin/ha = 391 × 1.92* = 750.70

(b) *Physical results*

Herd life (years)	4–5
Calving interval (days)	390
Cow mortality (%)	1–2
Calf mortality (%)	10
Size of cow (kg)	600
Winter feeding period (days)	185
Stocking (cows per hectare)	1.92*
Fertilizer use on grassland (kg N/ha)	
Grazing	250
Silage plus aftermath	275 (2 cuts 34 tonne yield)
Grazing season (days)	180

(c) *Net margins*

	£	£
Gross margin per ha (£392 × 1.92)		751
less Fixed costs		
Rent and buildings	94	
Machinery and power	176	
Labour (family and hired)	147	
Others	18	435
Net margin (per ha)		316

Information from The Scottish Agricultural Colleges' *Farm Management Handbook* 1981–82.

	Gross margin/cow	× Number of cows/ha	= Gross margin/ha
e.g. 1	£400	× 1.5	= £600
e.g. 2	£400	× 2.0	= £800
e.g. 3	£500	× 1.5	= £750
e.g. 4	£500	× 2.0	= £1000

Good grassland for grazing and conservation is the key factor which ensures high quality forage food and high stocking density.

Fixed Costs

These are the annual charges incurred for the use of land, labour, machinery and power and general overheads for keeping the herd. They could appear as follows on say a 46 ha farm keeping a herd of 80 cows and purchasing all replacement:

	£
Labour – farmer and 1 man	8 000
Machinery/power 46 ha @ £174/ha	8 096
Rent/rates 46 ha @ £94/ha	4 324
General overheads 46 ha @ £18/ha	828
Total	21 248
Net margin = £31 280 − £21 248	10 032

Fixed costs can vary enormously, depending mainly on the labour used, type and quality of buildings constructed, and the complement and age of machinery used. Generally speaking the managerial tasks are to:

i) keep labour costs at a reasonable level by an effective buildings layout which allows easy milking, feeding, disposal of slurry or manure and handling of cows;

ii) effectively mechanize for the
 (a) quick harvesting and storage of high quality forage crops;
 (b) storage, possible milling and mixing and rationing of home and purchased concentrates to cows;
 (c) disposal of manure or slurry.

It needs to be remembered that prices for output and input items are outside the farmer's control so that managerial skills need to be directed to the implementation and control of physical processes.

FORAGE PRODUCTION

Grass, whether grazed or conserved, is the cheapest food which can be fed to cows at present prices of different feeds. The principles governing the production and effective utilization of grass in relation to the dairy herd are described in chapter 9. Grass production varies considerably from one farm to another but the efficiency objective is to produce as much as possible; utilization by grazing and conservation is the 'cornerstone' of effective management to produce quality grass which reduces the concentrate feed for optimum milk production. Also, it is effective overall production and utilization which determines the stocking density attainable.

FEEDING FOR THE COW'S PRODUCTIVE CYCLE

The cow's productive cycle consists of a pregnancy followed by lactation after the birth of the calf; with the exception of the first pregnancy, a part of all other pregnancies occurs whilst the cow is producing milk. The lactation curve shows milk production increasing to a peak and then gradually decreasing to a dry period prior to the birth of the next calf. During this annual cycle the cow loses and gains body weight. The feeding task is to supply her varying energy and protein requirements within the daily dry matter intake which she is capable of eating. This balancing of energy and protein requirements and intakes is described in broad detail in chapter 8.

Because the cow is a ruminant her main forage feed consists of grass grazed in summer and eaten as conserved silage or hay in winter; the curve of grass growth and its accompanying concentrations of energy and protein have been described in chapter 9.

Ideally, it would be advantageous to perfectly match the milk lactation curve with the grass growth curve so as to reduce concentrate feeding. With a herd of cows it would be ideal to:

1. Calve all cows at the same time. This means that since all the cows are at the same stage of their productive cycles at any one time all the cows can be managed in the same way.
2. Calve all cows in late winter/early spring so that the milk production curve matches the grass

production curve, taking full advantage of summer grazing. Fig. 10.1 shows that if the cows calve in January/February, early concentrate

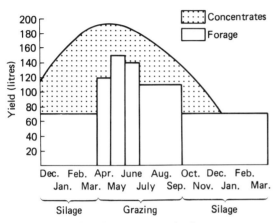

Fig. 10.1 Matching yield to grass production.

input having high energy concentration can ensure maximum peak yield and the remainder of the production requirement can be mainly supplied with cheap grazing.

If the above was true all herds in this country would be late winter/spring calving. The reasons why this does not occur in all herds are:

1. Simultaneous calving produces a heavy peak labour load and if calves are kept, a high capital cost for calf housing. Also, rigorous culling of those cows which do not calve is necessary because otherwise late winter/early spring calving slips into all-the-year calving, thus eliminating the advantages of matching milk to grass production (see p. 38).

2. The differential price paid for winter and summer milk coupled with existing concentrate prices makes autumn calving marginally more profitable. In many herds, all-the-year round calving is the rule, which is a compromise between the husbandry advantages of late winter/early spring calving and the existing financial margins of autumn calving. This situation, however, does not alter the three cardinal principles:

(a) cows calving in late winter/early spring should achieve maximum peak yield by concentrate input and subsequent milk production satisfied mainly by grazing;

(b) cows calving in autumn should achieve maximum peak yield by appropriate concentrate input and after reaching their peak yield, concentrates should be strictly rationed according to milk yield and cow condition required. Quality silage or hay is vital so as to reduce overall input of concentrates;

(c) high-stocking density ensures high gross margins per ha and profit per farm. High grass production should be matched with good grazing and conservation management.

COW AND GRASS MANAGEMENT

A high level of stockmanship linked with a high level of overall grassland management is very difficult to achieve in practice; in many farms the dual art of cow and grass management is as varied as the ability of the farmers who attempt the task. Broadly speaking there are four 'approaches' or 'net effects' in the difficult task of herd management.

1. Herds averaging over 5000 litres of milk per cow and fed mainly on high quality grass and silage. Concentrate feeding in winter is kept to a minimum and summer concentrate feeding is either non-existent or confined to cows giving high yields. High stocking rate, high milk yields and moderate concentrate feeding are the features of the best managed herds on this system.

2. Herds averaging over 5000 litres of milk per cow but relying mainly on concentrates to maintain high yields. Grass or grass products provide barely more than a maintenance ration for most of the year. Medium stocking rate, high milk yields and high concentrate feed in relation to milk yield are the features of the best managed herd on this system.

3. Herds giving moderate milk yields of around 3500–4500 litres of milk per cow. Heavy reliance is placed on quality grass and silage; concentrate feeding is usually kept below 750 kg per cow. High stocking rate, medium milk yields and low concentrate feeding are the features of the best managed herds on this system.

4. Herds averaging 4500 litres of milk per cow or less and relying too heavily on concentrates. These are really situations where the farmer 'falls between two stools', a situation which is unfortunately too common. Sub-standard cow and grassland management with inefficient con-

trol of concentrate feeding are the main causes. Low stocking rate, medium milk yields and high concentrate feeding are the features of this system.

ASSESSMENT AND ALLOCATION OF WINTER FOOD SUPPLIES

An assessment of the amount of home-grown foods available for the winter is advisable. After making a calculation of how much is required for young and other stock, it is possible to assess quantities available for the dairy herd during the winter. From then on, it is comparatively easy to assess how much is available for each cow by dividing the total quantity of each food by the number of cows in the herd. The amount fed to each cow per day is then calculated by dividing by the number of days in the winter. This will vary from 150 to 180, depending on when winter feeding starts in the autumn; it is always wise to assume that winter feeding will last until mid-April.

The following are simple examples of how this may be done:

Example 1

40 dairy cows
11 heifers (over 2 years old)
12 heifers (1–2 years old)
10 calves (under 1 year old)

The winter feed grown on the farm is hay, kale and barley; balanced concentrates are also purchased. The young stock receive only hay; the remainder of their nutritional requirement is met by feeding purchased rearing concentrates.

Assessment:
The quantities of hay, kale and barley grain available are assessed as follows:

Hay: Five bales are taken at random from the hayshed and weighed.

Weight of bales (kg)

No.	1	21.3
	2	22.7
	3	23.1
	4	22.7
	5	23.6
		113.4

Average weight per bale = 22.7 kg
Total No. of bales in stack = 3456
Total weight of hay = $3456 \times 22.7 = 78\,451$ kg

Kale: This crop is normally fed by grazing it in the field; the amount the cows receive each day is controlled by the electric fence. To estimate the kale yields fairly accurately, about five different one metre square patches are cut at random and their average weight calculated.

Average weight per square metre (m²) = 5.5 kg
Yield per ha $5.5 \times 100 \times 100 = 55$ tonnes (t)
(1 ha = 100×100 metres)
Total no. of hectares of kale = 2 ha
Total yield of kale $55 \times 2 = 100$ t.

If crop is grazed on the field, 1/10th of estimated yield should be subtracted to cover wastage, i.e. $110 - (110 \times 0.1) = 99$ t will be the total yield of the grazed crop.

Barley:
(a) In bags: No. of bags = 142
Average weight of bags = 50 kg
Total weight of barley = $142 \times 50 =$ 7100 kg = 7.1 t;
(b) In bins: size of bin = $7.8 \times 1.8 \times 0.9$ m
Volume = 12.6 cubic metres (m³)
740 kg of barley occupies 1 m³
Barley in bin = $12.6 \times 740 = 9324$ kg = 9.32 t
(c) Total weight of barley = barley in bags + barley in bins = $7.1 + 9.32 = 16.42$ t.

Thus the winter feeds available are:

Hay	78.45 t
Kale	99.00 t
Barley	16.42 t.

Allocation
Hay: Hay is fed to cattle in all age groups. In order to find out how much is available to each animal, all the cattle in the different age groups are converted into livestock units as follows (see p. 115).

Animals	Conversion factor	Livestock units (LUs)
40 dairy cows	× 1.00	40.0
11 heifers over 2 years old	0.80	8.8
12 heifers 1–2 years old	0.54	6.48 } = 18.28
10 calves under 1 year old	0.30	3.00
		58.28

The 33 young stock are equal to 18.28 adult cows in their food requirements.

So hay available for each LU during the winter will be $78\,451 \div 58.28 = 1346$ kg.

If it is assumed that hay may have to be fed from mid-October to mid-April, i.e. 180 days, this will allow $1346 \div 180 = 7.5$ kg per LU per day. In practice this means that if the average bale weight is 22.5 kg, each cow will receive about a third of a bale daily, i.e. $22.5 \div 3 = 7.5$ kg.

Kale: Kale is fed only to the 40 milking cows. Amount available per cow = $99 \div 40 = 2.50$ t. It is fed for three months (90 days), i.e. November, December and January. Amount of kale available per cow per day is therefore $2500 \div 90 = 27.8$ kg. In practice this means that if the average weight of kale per m² is 5.5 kg (5 kg after allowing for waste), the fence is moved each day so that there is about 5 m² of kale available for each cow.

Barley: On this farm the barley is fed only to the dairy cows. Barley feeding starts in mid-October to supplement the autumn grass and like the hay it is assumed that it may have to be fed for six months until mid-April. Hence it is fed for $6 \times 30 = 180$ days.

The quantity available for each cow per day is calculated as follows:

Annual quantity per cow = $16\,420 \div 40 = 411$ kg (approx.)

Daily quantity per cow = $411 \div 180 = 2.2$ kg (approx.)

The barley will be crushed or rolled and fed.

Thus daily allowances for the cows will be:

Hay (mid-Oct.–mid-April)	7.5 kg
Kale (Nov.–Jan.)	27.8 kg
Barley (mid-Oct.–mid-April)	2.2 kg

and daily rations during the two halves of winter read as follows:

	Nov.–Jan.	*Feb.–April*
Hay	7.5 kg	7.5 kg
Kale	27.8 kg	–
Barley	2.2 kg	2.2 kg

The daily milk production obtainable from each of the above rations can be assessed (see p. 98) and cows yielding above these production levels fed appropriate concentrate rations at a given kilogram rate per litre.

Example 2

There are 75 dairy cows (all replacements purchased as freshly calved heifers). The winter feed is self-feed silage, which is supplemented with purchased barley and balanced concentrates. The farm is 51 ha in area, and the cows are paddock-grazed on 15.2 ha during the summer, leaving nearly 36 ha for silage.

The silage feeding period is from early November until mid-April, a period of about 160 days. It is known that each cow will eat between 6 and 7 tonnes

of settled silage during this period, so a minimum of $75 \times 6 = 450$ tonnes of settled silage will be needed. On the 36 ha this will need a yield of 12.5 t/ha, which is an average yield.

Assessment

Before winter feeding commences, an assessment of the settled silage is made to obtain an indication of the quantity of silage actually available.

Dimensions of silo:	length	27 m
	width	13.5 m
	height of silage	1.8 m

Volume of silage = $L \times W \times H$
$$= 27 \times 13.5 \times 1.8$$
$$= 650 \text{ m}^3 \text{ (approx.)}$$

1 tonne of average consolidated silage occupies 1.35 m³

Weight of silage = $650 \div 1.35 = 480$ t, which is in excess of minimum requirements.

This calculation can be carried further knowing that on a self-feed system each cow consumes approximately 40 kg of silage daily. Therefore the daily consumption will be roughly:

$$40 \times 75 = 3000 \text{ kg} = 3 \text{ t.}$$

So 480 t would be sufficient for $480/3 = 160$ days.

The actual consumption and its relationship to the assessed consumption can be calculated by the rate at which the cows are eating into the silo. According to the above calculation the cows should be eating $27 \div 160 = 0.17$ m (170 mm) daily, horizontally averaged over the vertical height. If the actual rate of consumption is between 165 and 175 mm daily, the silage will last the calculated time. If on the other hand it is greater, a decision will be made whether to cut down consumption by restricting access to the silo.

As already mentioned, cows are self-fed, each cow being allowed to consume as much as she requires, and on average this will be about 40 kg daily. The nutrients supplied for maintenance and production will depend on the quality of the silage (see p. 113). Each cow will then be fed concentrates according to daily milk yield over and above that obtained from the silage.

CONCENTRATES

On most grassland farms, concentrates are purchased as proprietary balanced products. Their ME is 12.5 MJ/kg, crude protein percentage 12.5 and percentage dry matter 90 (see p. 98), e.g.

If ME requirement for 1 litre milk = 4.9 MJ

Then concentrates/litre milk = $\dfrac{4.9}{12.5}$

$$= 0.4 \text{ kg/litre}$$

1 kg cake supplies 0.125 kg protein

0.4 kg cake supplies $0.125 \text{ kg} \times 0.4 = 0.05$ kg protein/litre.

When foods are mixed on the farm the mix needs to be balanced to supply approximately 4.9 MJ of energy and 0.05 kg protein per litre of milk. Straight concentrates, commonly home-mixed, can be grouped as follows (their composition is shown in Table 8.1):

i) high protein, e.g. fish meal, soya bean meal, decorticated ground-nut and cotton cake;
ii) medium protein, e.g. linseed cake, bean and pea meal;
iii) energy/protein balanced, e.g. coconut and palm kernel cake, wheat middlings;
iv) low protein, e.g. barley, oats, flaked maize.

Foods in group (iii) are fairly balanced in themselves and can be fed at the following rates per litre:

| Palm kernel cake, coconut cake | 0.38 kg |
| Weatings | 0.40 kg |

Protein cakes in groups (i) and (ii) above are usually mixed with the low protein foods of group (iv).

Mixture 1: 4 parts by weight low-protein food with 1 part by weight of high-protein food. This means, for example, that 200 kg rolled barley could be mixed with 50 kg of decorticated ground-nut cake. To check and to calculate the kilos of cake to feed per litre, the following calculation is made:

	Energy (MJ)	Protein (kg)
1 kg ground-nut cake contains	12.9	0.45
4 kg barley 13.7 × 4:0.082 × 4	54.8	0.33
5 kg mix contains	77.7	0.78

77.7 MJ supplied by 5 kg mix
4.9 MJ supplied by $5/77.7 \times 4.9 = 0.32$ kg mix/litre.

Protein check:

| 5 kg mix supplies | 0.78 kg protein |
| 0.32 kg mix supplies | $\dfrac{0.78 \times 0.32}{5} = 0.05$ kg |

Mixture 2: 1 part by weight low-protein food with 1 part by weight of medium-protein food. This means that, for example, 100 kg of oats could be mixed with 100 kg of bean meal. To check:

	Energy (MJ)	Protein (kg)
1 kg oats	11.5	0.084
1 kg bean meal	12.8	0.209
2 kg mix contains	24.3	0.293

24.3 MJ supplied by 2 kg mix
4.9 MJ supplied by $2/24.3 \times 4.9 = 0.4$ kg mix/litre

Protein check:

2 kg mix supplies 0.293 kg protein
0.4 kg mix supplies $0.293/2 \times 0.4 = 0.06$ kg

Mixture 3: Mixtures 1 and 2 above can be combined in any desired proportion. For example, the following mixture could be constituted:

50 kg decorticated cotton cake
200 kg barley
100 kg linseed cake
100 kg oats

To check:

	Energy (MJ)	Protein (kg)
1 kg decorticated cotton cake	12.3	0.393
4 kg barley (13.7 × 4:0.082 × 4)	54.8	0.328
2 kg linseed cake (13.4 × 2:0.29 × 2)	26.8	0.580
2 kg oats (11.5 × 2:0.06 × 2)	23.0	0.120
9 kg	116.9	1.421

116.9 MJ supplied by 9 kg mix
4.9 MJ supplied by $9/116.9 \times 4.9 = 0.38$ kg/litre

Protein check:

9 kg mix supplies 1.42 kg protein
0.38 kg mix supplies $1.42/9 \times 0.38 = 0.06$ kg/litre.

A proprietary mixture of minerals must be added to such home-made mixtures at the rate of 1.3 kg of mineral to every 50 kg of the mixture.

Grain Balancer Concentrates

Many firms sell concentrates for mixing with cereals to provide a mixture balanced for milk production. These are called grain balancers and are mixtures of various protein-rich concentrates, plus the necessary vitamins and minerals. There are usually two types available according to the amount of protein they contain and they are mixed as follows by weight:

either 3 cereal to 1 concentrate
or 1 cereal to 1 concentrate.

These balancers can make farm mixing simpler and easier on a small scale.

Urea Feeding

It has already been described how ruminants synthesize proteins from urea. It is now possible to feed urea to dairy cows giving medium yields of 9 to 13.5 litres daily; its main advantage is that it is a cheap source of protein and consequently it lowers the cost of concentrate feeding. At the moment it is not clear whether it is advantageous for urea to be used as a source of protein for very high yielders.

It is available in either solid or liquid form for *ad lib.* feeding; it is also incorporated to supply part of the protein content of the more traditional concentrate.

In order to avoid digestive upsets, urea should be introduced gradually into the rations. Incorrect feeding resulting in too large a quantity being eaten can lead to some toxic effects. It is wise to follow the manufacturer's instructions carefully.

ANALYSIS OF A HERD'S PERFORMANCE

When the gross margin for a herd is divided by the number of cows in the herd this gives an average figure per cow which reflects the annual performance of the herd and which can be used to analyse possible weaknesses in the management of the herd. Simple effective records are required to make such an analysis meaningful.

Fig. 10.2 shows a diagnostic flow diagram which relates all the factors responsible for the ultimate efficiency measures of gross margin per cow and per hectare. Analysis involves comparing the figures for the farm with standard or target figures which are compiled by central agencies processing data collected from a wide range of farms. Each farm figure which is unsatisfactory compared with the standard figure pinpoints a cause of a low gross margin performance.

Margin over Concentrates

This is a quick check on the performance of a dairy herd enterprise and is calculated as follows:

Milk sales *less* purchased and home-grown concentrate costs

It is an efficiency measure incorporating the largest single item of enterprise output on the one hand and variable costs on the other. The result can be presented on a per cow or per hectare basis, the latter being particularly important on the small farm.

So as to take account of important forage costs, margin over concentrates and fertilizers per forage hectare is often used; to calculate, the fertilizer costs per forage hectare are deducted from margin over concentrates per hectare.

These measures can also be used to obtain a limited analysis of factors causing poor performance in the herd.

CONTROLLING A HERD'S PERFORMANCE

Analysis of a herd's performance indicates weaknesses which have occurred over the previous year. These defects need to be corrected but once corrected the herd's performance needs to be controlled daily so that the overall performance at the end of the year is as forecast. Controlling is thus the continuous managerial control of events which make up a continuous process.

Control implies:

forecasting possible performance
recording actual performance
comparing actual with forecast performances
diagnosing faults causing unsatisfactory actual performance
correcting faults immediately.

It is the physical events which are controlled and such controls have financial implications. The factors which are most easily controlled are:

breeding performance
input of concentrates and output of milk.

Breeding Performances

Records need to be kept of heat periods, natural or artificial service, pregnancy diagnosis, and birth. Careful scrutiny can ensure maximum reproductive output within the calendar year and rapid decisions on the culling of infertile cows. Several types of visual display boards are available for this purpose.

Milk Output and Concentrate Input

Two methods of control are described:

Method (a): Average daily milk output and concentrate intake for the whole herd

This is the method adopted by the M.M.B.'s Farm Management Services. The farmer provides monthly the following information:

Number of cows
Total milk production
Quantity and price of purchased concentrates
Calvings during next two months.

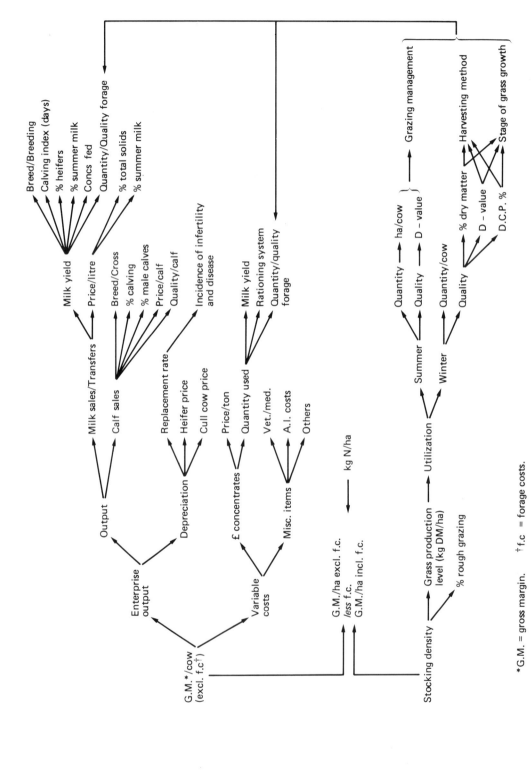

Fig. 10.2 Diagnostic flow diagram for the analysis of a dairy herd's performance.

*G.M. = gross margin.   †f.c = forage costs.

Computer print-outs can then predict for the next month, the average daily milk output and concentrate input.

The method is based on lactation curves according to the month of calving as shown in Table 10.3. These curves assume a peak yield of one two-hundredth ($\frac{1}{200}$) of predicted average yield of herd and a drop in yield of 2.5% per week after peak yield is obtained. The contribution of home-grown forage is estimated and the quantity of concentrates for remainder of milk output calculated at standard quantities per litre, e.g. 0.4 kg/litre. Average daily milk output and concentrate input can then be calculated as shown:

Example: Prediction of average daily milk output and concentrate input for whole herd for month of October (70 cows)

1. *Expected milk production in October for herd with 4000 litre average*

Calvers	No. cows	Lactation %		Litres milk
Dec.	10	× 0.3	× 4000 =	120
Aug.	10	× 12.8	× 4000 =	5 120
Sept.	20	× 14.5	× 4000 =	11 600
Oct.	20	× 7.2*	× 4000 =	5 760
Nov.	10	× 0	× 4000 =	0
				22 600

*Half of 14.4 because cows calved from mid-October onwards.

	Litres
Milk yield per cow/month = 22 600 ÷ 70 =	323
Milk yield per cow/day = 323 ÷ 30 =	10.8

2. Expected milk yield from silage = M + 5 litres
3. Daily milk yield from concentrates = 10.8 − 5
   = 5.8 litres
4. Expected concentrate input/cow/day = 5.8 × 0.4
   = 2.3 kg

Actual figures can be compared with predicted figures and if there are differences significant questions can be asked, e.g. should milk be dropping at all or is it dropping too fast; if milk is rising is it rising fast enough? Answers to these questions can give rise to quick corrective action so that performance can match predicted target.

Method (b): Average daily milk input and concentrate intake for a group of cows calving in the same month

With this system the herd is divided into groups according to month of calving. For each group, average milk yield can be predicted using standard lactation curves and average concentrate input calculated by estimating contribution of home-grown forage and then feeding cake at 0.4 kg/litre for the remainder of the milk yield as shown in example.

Example: Average daily milk output in October for a group of 10 cows calving in August

1. *Average expected milk yields*

Total	No. cows	Lactation %	Litres milk
Per month	10 ×	12.8 × 4000* =	5120
Per cow/month =	5120 ÷ 10		512
Per cow/day =	512 ÷ 30		17.4

2. Expected milk yield from silage = M + 5 litres
3. Daily milk yield from concentrates = 17.4 − 5
   = 12.4 litres
4. Expected concentrate input/cow/day = 12.4 × 0.4
   = 4.96 kg

* Predicted average annual milk yield.

The average milk output and concentrate input within each group is recorded weekly and any deviation from predicted figures noted and corrective action taken. This is a more detailed method of control than method (a).

Table 10.3. Milk production – lactation curves according to month of calving (100 = average yield for herd)

Month of calving	Jan.	Feb.	Mar.	Apr.	May	June	July	Aug.	Sept.	Oct.	Nov.	Dec.	Jan.	Feb.	Mar.	Apr.	May	June	July	Aug.	Sept.	Oct.
January	14.4	13.6	14.2	13.1	12.2	10.1	8.8	7.0	4.6	2.8	0.2											
February		12.6	15.1	14.4	13.8	11.7	10.7	9.1	7.0	5.1	3.1	0.4										
March			14.7	16.2	15.5	13.0	12.0	10.3	8.0	6.3	4.2	2.7	0.1									
April				15.1	16.7	14.1	13.1	11.6	9.4	7.9	6.1	4.6	3.2	0.2								
May					16.1	15.9	14.8	13.0	10.7	9.1	7.2	5.9	4.3	2.7	0.3							
June						15.0	16.7	15.0	12.4	10.7	8.8	7.6	6.3	4.4	3.7	0.4						
July							15.3	15.8	13.4	11.7	9.5	8.6	7.5	5.8	5.6	4.3	0.5					
August								14.9	14.5	12.8	10.5	9.4	9.2	6.5	6.6	5.8	4.4	0.4				
September									14.2	14.5	12.2	10.9	9.7	8.0	8.3	7.8	6.6	4.3	0.5			
October										14.4	13.9	12.9	11.3	9.2	9.6	9.1	8.1	5.6	3.6	0.3		
November											13.6	14.7	13.2	10.7	11.1	10.5	9.8	7.6	5.9	3.6	0.3	
December												14.4	14.8	12.2	12.5	11.7	10.9	8.8	7.3	5.2	2.9	0.3

*Add 3½% in leap year.
Derived by G. Allanson, Wye College, from data supplied by Production Division, Milk Marketing Board.
Figures for each month of calving weighted by the resulting lactation yield and the percentage of cows in the national herd calving in each month.

BUDGETING FOR MANAGERIAL CHANGES

When the performance of an enterprise has been fully analysed it may show up weaknesses. It is one of the functions of management to attempt to correct these weaknesses as this is a way of improving enterprise performance and in doing so the profit of the business.

When any change is contemplated in the management of an enterprise, budgeting to estimate the likely financial effect of such a change is essential to assist in the decision-making process; as factual a picture as possible of the effects of change is more desirable than mere guesswork. It needs to be appreciated that a budget is only valid for the changes involved in a specific farm situation; there is no such thing as a general budget for a range of farm situations.

When any planning is made four basic questions need to be asked:

1. What will be the strictly husbandry and technical effects of the change? This is probably the most difficult part of the exercise. It is asking exactly what is to be changed and the items emerging from such an exercise need to be isolated from those which will remain unchanged.

2. How much capital will be required to carry it out? This is set out as a capital budget and figures are calculated at current or estimated prices. It is convenient to prepare capital budget under the following headings:

Landlord's capital: land, buildings and fixed equipment
Tenant's capital: live and dead stock.

3. What profit or loss will result from the change? A profit or loss budget is prepared, this being a simple financial statement of the gains and losses which occur. The statement reflects the annual financial gain or loss after the contemplated change has come into full operation; it does not describe the position over the years when the plan is being phased in. It is only the technical items which alter as a result of the changes that are priced in the budget and it is prudent to under- rather than over-estimate any advantage.

4. Is the investment of capital worth while? Calculating the percentage return on the extra or marginal capital investment can help with this judgement. In the following examples weaknesses in the enterprise performance have been highlighted and the management approach to solving the problem is outlined.

Example 1: Improving the enterprise gross margin for an 80 cow herd from its current level up to the average performance (Table 10.2)

Per cow	Current figures for herd	Average
Gross margin (before forage) (£)	369	473
Milk yields (litres)	3900	5000
Concentrates: barley (tonnes)	0.45	0.45
16% protein (tonnes)	0.75	1.05

(a) *Husbandry effects*

No additional buildings or labour will be required but a larger bulk tank will be needed. Milk yields to be increased by more effective feeding of concentrates, improved grassland management and improved mastitis control. The stocking density will remain at the current level and forage costs will be unchanged.

(b) *Approximate marginal capital budget*

		£	£
i)	Landlord's	nil	
ii)	Tenant's:		
	Bulk tank (after grant) ÷ 2* (£3500 ÷ 2)		1750
iii)	Working:		
	Additional variable costs†		
	Concentrates ÷ 12		
	£3360 ÷ 12	280	
	Miscellaneous ÷ 12		
	£960 ÷ 12	80	
			2110
	less Capital released		
	Sale of original bulk tank		500
	Total		1610

*$\frac{1}{2}$ of total capital is taken in this calculation as this is the average investment for the bulk tank over its working life.

†$\frac{1}{12}$ of totals is taken in this calculation as the monthly milk cheque will bring this investment back to £0 when each cheque is received. Totals shown in Partial Budget.

(c) *Partial budget*

Loss		Gain	
Extra costs	£	Income gained	£
Concentrates:			
16% protein (0.3 t × 80 cows × £140/t)	3360	Additional milk (80 cows × 11 001 × 14.1p/l)	12 408
Miscellaneous (£12 extra × 80 cows)	960		
Depreciation of bulk tank (£3500 over 10 years)	350		
Additional maintenance and running costs of new bulk tank: 3% of £3000*	100		
Extra margin	7638		
	12 408		12 408

*New capital invested in tank = £3500 new tank minus £500 for old tank.

(d) *Return on marginal capital* (%)

$$\frac{\text{Extra margin}}{\text{Marginal capital}} \times \frac{100}{1} = \frac{7638}{1610} \times \frac{100}{1} = 474\%$$

Example 2: Increasing size of herd (Table 10.2) *by 15 dairy cows*

(a) *Husbandry effects*

No additional labour will be required. Housing will need to be increased by 12 kennels. Stocking density on the existing forage area will be improved by the application of additional fertilizer over the whole forage area (£1230). Milk yields will remain at 5000 litres per cow.

(b) *Approximate marginal capital budget*

	£
i) Landlord's:	
12 kennels at £250 each (after grant) ÷ 2, £3000 ÷ 2	1500
ii) Tenant's:	
15 dairy cows at £460 each	6900
iii) Working:	
Total variable costs including the extra fertilizer costs ÷ 12 (see table 10.2), £301* × 15 cows ÷ 12	376
Total	8776

*£219 variable costs + £82 forage costs (Table 10.2).

(c) *Partial budget*

Loss	£	Gain	£
Extra fertilizer costs	1230		
Extra fixed costs		Gross margins gained	
Depreciation of 12 kennels (£3000 ÷ 10 yrs)	300	15 cows at £473/cow (excluding forage costs)	7095
Repair and maintenance of 12 kennels (3% of £3000)	90		
Extra margin	5475		
	7095		7095

(d) *Return on marginal capital* (%)

$$\frac{5475}{8776} \times \frac{100}{1} = 62\%$$

This is a satisfactory return on the additional capital invested and is mainly due to the fact that existing fixed costs are now being spread over a larger herd.

During the process of farm planning there are occasions when more complicated changes than those outlined in these two examples have to be undertaken. Such changes can involve more than one of the farm enterprises and can have major effects on the farm's fixed costs. This may call for more complicated partial budgets or whole farm budgets.

11

Feeding and Management of Dairy Heifers

The management of a Dairy Heifer Replacement Enterprise is concerned with the rearing of female calves through their stages of growth and development until they give birth to their own first calves. They need to be housed, fed appropriate diets according to their stage of development and the daily growth rate required of them, given a routine of veterinary treatment to keep them healthy, and their reproductive development monitored so that they can be served to ensure down-calving of the heifers at an age appropriate to the system of management adopted.

ENTERPRISE GROSS MARGIN

A gross margin for a dairy heifer could be as shown in Figs. 11.1 and 11.2. It can be seen that the gross margin per head excluding forage costs is the difference between the sale value of the down-calving heifer *less* the market value of the calf making up enterprise output *less* the variable costs of milk substitutes, concentrates and miscellaneous items consisting of veterinary payments and medicines.

An acceptable gross margin per heifer depends mainly on producing a heifer of quality which has not been fed at too high a concentrate input because of the availability of high-quality forage. In many instances efforts are made to rear heifers so that they weigh about 510 kg when calving at two years of age: the alternative in specialist spring or autumn calving herds is to calve them when they are three years old. An example of this is shown in Fig. 11.2. A comparison of gross margins in Figs. 11.1 and 11.2 shows that the gross margin for a 2 year old heifer is less than for a 2.5 year old heifer because there has been a

greater input of concentrates to achieve a more rapid liveweight gain in the 2 year old heifer.

A more critical measure of enterprise efficiency is the gross margin per hectare. To appreciate stocking density in relation to this enterprise it is important to understand how it is calculated. A Dairy Replacement Unit (DRU) is defined as a calf and yearling and heifer over 2 years old. Thus in terms of livestock or 'cow' units, a replacement unit or heifer can be as shown in the table below.

Thus the age at calving has a bearing on the area of land required for the rearing process. Assume that the stocking density per forage hectare achievable on a farm was 0.5 ha/LU. The area of land required for heifers down-calving at different ages would then be as follows:

Calving age	ha land required per DRU
3 years	$0.5 \times 1.64 = 0.82$
2 years 9 months	$0.5 \times 1.44 = 0.72$

Age of down-calving heifer	3 yr	2 yr 9 mo.	2 yr 6 mo.	2 yr 3 mo.	2 yr
Calf: 1×0.3	0.30	0.3	0.3	0.3	0.3
+ yearling: 1×0.54	0.54	0.54	0.54	0.54	0.54
+ 2 year old heifer: 1×0.2 for every 3 months of feeding	0.8	0.6	0.4	0.2	0.0
Livestock units	1.64	1.44	1.24	1.04	0.84

136

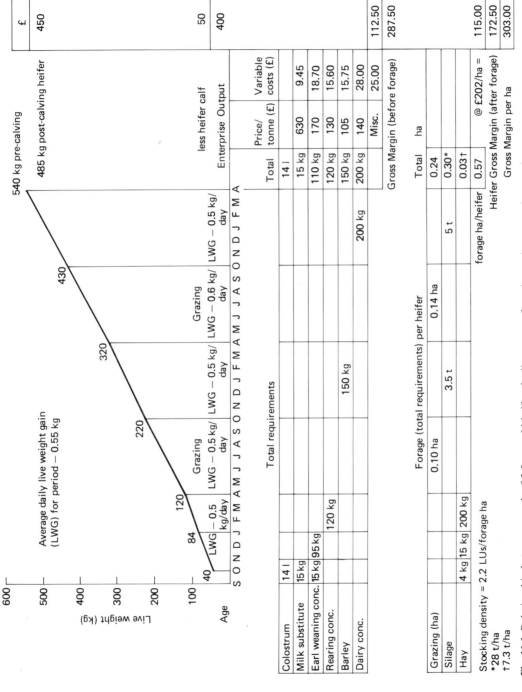

Fig. 11.1 Relationship between growth of 2.5 year old heifer, feeding, areas of grazing and conservation, resultant gross margin per heifer and per forage hectare.

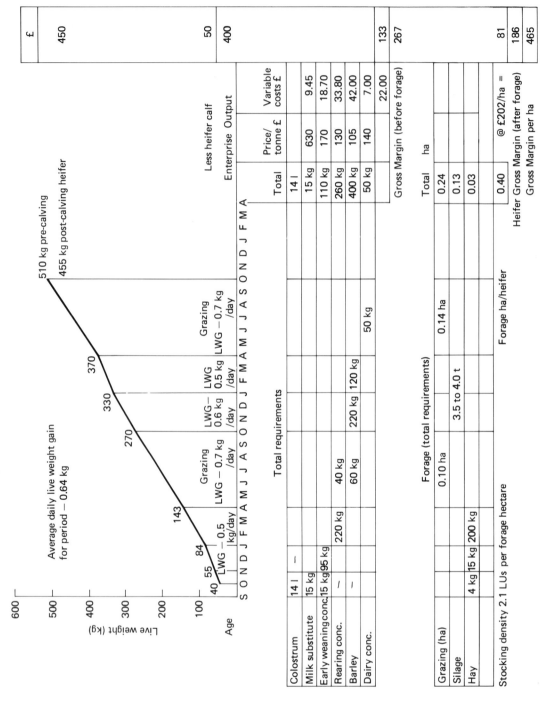

Fig. 11.2 Relationship between growth of 2 year old heifer, feeding, areas of grazing and conservation, resultant gross margins and per forage hectare.

2 years 6 months $0.5 \times 1.24 = 0.62$
2 years 3 months $0.5 \times 1.04 = 0.52$
2 years $0.5 \times 0.84 = 0.42$

This has a direct effect on gross margin per ha. If the gross margin for a dairy heifer is £186 then the gross margin per ha, if she calved at 3 years old, is $186 \div 0.82 = £227$/ha; if she calved at 2 years old it is $186 \div 0.42 = £443$/ha.

Thus the gross margin obtained per hectare depends on:

(a) Age of heifer at calving; the younger she calves the less land she requires;
(b) Stocking density achievable; high stocking density depends on good grassland management for producing and utilizing quality summer grazing and winter fodder. Reference to 'stocking density' in chapter 9 (p. 114) shows the principles involved.

GROWTH AND DEVELOPMENT

Figs. 11.1, 11.2 and 11.3 summarize the principles involved and should be referred to when reading this section.

There are several biological constraints which determine the husbandry possible:

1. Since a newly-born calf has but one stomach, it is essential to feed colostrum and milk during the early part of its life. The early feeding of solid and fibrous food encourages the oesophogeal pouches to develop into functional rumen, reticulum and omasum.

2. A calf needs to be around 120 kg at its first turn-out to grass for it to thrive and grow effectively. It needs to be placed on worm- and husk-free pastures and must never follow adult cattle in rotational pattern of grazing.

3. A heifer needs to have matured to about 510 kg in weight when she calves. With good management this is achievable in two years but

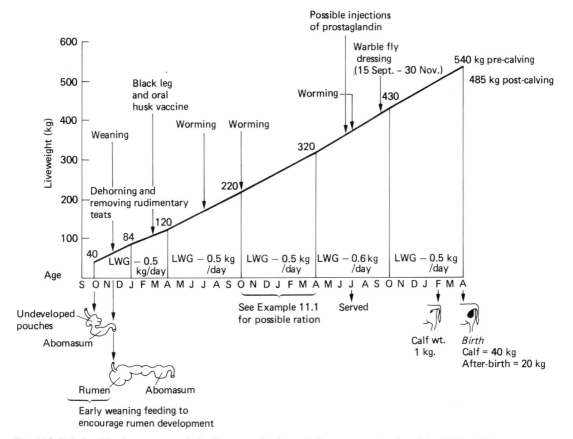

Fig. 11.3 Relationships between growth, feeding, reproduction and disease prevention in a dairy heifer calving at 2.5 years.

Table 11. 1. Once- and twice-a-day early weaning systems of calf rearing (source: British Denkavit)

Age in days	Twice per day feeding (litres)		Once per day feeding (litres)		Management
	Morning	Evening	Morning	Evening	
0–4	Colostrum		Colostrum		Offer dry food
5	1	1	1	1	and fesh
6	1.25	1.25	1.5	1	drinking
7	1.5	1.5	1.5	1	water
8	1.75	1.75	1.75	1	
9	1.75	1.75	2.25	0.75	Offer good
10–25	2	2	3		hay
26–39	1.75	1.75	3		
40	1.5	1.5	2.5		Wean according
41	1	1	1.5		to condition
42	0.5	0.5	0.5		

Concentration of mix:
  125 g powder per litre mixed milk for twice a day feeding system.
  150 g powder per litre mixed milk for once a day feed system.

it usually takes longer. The minimum age at which a heifer can be served for the first time is thus fourteen months.

Birth to Weaning (target 0.5 kg liveweight gain per day)

Under natural extensive systems of rearing, the calf suckles milk from its mother's udder for 4 to 6 months. This has proved too costly for intensive dairy-farming systems and the calf is reared using a milk substitute; dry food in the form of concentrates is introduced on the fourth day in order to encourage rumen development.

There are several systems of calf feeding practised for the 5 to 6 week period from birth to weaning. Two such systems are shown in Table 11.1. For the first four days colostrum must be fed either by suckling the mother or by bucket feeding (1.5–2.0 litres twice per day). Since colostrum is rich in minerals, vitamins and antibodies, its feeding confers a calf with a degree of resistance against disease.

Colostrum is then replaced by a milk substitute and this should be mixed and fed according to the manufacturer's instructions. Water, high quality hay and an early weaning concentrate are offered to the calf at an early stage. Early weaning concentrates need to be highly palatable and are usually purchased as proprietary 'pencils'. The energy value should not be below 12.6 MJ/kg dry matter, and containing 17% crude protein (Table 11.2).

Alternative systems following colostrum intake are:

i) whole milk feeding twice a day;

ii) cold milk substitute feeding either once or twice a day;

iii) stored colostrum instead of milk substitute. The production from the first eight milkings from a freshly-calved cow is stored and fed either fresh or sour. The maximum recommended per feed is 2.5 litres, and when supplies run out it is safe to change to a milk substitute. The cream should be well stirred in before each feed;

iv) acidified milk can be used but a high level of stockmanship is essential. The extra cost needs to be offset by an increased liveweight gain;

v) recent introductions as milk substitutes include products based on whey or non-milk proteins such as soya, fish-meal or single-cell protein plus whey proteins.

Table 11.2. Examples of concentrate mixes (kg) at the calf-rearing stage per tonne mix (source: Ministry of Agriculture, Fisheries and Food)

	0–3 mths	3–6 mths	6–24 mths
Protein concentrate (42.6 CP)	250	200	
Barley rolled or ground	400	500	982
Flaked maize	150		
Course wheat feed	100	100	
Molassed meal/molasses	100	50	
Maize meal		150	
Mineral and vitamins	included	included	18

Weaning should take place when the calf is eating 0.7 kg concentrates for three consecutive days (see chapter 12, p. 152 for additional information on calf rearing).

Routine calf tasks

1. *Umbilical cord and navel*. The hanging umbilical cord of the calf is always a possible source of infection. Navel-ill and joint-ill may develop as a result of infection. With newly born calves it is good practice to spray the animal with an antiseptic dressing.

2. *Disbudding*. It is the normal practice to remove the horn buds in the young calf. This should be done as soon as the horn buds can be properly located (3 to 6 weeks of age); the hot-iron method is the one most commonly used.

The Protection of Animals-Anaesthetic Act requires that the animal must be anaesthetized at any age, unless this is done by chemical cautery within the first week of life. The equipment needed to perform this task is:

i) scissors with rounded ends to clip the hair from around the horn bud;
ii) cotton wool swabs and antiseptic; 70% alcohol should not be used if a gas disbudding iron is used;
iii) 5 or 10 ml syringes with 19–20 gauge needles;
iv) local anaesthetic;
v) a disbudding iron heated either by electricity or gas.

The site for the injection of the anaesthetic is the occipital groove which is located between the bud and the back of the calf's eye (Fig. 11.4a). The needle is inserted gently, but firmly, to a depth of about 12 mm and the anaesthetic injected slowly and steadily. After the needle is withdrawn the site should be swabbed and massaged to disperse the anaesthetic. The hair around the horn bud is clipped (Fig. 11.4b) and the area around the base of each bud is tested for numbness by a pointed instrument (Fig. 11.4c). The cup-like end of the hot iron is firmly pressed

b. Clipping hair

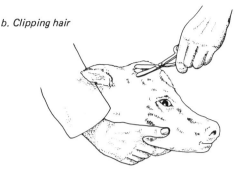

c. Testing buds for numbness

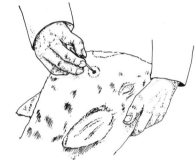

d. Making the first burn

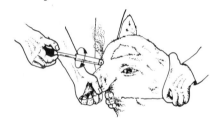

e. Undercutting horn bud

f. Removing horn bud

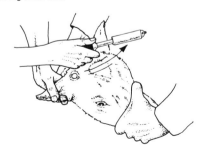

a. Injection Site

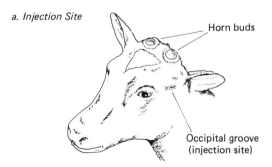

Horn buds

Occipital groove (injection site)

Fig. 11.4 Disbudding calves (hot iron) (source: Agricultural Training Board).

on the horn bud to achieve the first burn (Fig. 11.4d); this is followed by the undercutting of the bud (Fig. 11.4e) and finally removal by a scooping action (Fig. 11.4f). The cavity should be inspected to ensure that it is neat and round and that there is no visible white flesh and no bleeding. Dressing the area with an antiseptic or fly repellant or cream is advisable.

3. *Ear marking*. It is a statutory requirement that 'all cattle (with the exception of calves aged 14 days or under, which are retained on the farm or moved direct to a slaughterhouse) are required to be marked or otherwise identified in accordance with the National Herd Marking Scheme or in the case of pedigree animals, in accordance with the Rules of a Breed Society' (Tuberculosis Order).

The animal must be marked, in the right ear, by means of an approved tag or tattoo (Fig. 11.5). Examples of approved ear tags are shown in Fig. 11.6. It is important that when metal tags are used sufficient space is allowed for the continued growth of the ear. Under the Agriculture, Miscellaneous Provisions Act, the ear marking should be carried out by 'a competent operator so as to avoid unnecessary distress to the animals'.

4. *Identification (other than ear marking)*. In addition to ear marking, other methods of identification are used as aids to management. Freeze branding is such an example and involves the destruction of the pigment-forming cells of the hair follicles. This is achieved by the application of supercooled metal branding instruments to the animal's skin. Subsequent growth of hair at the site of branding is white and the technique is excellent for dark haired breeds. The animal must be effectively restrained during branding and the supercooled instrument held in position for 30 seconds. The technique needs to be carried out by a competent, properly trained operator (Agriculture Miscellaneous Provisions Act).

Electronic devices are now available and their

a. Loading pliers

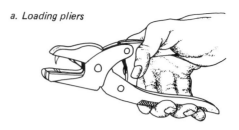

b. Fixing metal tag in ear

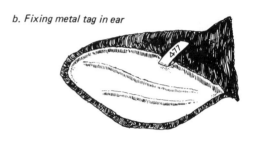

c. Fixing plastic tag in ear

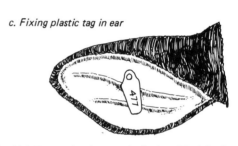

Fig. 11.6 Ear-tagging (source: Agricultural Training Board).

main value is for systems involving automatic feed-rationing and recording.

5. *Aftercare following all veterinary tasks*. Animals should be checked regularly after they have been subjected to any interferences, including the ones described in this section.

Rearing from Weaning to Calving

The rearing of heifers during this stage depends on time of birth and age at calving. The age at which heifers first calve has an effect on the number of animals in the rearing enterprise in relation to the size of the dairy herd (Table 11.3). Intensive systems of rearing aim to calve heifers at around 2 years of age as this reduces the area of land required for rearing. The area saved can then be used for more profitable enterprises, e.g. dairying (see Budget 2, p. 146).

The following system of rearing is for autumn born Friesian heifers to calve at 2 years of age:

5–12 weeks (target 0.5 kg liveweight gain per day). Concentrate feeding is continued up to a maximum of 2.3 kg per day and good quality

Fig. 11.5 Tattooing the ear (source: Agricultural Training Board).

Table 11.3. Number of replacements to be reared for a 100 cow herd with a replacement rate of 1:4 (source: Ministry of Agriculture, Fisheries and Food).

Age at 1st calving	2 years	2.5 years	3 years
0–12 months old	25	25	25
12–24 months old	25	25	25
24–36 months old		13	25
Total number of replacements on farm during any given year	50	63	75

hay is fed to appetite. If the hay quality is only moderate then the concentrate level can be increased to around 2.7 kg per day. The type of concentrate used is the same as for pre-weaning period.

3–6 mths (target 0.6 kg liveweight gain per day). Concentrates are fed to a maximum of 2.3 kg per day and hay is fed *ad lib*. The concentrate is gradually changed to a cheaper one (ME 12.7 MJ/kg DM; crude protein 15.5%) by reducing the number of ingredients and lowering the protein level (Table 11.2). Palatability is not so important as at the earlier stages.

6–12 mths (target 0.7 kg liveweight gain per day). The calf should be turned out on to a clean pasture as soon as soil and weather conditions allow and before the grass has made appreciable growth. If a gradual turn-out cannot be arranged, some form of temporary shelter should be provided. A clean pasture is one which has not carried cattle from the previous mid-summer. Where necessary, vaccination against husk is part of the routine before turn-out. Target weight gains can only be achieved by the provision of a continuous supply of good quality grass and effective parasitic control. The calf will benefit from supplementary feeding of concentrates for the first two weeks of the grazing season. As the rate of grass growth and quality declines in late summer, supplementary feeding in the form of mineralized rolled barley is necessary (Table 11.2).

Growth and Development from 12 Months Onwards

During this period the animal develops to a state of maturity and will be served at any time from 14 months onwards depending on physical development. It is important that the heifer does not become over-fat because otherwise fat may be laid down around the ovaries, and this can interfere with the normal functioning of these organs. Fat deposited in the udder retards the development of alveolar tissue and this means a reduced level of milk production in the subsequent lactation. Undue fatness may also cause calving difficulties.

Autumn-born Friesian heifers to calve at 2 years
12 months to service (15 mths) (target at least 330 kg at service). Heifers can remain on grass if ground conditions allow, provided they are supplementary fed and gaining about 0.7 kg per day. The full winter ration consists of 1.8–2.3 kg mineralized barley per day plus about 23 kg of 20% DM silage and straw to appetite; the silage can be substituted by the equivalent amount of hay. Heat period detection for possible service is around fifteen months as described on p. 1.

15–18 mths (target 0.5 kg liveweight gain per day). Unless grazing is likely to be very limited the following summer the level of concentrate feeding can be reduced to 0.9–1.4 kg per day with the bulk ration remaining as for the 12–15 month stage.

Examples 11.1 and 11.2 show how rations can be devised from the foods available on the farm.

18–24 mths (target 0.7 kg liveweight gain per day. Pre-calving weight 510 kg). The heifers should be turned out as soon as soil and weather conditions allow and they should be introduced to the dairy herd 3–4 weeks before calving. Levels of concentrate usage should be adjusted according to the condition of the grass and the aim is to keep the animals in a fit condition throughout pregnancy. A gradual introduction to the post-calving ration is recommended.

Example 11.1: To predict daily liveweight gain (D.L.G.W) from following ration fed to a 200 kg heifer

7.5 kg silage	(25% dry matter: 10.5 MJ/kg DM)
2.0 kg hay	(85% dry matter: 7.5 MJ/kg DM)
1.25 kg concentrates	(90% dry matter: 12.5MJ/kg DM)

	DMI (kg)	ME (MJ)
7.5 kg silage	1.9 (7.5 × 0.25)	20.00 (10.5 × 1.9)
2.0 kg hay	1.7 (2.0 × 0.85)	12.75 (7.5 × 1.7)
1.25 kg concen- trates	1.13 (1.25 × 0.9)	14.13 (12.5 × 1.13)
	4.73	46.88

Energy concentration of ration
(M/D) = 46.88 ÷ 4.73 = 9.9 MJ/kg DM.
Metabolizable energy required for maintenance
Mm = 27 (Table 8.2)
Metabolizable energy for production
(MEP) = 46.88–27 = 19.88 MJ
Net energy available for production
from 19.88 MJ/ME at concentration of 9.9 MJ/kg DM

Eg = 8.25 MJ (Table 8.7)
Daily liveweight gain
    D.L.W.G. = 0.65 kg (Table 8.8)

Example 11.2: To predict D.L.W.G. from following ration fed to a 400 kg heifer

25 kg silage	(25% dry matter: 10.5 MJ/kg DM)	
1.0 kg concentrates	(90% dry matter: 12.5 MJ/kg DM)	

	DMI (kg)	ME (MJ)
25 kg silage	6.25 (25 × 0.25)	65.6 (10.5 × 6.25)
1.0 kg concentrates	0.90 (1.0 × 0.9)	11.25 (12.5 × 0.9)
	7.15	76.85

Notation as for Example 11.1 above.
    M/D = 76.85 ÷ 7.15 = 10.7
    Mm = 45 (Table 8.2)
    MEP = 76.85 − 45 = 31.85.
    Eg = 13 (Table 8.7)
    D.L.W.G. = 0.7 (Table 8.8)

Autumn-born Friesian heifers to calve at 2.5 years
Calving at 2.5 years old requires a lower average growth rate than for 2 year old calving. Target weights are easier to achieve and the level of concentrate feeding can be reduced. It is preferable to aim for a higher liveweight at calving – 540 kg as compared with 510 kg (Fig. 11.1).

Spring-born Friesian heifers
The general principles of rearing spring-born heifers are the same as for autumn-born heifers. The difficulty with getting these animals to calve at 2 years of age is that they are too small to make efficient use of grass in their first year.

To ensure that the target weight during this period is achieved, the supplementary feeding of concentrates is required for the major part of the grazing season. The liveweight gain during the winter period needs to be higher than for autumn-born calves and in order to achieve calving at 2 years of age a greater input of concentrates is required overall.

Dentition and Age

Two sets of teeth develop in a cow during its life – a set of temporary or milk teeth which are replaced later by a set of permanent teeth. When a cow is about 18 months of age it has a full set of temporary teeth, i.e. 20 teeth. The number of teeth in a full set of milk teeth are shown in Fig. 11.7. The number of teeth in a set are usually written in the form of a dental formula as follows:

Dental formula for a full set of milk teeth
$$\frac{\text{Teeth in one half of upper jaw}}{\text{Teeth in one half of lower jaw}} \times 2$$

i.e.

$$\frac{\text{I}(0)\ \text{C}(0)\ \text{P}(3)\ \text{M}(0)}{\text{I}(4)\ \text{C}(0)\ \text{P}(3)\ \text{M}(0)} \times 2 = (3+7) \times 2 = 20$$

where   I = incisors,   C = canines,   P = premolars, M = molars.

When the animal has reached the age of about 1 year 9 months, the two front broad teeth (permanent incisors) push out and replace the first two milk teeth in the lower jaw (see Fig. 11.7)

At six-monthly intervals the milk teeth on each side are shed and replaced by broad teeth. Thus, the age of the cow can be assessed as follows:

4 broad teeth	– about 2 years 3 months
4 broad teeth well up	– about 2 years 6 months
6 broad teeth	– about 2 years 9 months to 3 years
8 broad teeth	– about 3 years 9 months to 4 years.

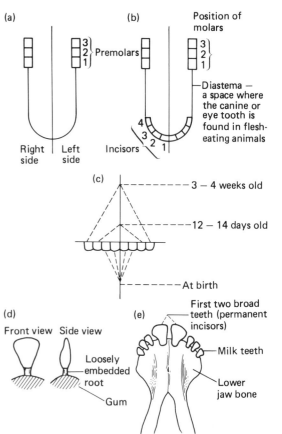

Fig. 11.7 Dentition of cattle: (a) full set of milk teeth in upper jaw; (b) full set of milk teeth in lower jaw; (c) appearance of incisors (milk teeth); (d) incisor tooth; (e) appearance of first broad teeth.

ANALYSIS OF A DAIRY HEIFER REARING ENTERPRISE

Figs 11.1 and 11.2 show the relationship between feeding and management requirements and the annual gross margins which result from the completed rearing process.

For a given farm situation physical information is available for the rearing enterprise as a whole and it could read as follows:

Example 1

Stocking Heifers	Number	× Livestock unit factor	LUs
0–1 yr old	20	× 0.30	= 6.00
1–2 yrs old	20	× 0.54	= 10.80
2 years and over	20	× 0.40 (2½ yr calving)	= 8.00
Replacement units (RUs)	20	1.24	24.80

Concentrates used	Total	Per RU
Milk substitute	350 kg	17.5 kg
Concentrates	17 t	0.85 t
Miscellaneous costs	£540	£27

Allocated area of forage (ha)		
Grazing	7	0.35
Silage	6	0.30
Hay	1	0.05
	14	0.70

i.e. stocking density = 24.8 LUs ÷ 14 forage hectares
= 1.77 LUs per forage hectare
or
14 forage hectares ÷ 24.8 LUs
= 0.56 forage hectare per LU
= 0.56 ha × 1.24 LU
= 0.7 ha/RU

Fertilizer application: 120 kg N/ha plus base dressings of phosphate, potash and lime.

At current prices the gross margins could be calculated thus:

	Enterprise			Per heifer	
	Nos. Quantity	Price	£	Nos. Quantity	£
Heifers reared, *less*	20	£450	9000	1	450
Calves	20	£50	1000	1	50
Enterprise ouput *less*			8000		400
Variable costs					
Milk substitutes	350 kg	£630/t	221	17.5 kg	11.1
Concentrates	17 t	£145/t	2465	0.85 t	123.3
Misc. items			540		27.0
Total variable costs			3226		161.4
Gross margin excluding forage costs			4774		238.6

Gross margin/ha excl. forage costs
= £238.6 ÷ 0.7   = £341
less Forage costs: 120 kg N @ £0.40/kg plus P and K   = £48
Gross margin/ha incl. forage costs   £293

These average per heifer and per ha figures for the enterprise can now be compared with the standard or target figures compiled by central agencies as described for the dairy herd (p. 131) and an analysis made to ascertain the possible factors causing low gross margin figures. Fig. 11.8 shows a diagnostic flow diagram which relates all the factors responsible for the ultimate efficiency measures of gross margin per heifer and per hectare.

BUDGETING FOR CHANGES

The economic policy choices for the farmer depend completely on the husbandry skill level which he is capable of attaining. There are three areas of choice:

i) whether to rear, buy or contract rear replacements (Table 11.4)
ii) the age at which heifers should calve;
iii) the rate at which cows in the dairy herd can be replaced.

Assume that an enterprise exists in a farm situation as described above, and that the husbandry and financial implications of the above three categories of change are being considered; the following examples demonstrate the principles involved:

Example 1: To consider purchasing heifers instead of rearing them

(a) *Husbandry effects*
By purchasing the heifers, 14 ha of land now used for their rearing can be used for other farm enterprises, e.g. 7 ha for barley and 7 ha for dairy cows. At a stocking rate of 1.77 LU per hectare the herd can be increased by 12 cows (7 hectare × 1.77 LU). No extra housing is assumed.

(b) *Real costs of rearing*
These consist of:
i) the gross margins attainable from the additional barley hectares and dairy cows;
ii) the existing variable costs of rearing the replacements which can be saved.

Thus:

Extra gross margins attainable:

		£
12 dairy cows at say £391 gross margin per cow (including forage)	=	4692
7 ha of barley at say £360 gross margin per hectare	=	2520
variable costs saved on 20 replacement units	=	3226*
Total		10 438

Real cost per heifer reared
= £10 438 ÷ 20 (heifers needed) = £522

* table on p. 145.

From a purely economic standpoint it would be cheaper for the farmer to purchase his heifers if ones of equal quality could be purchased for less than £522 each; the reverse argument would be true if they cost more than £522 to buy.

Such financial calculations on the break-even price of heifers (£522) can assist a farmer to decide on his policy. It would be one factor to consider in addition to other factors, which favour home-rearing.

Example 2: Consider reducing the age of calving from 2.5 to 2.0 years in the rearing enterprise described on p. 145.

(a) *Husbandry effects*

i) The area of land required for rearing would be reduced

Land required by 2.5 yr old heifers
= (0.56 ha × 1.24 LU)   = 0.69 ha

Land required by 2.0 yr old heifers
= (0.56 ha × 0.88 LU)   = 0.49 ha

Land saved per heifer reared   0.20 ha

Land saved for 20 heifers = 20 × 0.20   = 4.0 ha

This land could be used to increase the dairy herd and also for rearing replacements for the additional cows. It is assumed that the replacement rate is 1 in 4.

The number of additional cows is:

$$\frac{4.0\ \text{ha} \times 1.77\ \text{LU/forage hectare}}{1.0\ \text{LU [dairy cow]} + [0.84\ \text{LU} \div 4\ \text{(proportion of replacement unit per cow)]}} = 6\ \text{cows}$$

ii) 5 extra cow kennels would be needed.
iii) The quantity of concentrates required per heifer would be increased by 0.3 tonnes to achieve a faster growth rate.
iv) The stocking density would remain at the same level and consequently the forage costs would remain unchanged.

(b) *Approximate marginal capital budget*   £
  i) Landlord's
    5 kennels at £250 each (after grant) ÷ 2
    = £1250 ÷ 2   625

ii) Tenant's
    6 dairy cows × £460 each   2760
iii) Working
    Total variable costs inc. forage for dairy
    cows (Table 10.2) ÷ 12
    = £301 × 6 cows ÷ 12   151
    Value of 1.5 calves + their variable costs
    1.5 × (£50 + £205*)   383
          Total   3919

* Existing variable costs of £161.4/heifer + extra concentrates of £43.5 (table, p. 145).

(c) *Budgeting*   £   £
  i) The new gross margin per heifer.
    Existing gross margin per heifer
    (p. 145)   238.6
    less 0.3 t additional concentrates
    at £145/t   −43.5
          195.1
ii) Gross margin per cow (before forage)   473.0
    (Table 10.2)
iii) Partial budget:

Loss		*Gain*	
Gross margins lost	£	*Gross margins gained*	£
Reduced gross margins on 20 heifers (20 × £43.5)	870	6 cows × £473	2838
Extra fixed costs		1.5 heifers* as replacements for additional cows £195 × 1.5	293
Depreciation of 5 kennels (£1250 ÷ 10 yrs)	125		
Repairs and maintenance of 5 kennels (3% of £1250)	36		
Extra margin	2100		
	3131		3131

* In practice probably 2 heifers would be kept in one year and 1 heifer the following year.

(d) *Return on marginal capital (%)*

$$\frac{2100}{3919} \times \frac{100}{1} = 54\%$$

Example 3: To consider reducing the replacement rate within the dairy herd from 1 in 4 to 1 in 5 cows

(a) *Husbandry effects*

  i) With a dairy herd of 80 cows this would mean that the down-calving heifers required annually would be reduced from 20 to 16.
 ii) Land required by the heifer rearing enterprise would be reduced (4 × 0.7 ha/replacement unit) = 2.8 ha.
iii) The number of additional cows that could be kept on the land released is:

$$\frac{2.8\ \text{ha} \times 1.77\ \text{LU/forage hectare}}{1.0\ \text{LU (dairy cow)} + *(1.24 \div 5)\ \text{(proportion of replacement unit per cow)}} = \frac{4.956}{1.248} = 4\ \text{cows.}$$

* Calving at 2.5 years is assumed.

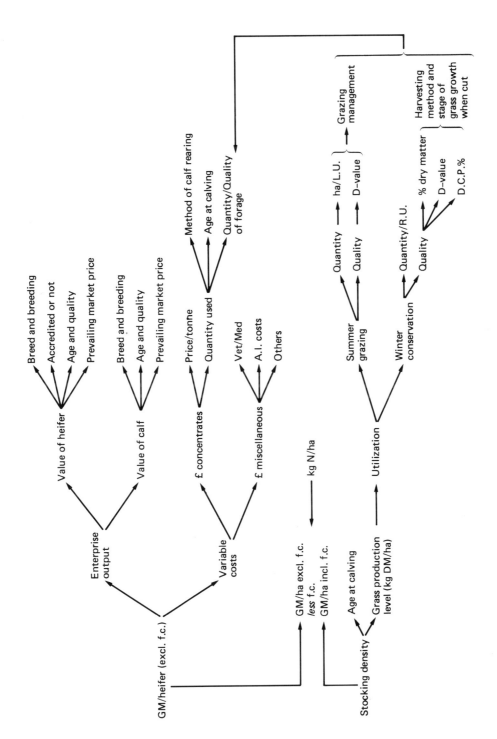

Fig. 11.8 Diagnostic flow diagram for analysis of a dairy heifer rearing enterprise.

Table 11.4. Advantages and disadvantages of purchasing, home rearing or contract rearing (source: MLC and MMB).

	Purchasing	Home rearing	Contract rearing
1. Quality of heifer	Animals can be selected or rejected at the point of calving	It is possible to breed for improved quality of heifer (yield and conformation). The management before calving can be correctly controlled.	It is possible to breed for improved quality of heifer. Some degree of control pre-calving is possible.
2. Disease	There is appreciable risk of introducing disease onto the farm.	There is no risk of introducing disease onto the farm.	There is a slight risk of introducing disease, especially if the rearer keeps heifers from more than one farm.
3. Labour and management	No labour or management time is devoted to heifer rearing. This enables specialization in producing milk or beef.	Labour and management time must be devoted to the enterprise.	No labour or management time is required (except in the calf stage before transport to the rearer). The rearer will be a specialist who can devote all his time and skill to the task.
4. Land	No land is committed to the rearing enterprise.	Land is devoted to rearing. This would be more profitable if devoted directly to producing milk or beef. On the other hand rearing may utilize land not suitable for milk production, because of topography or distance from the dairy unit.	No land at the home farm is committed to rearing.
5. Capital	No capital is invested in replacements.	Considerable capital is required, to cover the A.I. fees, loss of calf income, and costs of rearing.	Considerable capital is required, to cover the A.I. fees, loss of calf income and contract payments.
6. Others	(a) In cross-bred suckler herds, purchasing replacements simplifies the breeding programme. (b) The cost of purchasing is relatively unpredictable.		(a) It is extremely difficult to find a competent contract rearer. (b) The contract payment represents a considerable drain on cash resources.

iv) 3 extra cow kennels would be needed.

v) To achieve this reduced replacement rate a more effective monitoring of breeding performance would be required, e.g. pregnancy testing and also a more rigorous regime for mastitis prevention.

(b) *Approximate marginal capital budget*

		£	£
i) Landlord's			
	3 kennels at £250 each (after grant) ÷ 2 = £750 ÷ 2		375
ii) Tenant's			
	4 dairy cows × £460 each		1840
iii) Working			
	Total variable costs including forage for dairy cows ÷ 12 £301 × 4 cows ÷ 12		100
			2315

less capital released

Cost of 3 calves + variable costs for 3 replacement units 3 × (£50 + £205)		766
Total		1549

(c) *Partial budgeting*

The gross margin per cow would be improved as depreciation per cow would be reduced.

	Replacement Rate	
	4.1	*5.1*
	£	£
Value of replacement heifer	460	460
Value of cull cow	280	280
Total depreciation	180	180

	£	£
Depreciation/cow/year (£)	45	36

Improved gross margin per cow
    = 45 − 36 = £9

Loss	£	Gain	£
Gross margins lost		4 cows × gross margin	
3 down-calving heifers (£239 × 3)	717	£473/cow	1892
Extra fixed costs		*plus* reduced depreciation 84 cows × £9/cow	756
Depreciation of 3 kennels (£750 ÷ 10)	75	*less* additional vet and medical	
Repairs and maintenance of kennels (3% of £750)	23	charges (pregnancy diagnosis and mas-	
Net gain	1413	titis control)	
		84 cows × £5	−420
	2228		2228

(d) *Return on marginal capital* (%)

$$\frac{1413}{1549} \times \frac{100}{1} = 91\%$$

These three examples highlight the inter-relationship between the dairy herd and the heifer-rearing enterprise and how a change in one enterprise affects the other.

12

Feeding and Management of Beef Cattle

The main sources of home-produced beef in Britain and the contributions from each source are as follows (Figures supplied by the Meat and Livestock Commission):

	Per cent		Per cent
Culled dairy breeding cows	19	Pure-bred calves from dairy herds	16
Culled beef breeding cows	6	Cross-bred calves from dairy herds	23
Suckled calves from beef herds	28	Imported Irish stores	8

SYSTEMS OF PRODUCTION

There are many systems of beef production (Table 12.1). Historically, cattle were expected to grow at grass, and have a nil or low store growth rate during the winter; the slaughter age was generally 2.5 to 3 years. The development of modern production systems has resulted in a reduction in the age and weight at which cattle are slaughtered. This change is linked to the development of systems which result in higher daily liveweight gains due to better grazing management, improved forage conservation and more effective utilization of concentrates. The changes have virtually eliminated the store period in the development of the animal.

Beef breeding herds are kept to rear calves by the natural suckling of dams by their calves; some of the commercial systems of suckler beef production are shown in Table 12.2. Suckled calves are normally sold at the autumn sales, the heavier, older calves subsequently finishing at around 18 months of age and the lighter calves at 20–24 months of age. Often the calves are not sold but finished on the same farm as a separate enterprise.

Other systems of beef production differ according to whether they utilize the dairy or beef-bred calf and the proportion of the production cycle which occurs on a single farm. Complete systems represent those where the full production cycle of rearing and finishing occurs on one

farm; partial systems are those devoted either to the rearing of stores or to the purchasing of stores for finishing or resale as heavier stores.

The terms 'grass systems' and 'grass/cereal systems' refer to methods of using dairy-bred calves depending on the time of the calf's birth, level of concentrates fed and whether one or two grazing seasons are involved. The most common method is to use autumn- and winter-born calves and aim to finish them out of yards at about 16–20 months of age; with higher levels of concentrate feeding, finishing at a younger age can be achieved. These systems are not rigid and are often adapted to suit the time of calf purchase and the resources of individual farms.

Cereal beef production was introduced on a commercial scale in the early sixties. The system was based on dairy-bred calves (usually Friesian steers) which had been early weaned at 5–6 weeks old and weighing approximately 100 kg; the animals were introduced to an *ad lib.* diet based on rolled barley with protein/vitamin/mineral mix. The cattle were slaughtered at 10–12 months old.

In all forms of meat production there tends to be a relationship between rate of growth, feed conversion efficiency and net margin. Systems of beef production demand high levels of feeding to achieve target liveweight gains and the use of late-maturing breeds and crosses are more

Table 12.1. Beef production systems (source: MLC)

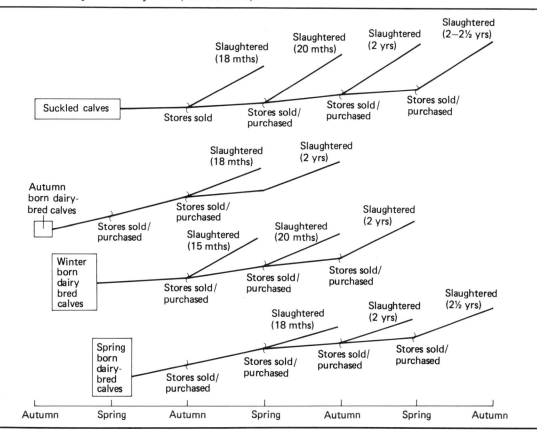

suitable for intensive systems as they can grow to heavy weights without excess fat deposition.

The rearing system is either natural suckling or artificial feeding with milk substitutes; suckling can be either single or multiple. The former is the traditional system in beef herds where the cow suckles the calf for the first 6–8 months; many pure-bred and cross-bred cows are used. Multiple suckling uses a dairy cow to rear several calves in a lactation.

BEEF ENTERPRISE NET MARGIN

Annual net margin is the difference between enterprise gross margin and the proportion of fixed costs which is used for its effective management. With a breeding herd, enterprise output is expressed as calf sales (plus any premiums) less cow and bull depreciation together with purchases of any additional calves. With other beef systems, enterprise output is expressed as the sale of livestock less the purchases of calves or stores including an allowance for mortality. Enterprise output less the variable costs for concentrates, miscellaneous items and fertilizer, seeds and sprays required on the forage area for both grazing and conservation, gives the gross margin figures.

Gross margin per hectare depends on the gross margin per head and the number of stock kept per hectare, i.e. stocking density. Up to a certain point an increase in stocking density will increase the gross margin per hectare, but beyond this the rate of liveweight gain drops and this adversely affects the per hectare performance. A high degree of skill is required to link stocking density to the available grass throughout the growing season.

An acceptable level of gross margin for a beef enterprise depends on the following factors:

1. Breeding
Selection of the best breed or cross-breed for specific farm conditions is important. The choice for both upland and lowland conditions requires

Table 12.2. Some commercial systems of suckler beef production

Environmental conditions	Breeds and crosses	Phenotype performance
1. *Hill land:* Weather: extremely wet, cold and windy Feeding: poor quality summer grazing; occasional out-wintering supplemented by limited hay or straw	*Cows:* extremely hardy breeds or crosses, e.g. Galloway, Highland, Welsh Black, Highland × Beef Shorthorn, Blue Grey (Galloway × White Shorthorn bull) *Bull:* usually Hereford	*Cow:* hardy with a short, steep lactation curve (the Welsh Black is an exception) suitable for single suckling a spring-born calf *Calf:* grows into a well fleshed calf at 7 months old. Colour marking and conformation command good autumn prices. Capable of finishing at 16 months or over under lowland conditions (see 3 below)
2. *Marginal land:* Weather: wet, cold and windy Feeding: adequate summer grazing; majority are in-wintered on better quality forage, i.e. some land is usually available for conservation	*Cows:* hardy breeds or crosses, e.g. Welsh Black, Blue Grey, Angus or Hereford crosses *Bulls:* Hereford, Angus, Charolais, Limousin, Simmental	*Cow:* hardy with a longer, more gradual lactation curve capable of single suckling calf for up to 10 months. In-wintering makes autumn calving possible *Calf:* grows well into a well fleshed animal. Capable of finishing at 16 months or over under lowland conditions
3. *Lowland:* Weather: favourable Feeding: adequate summer grazing; winter feeding on quality silage or hay with cereal supplement. High stocking rates possible	*Cows:* usually beef breed × Friesian crosses *Bulls:* usually heavier beef breed	*Cow:* capable of suckling one or two calves in any season *Calf:* grows well into well fleshed animal capable of finishing at 16 months or over

careful selection. The potential for liveweight gain under differing conditions varies between breeds and also within individual breeds.

2. Feeding
Daily liveweight gain and rate of development are controlled by the kind, quantity and quality of food fed. In the 'grass/cereal systems' grazing management and conservation are the main problems.

(a) *Pasture grazing*
The size and weight of individual animals is increasing throughout the growing season but the quantity and quality of the grass is decreasing. Parasitism can also become an increasing problem.

(b) *Conservation*
Expertise in making high quality silage or hay is needed and these fodders are usually supplemented with barley.

Apportioned fixed costs are the annual charges incurred for the use of land (rent), labour, machinery, power and general overheads. These costs can vary enormously depending upon factors such as the type and quality of the buildings and the range and age of the machinery used.

Average gross and net margin figures for an 18–20 month system as shown in Table 12.3 illustrate the budget format for beef enterprises.

ARTIFICIAL CALF REARING

Calves are bought in batches and reared by hand on milk replacer. It is essential that all calves receive colostrum, which is rich in protein and vitamins A, D and E, since it confers passive immunity to disease. Those that have not received colostrum have a reduced survival capacity and are susceptible to infections, particularly by *E. coli* which causes scouring.

When a calf has been purchased under 4 days old, small quantities of high fat substitutes are

Table 12.3. Physical and financial results for 18–20 months old finished beef animal (autumn-born) (source: Scottish Agricultural Colleges – Farm Management)

a) *Gross margin*

	Per head		
	Quantity	Price/Unit	£
Sale value	1	£463	463
less Calf purchase price	1	£105	−105
			358
Enterprise output			
less Variable costs			
Rearing to 12–14 weeks (100 kg lw)			
Milk substitute	13 kg	£630/t	8
Calf concentrates	160 kg	£150/t	24
Hay (purchased)	35 kg	£160/t	2
Miscellaneous			6
12/14 weeks to Turn-out			
Rearing concentrates	275 kg	£135/t	37
First winter			
Barley	50 kg	£195/t	5
Second winter			
Barley	570 kg	£95/t	54
Miscellaneous			24
Gross margin (excluding forage)			198
Forage costs			42
Gross margin (including forage)			156

Physical results
Liveweight (kg):

Birth	38
Purchase	45
Weaning	100
Turn-out	189
Housing	311
Slaughter	482
Overall daily gain	0.75
Age at slaughter (days)	580
% Mortality/Culling	5

Forage:

Silage feeding	Tonnes
First winter	0.6
Second winter	4.8
Area required	*ha*
Silage and aftermath grazing	0.18
Hay and aftermath grazing	0.01
Grazing	0.14
Total	0.33

Fertilizer	N (kg/ha)
Silage	200
Hay	125
Grazing	175

b) *Net margin*

	£	£
Gross margin per ha		473 (£156 ÷ 0.33)
Estimate fixed costs		
Rent and buildings	78	
Machinery and power	146	
Labour (family and hired)	130	
Others	17	
		−371
Net margin per ha		102

preferred. Once- or twice-a-day feeding can be adopted. Once-a-day feeding economizes on labour and the results can be equally good; the same amount of powder is used but mixed at a higher concentration. The calves should be introduced to once-a-day feeding from the beginning of bucket rearing.

It may be necessary with some calves to teach them to drink from a bucket. The calf is allowed to suckle the handler's fingers as they are lowered gradually into a bucket. The fingers are then removed slowly to encourage a drinking action rather than sucking; if the calf lifts its head the fingers are placed back into its mouth. Some continental breeds are particularly difficult and the use of a nipple feeder may be necessary. The quantities of substitutes to be fed are shown in Table 12.4(a).

Table 12.4. Artificial calf rearing (source: MLC)

(a) *Daily quantities of milk substitutes for young calves*

	Day					
	1–2	3–4	5	6	7–28	29–35
High fat milk powders (kg/day)	0.2	0.3	0.35	0.38	0.4	*Abrupt or gradual weaning*
Liquid replacer twice daily (litres)	2.0	3.0	3.5	3.75	4.0	
once daily (litres)	1.0	1.5	2.0	2.5	2.75	

(b) *Comparative performance (to weaning at 5 weeks) with bucket and machine rearing*

	Bucket once daily (kg)	Bucket twice daily (kg)	Machine (kg)
DLWG* 0–5 wks	0.4	0.4	0.7
DLWG 5–12 wks	0.9	0.9	0.7
Liveweight at 12 wks	103	103	105
Milk powder consumed	12.5	13.1	28.5
Concentrates consumed	158	150	130

*Daily liveweight gain.

A clean supply of water, good hay and early weaning concentrates should be on offer from the first week. Early weaning concentrates should contain 17% crude protein and this can be reduced to 15% during the post weaning period; they are fed *ad lib.* up to 12 weeks when the calves should weigh 100 kg. It is essential that calves take readily to weaning concentrate, so that early rumen development can occur. The aim should be an intake of at least 0.7 kg per day over 3 consecutive days at five weeks of age before the calves are weaned. Best quality hay is also essential to rumen development but its contribution may be low due to the calf's small intake.

Automatic Rearing

Since most systems of beef production involve batch rearing, mechanical methods of feeding have been adopted to ease labour; formal penning arrangements are needed. The main advantages and disadvantages of the system are:

Advantages	*Disadvantages*
Very good growth rate	High milk usage
Good food conversion	Variation in food intake
Less labour	Low concentrate intake to
Convenience	5 weeks
Less human error	Reduced rumen
Lower establishment	development
cost	Greater check at weaning
Simpler housing	Higher litter requirements
Calves of mixed ages	Better stockmanship
can be penned	needed
separately but served	Less individual control
by one machine	Risk of disease
	High standard of hygiene
	essential

Acidified Milk Powders

These powders contain small quantities of acetic and propionic acids which allow a mix to be kept for about three days. This treatment enables the milk substitute to be fed cold using simple plastic containers from which the milk is drawn through plastic pipes to a series of teats. The advantages and disadvantages of acidified treatment are:

Advantages	*Disadvantages*
Prolonged keeping	Unpalatable to some
quality	calves
Reduced risk of scouring	Variation in consumption
Reduced labour	Poorest conversion rate of
Less cleaning of utensils	all systems
Very good liveweight	Large volume to be mixed
growth	every 3rd day
	Low level of individual
	attention

Comparative performance with different systems are shown in Table 12.4(b). By the age of 12 weeks the calves should be eating 2.5 kg concentrates per day and weighing around 100 kg.

Routine Tasks

Dehorning
This is usually undertaken with the hot iron method at 3–4 weeks of age using a local anaesthetic (p. 141).

Castration

Young bulls which are not required for future breeding or bull beef production are castrated. The three recognized methods are the:

1. *Bloodless method using the burdizzo*

This technique is commonly used by stockmen for calves and lambs. The advantages and disadvantages as stated by the NPTC are:

'a) *Advantages*

    i. No open wound or risk of haemorrhage.

b) *Disadvantages*

    i. The scrotum may swell after castration.

    ii. Not completely reliable as the cord may slip out.

    iii. If the instrument is applied too high the penis may be crushed. This has serious consequences as the flow of urine may be prevented.

    iv. If the crush wounds join, the scrotum may slough off leaving an open wound.'

(NPTC)

The jaws of the burdizzo are applied about three-quarters of the way up the scrotum with the cord-stops pointing towards the operator (Fig. 12.1a). The procedure for crushing the spermatic cords is shown in Fig. 12.1a and b. After crushing, the cords should be felt for breaks in continuity which indicates a successful operation. The effect of the operation is to cut off the blood supply to the testes – they then shrivel up and die.

2. *Cutting method*

The NPTC gives the following as the advantages and disadvantages of this method:

'a) *Advantages*

    i. Immediate and effective.

b) *Disadvantages*

    i. Leaves an open wound which may become infected.

    ii. Animals (especially calves and lambs) may die of haemorrhage following castration. On occasions the intestines may prolapse through the wound. This is an emergency and a veterinary surgeon should be called without delay.

    iii. In cases of severe haemorrhage the following first aid procedure is recommended: Keep the animal still. Do not explore the wound as this may

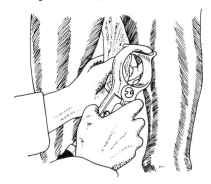

(a) *Making the first crush*

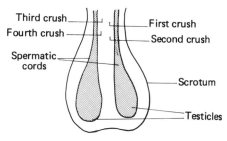

(b) *Making second, third and fourth crushes*

Third crush
Fourth crush
Spermatic cords
First crush
Second crush
Scrotum
Testicles

Fig. 12.1 Castrating calves (burdizzo): (a) making the first crush; (b) making second, third and fourth crushes (source: Agricultural Training Board).

introduce infection. Pack the wound with moist cotton wool or alternatively place a clean towel over the scrotum and apply gentle pressure upwards.'

(NPTC)

The testicles are grasped in turn and manipulated to the bottom of the scrotal sac (Fig. 12.2a). The grasp is maintained on the testicles and a cut made across the bottom of the scrotum, exposing the testicles (Fig. 12.2b). Each testicle is pulled away separately (not cut with the scalpel) after several twists of the cord/vessels (Fig. 12.2c). Before releasing the animal the wound should be dusted with an antiseptic powder and the animal then returned to a building with fresh bedding. An hour after the operation the animals should be inspected for excessive bleeding and checked for any infections for the next seven days.

3. *Rubber ring method*

Again quoting the NPTC:

'a) *Advantages*

    i. A simple technique suitable for calves and lambs.

(a) *Preparing for incision*

(b) *Making the incision*

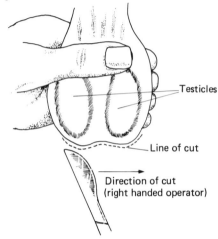

Testicles

Line of cut

Direction of cut
(right handed operator)

(c) *Removing testicles*

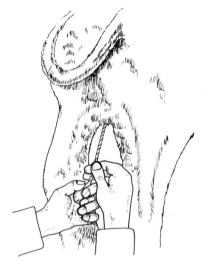

Fig. 12.2 Castrating calves (knife): (a) preparing for incision; (b) making the incision; (c) removing testicles (source: Agricultural Training Board).

b) *Disadvantages*
   i. It may be slow and painful.
   ii. The scrotum sloughs off leaving a wound.
   iii. The ring may accidently be put on either below or through a testicle.

Fig. 12.3 Castrating calves (rubber rings): placing the ring on the calf's scrotum (source: Agricultural Training Board).

   iv. If the ring is put on too high the penis may be trapped, so preventing urination.
   v. It may predispose to tetanus.'

(NPTC)

A rubber ring is applied to the 'neck' of the scrotal sac by means of an instrument called an elastrator. Both testicles must be in the scrotal sac below the ring (Fig. 12.3). The ring is allowed to stay in position until it drops off with the testes.

Legal requirements
   1. The operator must be over 18 years of age unless he/she is receiving instruction at an approved institution or is under the supervision of a veterinary surgeon when he or she must be over 17 years of age (Veterinary Surgeons Act).
   2. The age at which animals can be castrated by lay people (Veterinary Surgeons Act) and when an anaesthetic is required (The Protection of Animals Anaesthetic Act) are shown in Table 12.5.
   3. Rubber rings must be applied within the first week of an animal's life (The Protection of Animals Act).

For other routine calf tasks and dentition see chapter 11 – Feeding and Management of Dairy Heifers.

Table 12.5. Castration ages in the Veterinary Surgeons and Protection of Animals (Anaesthetic) Acts (source: Royal College of Veterinary Surgeons)

Species	Veterinary Surgeons Act	Anaesthetic Act
	Unqualified persons may only castrate animals which have not reached the age of:	*No anaesthetic required if animal is under:*
Bull	2 months	2 months
Sheep/Ram	3 months	3 months
Pig/Boar	3 months	2 months

GRAZING AND CONSERVATION

The principles underlying summer grazing and the conservation of grass for winter feeding have been described in chapter 9 (see p. 111).

Compensatory Growth

Cattle fed over winter in readiness for grazing do best at grass if the winter growth can be in the region of 0.4 to 0.6 kg per day. Gains above this cause an increase in costs and result in depressed gains at grass.

Winter gains lower than 0.4 kg per day result in high grazing gains but overall weight of animal is not as great. Some cattle fail to finish by the end of the season and have to be sold as stores.

Stocking Rates

With growing cattle, numbers of animals per hectare need to be adjusted throughout the grazing season depending on the quantity and quality of herbage available. Stocking rates which match grass production are described in chapter 9 (p. 121).

WINTER FEEDING

Suckler Cows

Rations can be worked out using the method described for dairy cows (chapter 8). Difficulties can arise because there is wide variation in their voluntary food intake depending on the quality of the food offered; their dry matter intake tends to decline rapidly as roughage quality decreases.

Growing Cattle

There are two requirements in practice:

i) ability to predict the daily liveweight gain from a given ration of food;
ii) ability to devise a ration to meet a given daily liveweight gain expectation.

These have been described in chapter 8 (Examples 8.2 and 8.3).

Protein and Mineral Supplements

The suckler cow's requirement of protein is similar to that of the dairy cow (Table 8.5). Table 8.12 shows the level of protein requirements for growing cattle.

Rations based on grass silage are rarely deficient in protein. Soya bean meal, groundnut cake and urea are the usual protein supplements for beef cattle; distiller's grains or brewer's grains may also be used. Urea can be obtained in powdered, feed block or liquid forms. The latter two are more convenient but are more difficult to measure correctly. The powdered form must be accurately and carefully mixed into an energy or a mineral/vitamin supplement to avoid any risk of urea toxicity.

In most systems of production there is a need to provide a full range of trace elements and in particular copper and cobalt; selenium may also be important in suckled-calf systems, especially if fed on hay and straw diets. Major elements are required; calcium in particular for lactating cows and phosphorus for cows during their breeding period. Magnesium is needed by suckler cows and calves at the beginning and end of the grazing season as well as for cows that calve-down in mid-winter; up to 50 g magnesium per cow per day are fed.

Assessment of Winter Food Requirements

Winter food assessment is difficult because the animals are constantly growing and their daily food requirements increasing. A simple approximate method of dealing with the situation is to devise a ration for the mid-period of growth and subsequently calculate the total food and hectare requirements.

Example 1
If the growing period is 140 days and if the target is 0.75 kg/day, add 70×0.75 kg to the weight of the animal at yarding; assuming the latter to be 300 kg then the ration is based on $300 + (70 \times 0.75) = 352.5$ kg liveweight. Total requirements for a group of say 30 bullocks based on a mid-period daily ration of 20 kg silage and 3 kg barley would be:

20 kg silage $\times$ 150 days = 3 t $\times$ 30 = 90 t
3 kg barley $\times$ 150 days = 0.45 t $\times$ 30 = 13.5 t

Hectares required:
90 t silage @ 25% DM = 22.5 t DM.
DM yield per ha 1st cut = 6 t ⎱ 8 t
DM yield per ha 2nd cut = 2 t ⎰
Therefore hectares required = 22.5 ÷ 8 = 2.8 ha
Hectares of barley required assuming a yield of 4 t/ha = 13.5 ÷ 4 = 3.38 ha.

BEEF SYSTEMS

Although specific systems have emerged in recent years many farmers still buy and sell cattle to suit their farming system and market trends.

Complete systems in the main are:

i) 18 month old grass/cereal beef utilizing the autumn-born calf (Table 12.6);
ii) 20 month old grass beef utilizing the winter-born calf (Table 12.6);
iii) suckler cow and her weaned calf.

Breed has a major effect on matching cattle numbers to feed consumption in any system (Table 12.7). Size is a key factor which has a bearing on daily feed intake; growth rate and the rate of maturity determine age at slaughter and therefore the amount of time cattle remain on the farm.

Early maturing cattle, such as the Angus and Hereford crosses, produce cattle for slaughter at a younger age than heavier Simmental and Charolais crosses (Fig. 12.4). Care is therefore necessary in matching numbers of cattle to hectares of grass (p. 121); heifers fatten early while bulls produced on the same system grow faster and reach heavier weights than steers. The comparative advantages of early and late maturing breeds and crosses are:

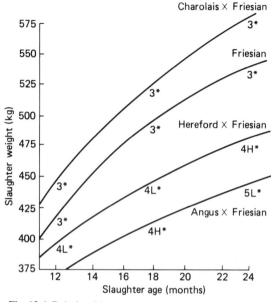

Fig. 12.4 Relationships between slaughter age, slaughter weight and carcass fatness in beef production from dairy-bred cattle. Fat class on scale:1 (leanest), 2, 3, 4L, 4H, 5L, 5H (fattest) (source: MLC).

Early maturing	*Late maturing*
Early slaughter – quick turnover	Late slaughter – slower turnover

Table 12.6. Recorded results from beef systems (1978) (source: MLC)

		18 months grass/cereal beef		*18 months grass/cereal bull beef*		*20 months grass beef*	
		Ave.	*Top third*	*Ave.*	*Top third*	*Ave.*	*Top third*
Daily gain (kg)	First winter	0.7	0.7	0.8		0.6	0.6
	First summer	0.7	0.8	0.7		0.5	0.7
	Second winter	0.8	0.8	1.0		0.6	0.5
	Second summer					0.8	1.0
	Overall	0.7	0.8	0.9		0.65	0.7
Slaughter	Age (days)	580	547	535		638	624
	Weight (kg)	482	485	501		487	498
Stocking rate (cattle/ha)	Grazing only	5.1	5.9	5.1	5.9	–	–
	Grazing and conservation	3.1	3.5	3.1	3.5	2.2	2.7
Concentrates	kg/head	1050	900	–	–	910	840
Carcass composition*	Fat %	19.6 †		13.4			
	Lean %	62.4		69.0			
	Bone %	15.5		15.7			
	High priced cuts %	49.0		46.6			

*Excluding kidney knob and channel fat.
†Steers only.

Finished carcass from high quality forage diets

Low feed requirement – high stocking rate

Short final grazing period

Good liveweight gain on spring grass

Early slaughter releases grass for remaining finishing stock, younger cattle or an additional batch of cattle.

Heavier carcass from good quality forage diets

High feed requirement – minimum stocking

Long final grazing period

Liveweight gain drops in late season as grass yield and quality fall

Late slaughter causes competition for grass from mid-season.

Table 12.7. 18 months old beef production – comparative data for breeds (source: MLC)

(a) *Comparative output and feed consumption of different breeds*

	No. of cattle to produce same slaughter weight	No. of cattle to eat same quantity of food
Charolais × Friesian	1.00	1.00
Angus × Friesian	1.37	1.46
Devon × Friesian	1.32	1.45
Friesian	1.16	1.15
Hereford × Friesian	1.28	1.45
Simmental × Friesian	1.04	1.07
South Devon	1.12	1.14

(b) *Comparative performance of breeds (% above (+) or below (−) contemporary Friesian steers)*

Breed or cross	Daily gain (kg)	Slaughter weight (kg)
Friesian	0.8	495
Charolais × Friesian	+10.4	+7.2
Simmental × Friesian	+10.3	+5.4
South Devon × Friesian	+ 8.9	+4.4
Devon × Friesian	+ 6.7	+2.4
Hereford × Friesian	+ 3.1	−10.4
Angus × Friesian	−11.4	−15.7

Eighteen Month Old Beef Production

This has proved the most popular method of production. Autumn-born calves are reared during their first winter, grazed during their first summer and finished during their second winter on silage and concentrates. Tables 12.6 and 12.8 quantify performance and some feeding strategies for this system.

Autumn-born calves are early weaned on to hay and fed concentrates to a maximum of 2.5 kg per day. The system aims for a liveweight gain of 0.8 kg per day so that calves at turn-out weigh 180 kg. Excessive concentrate feeding during the rearing period depresses liveweight gain at

Table 12.8. Feeding data for 18 months old beef production (source: MLC)

(a) *Effect of silage quality on winter finishing diets*

	65 D	60 D	55 D
Silage quality: Daily gain (kg):	*0.8*	*0.8*	*0.8*
Rolled barley (kg)	1.25	3	4
Silage to appetite (kg)	26	20	16
Total requirement:			
Rolled barley (kg)	263	530	840
Silage (tonnes)	5.5	4.2	3.4

(b) *Examples of alternative feeding strategies for Friesian steers and Hereford × Friesian steers weighing 325 kg at the start of finishing winter*

	FR			H × FR	
Daily feed allowance:					
Rolled barley (kg)	0.75	1.25	1.75	0.8	0.75
65 D silage to appetite (kg)	27	26	25	27	26
Results:					
Daily gain (kg)	0.7	0.8	0.9	0.7	0.8
Finishing period (days)	260	210	165	210	165
Slaughter weight (kg)	520	500	475	475	450
Total feed required:					
Rolled barley (kg)	195	263	289	105	125
Silage (tonnes)	7.0	5.5	4.1	5.7	4.3

grass and late-born calves, because of their small size, fail to do so well. Supplementary feeding at grass continues at 1.5 kg/day for two to three weeks depending on weather conditions. Good management of the grass is essential; of the grazing systems mentioned in chapter 9, probably the best system is to graze one-third and conserve two-thirds in the early season. The order can be reversed for second-cut and thereafter all the area is grazed. This helps to maintain liveweight gains at a time when herbage quality decreases and worm infestation increases.

From mid-August the decline in herbage quality is rapid and rejection is increased and consequently supplementary feeding is necessary to maintain liveweight gains. At yarding, cattle should weigh 300–350 kg.

The aim in the second and finishing winter is to feed high quality conserved forage to reduce concentrate intake and achieve the target liveweight gains. With good quality silage, mineralized barley should be an adequate supplement.

The early maturing Hereford × Friesian cross reaches a finished condition earlier on the same ration (Fig. 12.4); they can therefore be pushed along to slaughter weight at younger ages and lighter weights or they can be fed a lower quality, high forage diet to achieve market finish at the same slaughter age as Friesians.

Carcasses from the 18 month old system fall into the middle weight range and those from Friesian steers have a fat class 3 and conformation class O or R based on the E.E.C classification scheme (see p. 165); on average they produce 72% saleable meat. Hereford × Friesian crosses show a 71% saleable product while the Charolais × Friesian crosses show a 73% saleable product with a fat class 2 and conformation class U.

Grass Beef Production

Calves born at the turn of the year do not fit well into an 18 month old system but are suited to grass finishing in their second summer at around 20 months of age; Table 12.6 gives results which can be expected from this system.

Calves on turn-out in their first summer are better suited to a system of grazing that relies on older stock to control the grazing. A system such as the leader–follower is ideal where young calves select the best grass ahead of older cattle following behind. It is often necessary, however, to feed concentrates to maintain a liveweight gain of 0.7 kg per day.

When the calves are yarded in the autumn they should weigh about 250 kg. During this period a silage based (18 kg) ration supplemented by barley is sufficient to achieve a target liveweight gain of 0.5 kg/day. The aim is to have cattle at turn-out which are well grown but lean to make best use of the grass available. If this has been achieved they should come to slaughter in the late summer to early autumn weighing between 450 kg and 550 kg.

With this system of production the early maturing breeds and crosses are more suitable because the competition among finishing cattle as grass quality and quantity fall after mid-season is reduced. It also allows a redress of the balance between the two age groups of cattle since the younger group outgrow the leader–follower system towards the end of their first season at grass.

The rate of liveweight gain during the finishing period at grass can be increased by using implants; Table 12.9 illustrates results that have been obtained. A slight discolouration of the fat may feature in this system. The carcass classification of Friesian steers on this system gives a fat range of 3–4L and conformation of O or R. The Hereford × Friesian crosses produce 4H fat and R–U conformation whilst the Charolais × Friesian crosses give fat class 3 and conformation U to E.

Table 12.9. Responses to growth promoting implants during grass finishing (source: MLC)

	Daily gain (% above control)	
	Steers	Heifers
Finaplix	+6	+11
Ralgro	+12	+5
Hexoestrol	+18	*
Finaplix + hexoestrol	+29	*

*Not to be used because of side effects.

Suckled Calf Production

One of the main objectives with suckler cow management is to determine the time of year to calve; the options are the four seasons of the year with their inherent advantages and disadvantages. A factor which probably influences this choice more than anything else is altitude. Hill farms have the problem of the availability in terms of quantity and quality of conserved fodder. On the lowland and better upland farms which can produce sufficient winter forage, autumn calving is possible provided that housing is adequate. The autumn-born calf is obviously much bigger at sale than the spring-born calf. The choice of calving date can have a marked influence on the length of the calving period since this is so dependent on the nutritional status of the cow at service. Once a decision has been taken it is important to maintain as compact a calving period as possible since this allows the herd to be fed as economically as possible, it reduces the time over which the herd needs to be closely supervised and allows for a more uniform group of calves to be marketed.

The type of cow used should be related to farm conditions and in particular winter feed supplies (see Table 12.2); the best results are normally achieved from three-way cross calves. Hardiness of cow may have a low priority except on the hill.

Good management entails identifying cows which require special attention and body condition scoring is a good guide for this purpose. A cow with an inadequate food intake to satisfy her maintenance requirements and the demands of her calf will tend to draw on her body reserves to compensate for this deficiency. Target weights for some cross-bred cows at service and pre-calving are shown in Table 12.10.

Body condition scoring
This method applies a score to what was previously a descriptive assessment of an ani-

Table 12.10. Average mature cow weights of some crosses and target weights at service and pre-calving

Breed crosses	Cow body weight (kg)	Target weight at service (kg)	Target weight at calving (kg)
South Devon × Friesian ⎱ Simmental × Friesian ⎰	640	350	540
Charolais × Friesian	660	370	560
Limousin × Friesian	610	340	520
Hereford × Ayrshire	520	290	440
Charolais × Ayrshire	570	320	490

mal's condition; the aim is to ascertain the nutritional status of the animal. The cow's performance depends on its body condition, particularly during the critical times of calving and conception.

The procedure is to grip the loin between the hook bone and last rib, with the fingers on top pointing towards the spine and the thumb curled around the transverse process to feel the fat cover at this point.

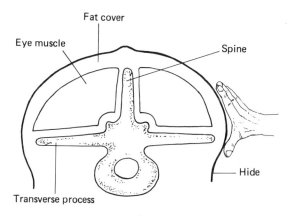

There is a six-point scale from 0 to 5:

0. Spine is prominent and transverse processes very prominent.
1. Spine is prominent but transverse processes less sharp.
2. Transverse processes have a thin layer of fat.
3. Separate transverse processes can only be felt with pressure.
4. Transverse processes cannot be felt.
5. Transverse processes covered with a thick layer of fat.

The tail-head area also acts as an indicator of the cow's body condition (Fig. 12.5). The scoring is equally important to both dairy and beef cows. In order to achieve maximum performance at service and calving the NIRD and MLC respectively suggest the following scores:

Dairy cows (NIRD)

At calving	3.0–3.5
At first service	2+
At drying-off	3.0–3.5

Beef suckler cows (MLC)

	Mating	Mid-pregnancy	Calving
Autumn calving	2.5	2	3
Spring calving	2.5	3	2.5

Target condition scores in relation to feed requirements throughout the productive cycle of spring- and autumn-calving cows are shown in Fig. 12.6.

Mating is the key point in the production cycle. Unless the cow comes on heat and conceives within 3 months of calving, performance and profit suffer. The cow may be barren or conception may be delayed, reducing the number of calves produced annually and extending the calving period. With cows at different stages of their productive lives, accurate rationing becomes difficult and often calves offered for sale do not conform to the demands of the market.

An associated problem that never fails to cause problems within the beef herd in particular is that of identifying oestrus. This is particularly serious for systems that use artificial insemination, which allows the herds to be serviced with a wider range of breeds and with progeny tested bulls of such breeds. Frequently, aids in oestrus detection are necessary and vasectomized bulls or heat detectors are often used. Oestrus synchronization offers considerable potential for securing a more contracted calving pattern.

Beef cow and sire

Most dams are cross-bred and consequently herd replacements are purchased; the Hereford × Friesian cow in particular has become very popular. A wise selection of sire breed and of a performance-tested sire within that breed should produce the best type of calf. The breed of cow

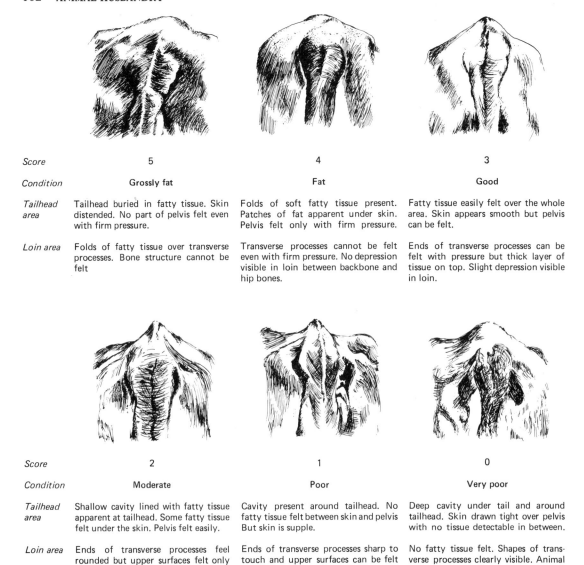

Score	5	4	3
Condition	**Grossly fat**	**Fat**	**Good**
Tailhead area	Tailhead buried in fatty tissue. Skin distended. No part of pelvis felt even with firm pressure.	Folds of soft fatty tissue present. Patches of fat apparent under skin. Pelvis felt only with firm pressure.	Fatty tissue easily felt over the whole area. Skin appears smooth but pelvis can be felt.
Loin area	Folds of fatty tissue over transverse processes. Bone structure cannot be felt	Transverse processes cannot be felt even with firm pressure. No depression visible in loin between backbone and hip bones.	Ends of transverse processes can be felt with pressure but thick layer of tissue on top. Slight depression visible in loin.

Score	2	1	0
Condition	Moderate	Poor	Very poor
Tailhead area	Shallow cavity lined with fatty tissue apparent at tailhead. Some fatty tissue felt under the skin. Pelvis felt easily.	Cavity present around tailhead. No fatty tissue felt between skin and pelvis But skin is supple.	Deep cavity under tail and around tailhead. Skin drawn tight over pelvis with no tissue detectable in between.
Loin area	Ends of transverse processes feel rounded but upper surfaces felt only with pressure. Depression visible in loin.	Ends of transverse processes sharp to touch and upper surfaces can be felt easily. Deep depression in loin.	No fatty tissue felt. Shapes of transverse processes clearly visible. Animal appears emaciated.

Fig. 12.5 Condition scoring by reference to the tail-head area (source: the National Institute for Research in Dairying).

does have an effect on the weaning weight of the calf (Table 12.11) but it is less than the effect caused by the breed of bull used. The breed and type of cow selected must be suited to the farm's position, altitude and topography. The milk-producing ability of cows varies between breeds and crosses but all cows are required to have consistency of performance, longevity, hardiness and the ability to convert medium quality forage into milk.

Finishing of Suckled Calves

These calves are weaned at different times of the year and at a wide range of weights and finished quality. There is a considerable variation in their subsequent liveweight gain according to the breed crosses used and the level of feeding given. Progressive management and feeding can improve profit margins but these margins are probably affected even more by the current market prices of weaned calves and finished animals; prudent buying and selling is essential for success. Market trends may often induce a producer to deviate from his intended policy as is the case when he sells his growing animals as stores in a favourable market instead of finishing them at an older age as intended. Policy decisions are often difficult but market opportunities,

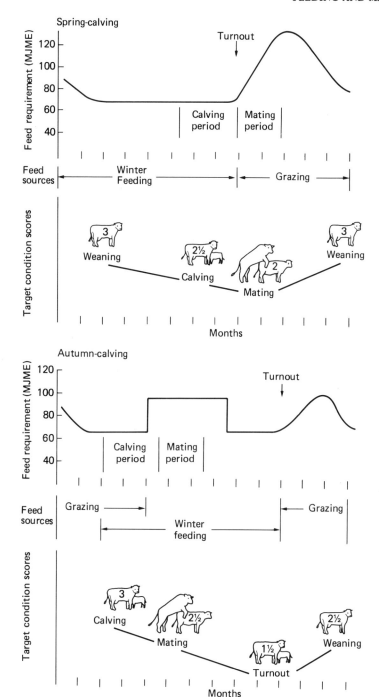

Fig. 12.6 Pattern of feeding requirements (MJME) for a 500 kg mature suckler cow, feed sources and target condition score (source: Scottish Agricultural Colleges).

availability and quality of grass/forage and the farmer's own cash flow situation are the main factors which affect his decision.

Successful finishing of weaned suckled calves depends on:

i) a smooth transfer from the suckling to the rearing stage;

ii) good clean pasture supplemented by concentrates;

iii) quality forage supplemented by concentrates.

Autumn-born calves from suckler herds can be finished during their second winter and slaughtered at 15 to 18 months. Later-born calves,

Table 12.11. Effect of cow type on 200 day calf weight (source: MLC)

Cow type	Calf 200 day weights (kg) Herd type: Lowland	Upland	Hill	Comparison with calves born out of Hereford × beef cows in same herd	Weight of weaned calf produced per 50 kg of cow body weight
AA × beef	201	186	176	−9	19
AA × Friesian	204	200	195	+11	20
Blue Grey	203	197	190	+6	20
Irish AA crosses	202	192	188	+5	20
Irish Hereford × Sh/horn	212	209	196	+7	19
Hereford × beef	202	191	181	0	18
Hereford × Fr	217	211	198	+19	20
Devon, Lincoln Red and Sussex's	208	196	191	+15	17
S Devon crosses	215	210	194	+16	16
Charolais crosses	221	214	193	+16	16

because of their small size, will have to be stored through the winter and finished off grass at 18 to 24 months.

Finishing in yards
Target daily liveweight gain varies between breed, sex, weight at yarding and when cattle need to be finished; a target daily liveweight gain of 0.75 kg for heifers and 1.0 kg for steers is often set but this could be lower if finished cattle are not required until the end of winter.

An assessment of quantity and quality of winter feed stocks precedes yarding to establish if the target liveweight gains can be achieved. The calves are grouped according to weight and sex and brought in before any loss of condition occurs; it may be necessary to clip along the back to avoid excessive sweating. They are often dusted with anti-louse powder and wormed.

Buildings need to be well ventilated and draught free with a square area allowance per animal of 3.25 m² to 3.27 m² with a trough length of 500 mm per head. Typical daily rations per head are given in Table 12.12.

Table 12.13 highlights how important it is to assess the winter food supply and to match this with the required number of cattle. It needs to

Table 12.12. Typical daily rations for winter finishing of suckled calves

Liveweight (kg)	Silage (65 D 250 g/kg)	Mineralized barley (kg)
300	22 kg	1
350	24 kg	1.5
400	26 kg	2
450	28 kg	2.5
500	30 kg	2.75

Table 12.13. Comparison of crosses during the finishing period (source: MLC)

	Angus cross	Hereford cross	Charolais cross
Start weight (kg)	260	270	300
Finishing period (days)	170	200	200
Slaughter weight (kg)	390	430	480
Daily gain (kg)	0.75	0.8	0.9
Carcass fat class	3H	3H	3L
Mineralized barley (kg/day)	1.25	1.5	2
65D silage (kg/day)	23	24	26
Total concentrates (kg)	210	300	400
Total silage (tonnes)	3.9	4.8	5.2

be noted that Charolais crosses consume one-third more silage than Angus crosses. It also needs to be noted that heifers of early maturing breeds tend to get too fat too young at light carcass weights.

Finishing off grass
The aim during the winter period is to utilize home grown fodder with a minimum of concentrate supplement and subsequent intensive grass management to finish animals before the seasonal price trough.

The calf is maintained on a roughage and limited cereal ration over winter, turned out at about 270 kg for heifers and 330 kg for steers so as to attain slaughter weights of 350 kg and 480 kg respectively at grass; typical daily rations for the yarded period are shown in Table 12.14.

Spring-born calves are yarded at weaning, while summer-born calves are yarded with their dams and subsequently weaned. They are turned out to grass as early as possible in the spring, supplementing the grass with 1–2 kg cereal per head per day; they are treated against stomach worms and lung worms. One hectare of well

Table 12.14. Typical winter rations for suckled calves finished at grass

Live weight	Silage (kg)	Mineralized barley (kg)
250	20	0.5
300	32	0.5
350	28	–
400	30	–

managed clean grass should satisfy the grazing needs of 7.5 animals. Selection for slaughter is based on weight and finished condition of the animal.

Bull Beef

Bull beef is a further outlet but it is necessary to carefully plan the system in detail, especially the marketing, before adopting such a system. Bulls react differently to steers since they are more independent and aggressive; attention to safety is therefore a priority of the system. The Code of Practice for Bull Beef Premises (MAFF) demands that hedges, fences and gates be stock-proof and entrances display the sign 'DANGER – BULLS – KEEP OUT'.

Traditional buildings presently used for steers may not be suitable for bulls. The Code of Practice for Bull Beef Premises lists the following requirements:

1. Feeding and bedding must be carried out without the necessity of stockmen to move among the bulls. If this is not possible two men must be present at all times.
2. Races and crushes should be available for safe handling.
3. Divisions between pens must be strong and gates secure and childproof.
4. Each pen should not contain more than 20 bulls.

Due to the inherent problems of management and the difficulties of achieving high daily liveweight gains while at grass, current thinking revolves around a system of fattening young bulls indoors on silage supplemented with barley.

The Hereford × Friesian bull calf which remains as a standard product of the dairy herd is placed on the once-a-day bucket feeding of *ad lib.* acid milk system and standard feeding practised to ten weeks when a gradual change to rolled barley and fishmeal is fed at about 2 kg per head per day.

Good quality silage is offered from about 14 weeks and fed to appetite. From ten months onwards barley alone is fed. Trials at Rosemaund Experimental Husbandry Farm suggest the following results:

Total silage	3.8 t
Hay	25 kg
Compound	720 kg

Bulls slaughtered at just over 1 year old weighing 407 kg.

Advantages	Disadvantages
Better liveweight gain	Silage must be available all year round
Turn-out and yarding checks avoided	Best suited to tower systems
Planned marketing easier	Higher capital cost
Higher stocking rates.	Safety precautions necessary.

ASSESSMENT OF LIVE CATTLE FOR SLAUGHTER

The visual assessment of finished cattle is an art which can only be acquired with experience. Since most cattle are still sold on the hoof, this art needs to be promoted. The first requirement is the ability to assess the liveweight with a certain degree of accuracy and then from handling to estimate the dressing-out percentage. The following points need to be observed:

i) general conformation should give a blocky appearance;
ii) handling by passing the hand over the ribs and shoulder should indicate evenness of fat cover and firmness;
iii) loin should be wide and firm;
iv) the loin should run smoothly into the rump, the latter to be long and wide;
v) the hindquarters should be full of muscle and firm to touch;
vi) the skin should feel soft and pliable.

The demands of present markets emphasize the need for standard grading schemes, and the EEC has developed a classification system which can be used for grading purposes. The scheme is based on a grid system with a fat classification from 1 (lean) to 5 (fat) and a conformation scale from E (very good) through U,R,O to P, the latter letter indicating a grossly overfat beast or one with an extremely poor conformation.

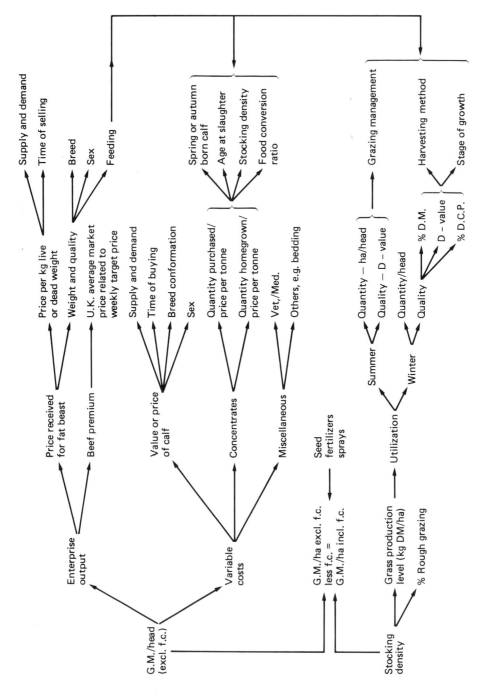

Fig. 12.7 Diagnostic flow-diagram to analyse factors responsible for gross margin performance of a beef fattening enterprise.

FAT CLASS

	1	2	3	4L	4H	5L	5H
E							
U+							
U							
R							
O							
O−							
P							

CONFORMATION

ANALYSIS OF A BEEF ENTERPRISE'S PERFORMANCE

When the gross margin for a beef enterprise is divided by the annual throughput, a per head figure is reached. This reflects the level of annual performance and can be used to analyse possible weaknesses in the enterprise management. Simple but effective records are required to make such an analysis meaningful.

Fig. 12.7 shows a diagnostic flow-diagram which relates all the factors responsible for the ultimate level of gross margin per head and per hectare. As for any other enterprise, analysis involves comparing the figures of an individual farm with standard or target figures which are compiled by central agencies processing data collected from a wide range of farms. Each farm figure which is unsatisfactory compared with the standard figure pinpoints a weakness in the gross margin performance.

13

Feeding and Management of Sheep

There is a continuous supply of lamb to the consumer market throughout the year; some 50% of lamb supply is imported, mainly from New Zealand and Australia, and a limited quantity of home-produced lamb exported into Europe. Commercial home producers operating different systems of production supply this annual demand for lamb. Spring lambs are produced from early lambing lowland flocks. Summer and early autumn lambs come mainly from the lowland grassland flocks supplemented by fat lambs from upland and hill flocks. Late autumn lambs and winter hoggets are produced from the lowlands by extensive usage of forage crops such as kale, rape, stubble turnips, hay and silage supplemented by cereal-based concentrates.

There is a general pattern concerning finished lamb weights – they increase from early spring to late winter production, the lowlands producing heavier lambs than the uplands and hills; also, concentrate usage is high for early lambs and winter hoggets because they are produced when nutritious grass for grazing is limited or unavailable.

SYSTEMS OF COMMERCIAL SHEEP PRODUCTION

Physical data concerning the main systems of commercial sheep production are summarized in Table 13.1.

Lowland

(a) *Early lambing flocks*
Lambing usually occurs in December/January and an attempt is made to market finished 'light weight' lambs before the end of May when high prices prevail. The concentrate input to the ewe and growing lambs is appreciable.

(b) *Grassland flocks*
Lambing occurs in March and consequently the grass growth curve matches the energy and protein requirements of the ewe during her productive cycle. An attempt is made to market as many finished lambs as possible before the price drops in August and the remainder are either sold as store lambs or gradually sold off in the autumn as they reach heavier finishing weights. Concentrate input to the ewe is considerable but the concentrate input to the lambs is low and used mainly for those lambs not finished on summer grass.

(c) *Grass and forage flocks*
Lambing occurs in March but the system is geared to the production of finished lambs over a more extended period than grassland flocks, sales occurring from June to early winter. Concentrate input for lamb growth is consequently greater than for grass flocks because of the greater number of lambs which need to be finished after the flush of summer grass.

(d) *Hogget production*
After the 31st December of the year in which a lamb is born it is called a hogget. In some flocks a proportion of the lambs are finished off to be sold as hoggets in the subsequent winter after their birth so that the lamb production is even more protracted than grass and forage flocks; as a consequence the amount of concentrates consumed by lambs is greater.

Often fattening of store lambs into hoggets becomes a separate enterprise on some lowland

168

Table 13.1. Average physical data relating to commercial systems of sheep production (source: MLC 1979 data)

	Lowland flocks				Upland flocks			Hill flocks
	Early lambing	Grassland	Grass and forage	Hogget production	Selling fat and store lambs	Selling breeding stock	Extensive	
Lambing time	December/ January	March	March	March	March	March	April	April on
Time of lamb sales	April/May	June on	June on	June on	August on	August on	August on	September on
No. of lambs reared	133	137	136	133	125	123	116	100
No. of lambs sold fat	110	62	127	124	45	20	24	0
No. of lambs sold for breeding	0	0	0	0	0	44	17	0
No. of lambs sold or retained as stores	14	56	0	0	60	48	67	69
No. of lambs retained for breeding	9	8	9	9	11	11	8	31
Draft ewes	0	0	0	0	0	0	0	24
Ewes/ha grass and forage	12	11	10	10	9	9	<6.5	<6.0
kg N/ha	145	138	133	120	86	86	50	45
kg concs/ewe	55	50	47	45	38	30	26	} 23
kg concs for lambs reared per ewe	33	6	13	15	1	1	1	

farms. Store lambs are purchased from flocks and forage crops supplemented by concentrates are fed to fatten them.

Upland

(a) Flocks selling fat and store lambs
Under upland conditions the stocking density and the number of lambs which can be finished is dependent on the proportion of marginal land which has been improved by drainage, liming, applying phosphates and re-seeding and subsequently fenced for better pasture management by controlled grazing; the high proportion of store lambs are usually sold to the lowland farmers for finishing. Fertilizer usage is lower than for lowland and little or no concentrates are used for lamb growth.

(b) Flocks selling breeding stock
These are flocks which supply the lowland farmer with a high proportion of pure or crossbred ewe lambs or two-teeth ewes. Usually within each flock a greater proportion of breeding stock is sold than finished lambs for the meat market because they command higher prices.

(c) Extensive flocks
Because of the low proportion of 'improved land' these flocks graze extensively and the overall stocking density is lower than 6.5 ewes per

hectare of grass and forage. The number of lambs which can be finished are limited and a high proportion are sold as stores.

Hill

Hill flocks are managed in a distinct way because of the rough terrain, inclement weather and the inferior herbage such as heather, nardus, molinia and fescue grasses which exist in the hill areas. Such an environment reduces the productive life of the ewe to four lamb crops before she is drafted to lower land as a broken-mouthed ewe incapable of grazing the tough vegetation.

Consequently either all or at least three-fifths of ewe lambs are retained for breeding and the male lambs sold usually as stores; although the vast majority of ewe lambs are over-wintered or 'tacked' on lowland farms some are now being winter housed on the hill farm.

Stocking density and the capacity to finish lamb and not to sell them as stores depend in each farm situation on the proportion of lower slope and flat land available. Systems of production are thus largely dictated by the climatic, topographic and soil conditions which exist in any given farm situation; each lowland and upland farmer has a limited choice concerning which system to adopt whilst the hill farmer has little or no choice.

Inter-farm comparisons within any given system of sheep production reveal that some farmers manage the enterprise more effectively and profitably. Over the complete range of production systems the main management factors which enable the best farmers to better their contemporaries are:

i) more skilful marketing by meeting a 'best price' deadline with the maximum number of finished lambs at the weight and quality demanded by the specific market;

ii) higher percentage of lambs reared;

iii) superior grassland management which ensures a plentiful supply of better quality grazing and conserved forage resulting in a:

    (a) higher stocking rate per hectare of land, and

    (b) reduced intake of concentrates.

FLOCK NET MARGIN

Within any given production system the net margin of the enterprise is the difference between the gross margin for the flock and the proportion of the farm's fixed costs which are used for its effective management. In order to illustrate the method of calculation involved, data for a lowland grassland flock are based on average 1980 price figures; the same method applies to all production systems.

A yearly summary of an enterprise's performance is conveniently structured in the form of a gross margin budget; Table 13.2 presents such a budget for a lowland flock of 300 ewes. Output items consist of the sales of fat or store lambs, the value of lambs retained at the end of the financial year as stores or breeding ewe lambs, and the sale of wool fleeces. On average a fifth of the older ewes are sold as culls and shearling ewes purchased to replace them; the difference between cull ewe sales and shearling purchases is a measure of the flock's replacement cost or depreciation; to this needs to be added the depreciation of the rams whose productive life is 3 years. In the example quoted the total depreciation for the flock is

$$(3600 + 438) - (1620 + 50) = £2368$$

When this figure is divided by the number of ewes in the flock a per ewe depreciation figure is calculated, i.e.

$$£2368 \div 300 = £7.89 \text{ (i.e. } £6.60 + £1.29).$$

It can be quickly appreciated that a favourable financial output depends primarily on the number of finished lambs which can be reared and sold at given weights when market prices are at their best; lower prices prevail for store lambs. This performance hinges on effective management of the ewe throughout her productive cycle and adequate feeding of the lamb for rapid liveweight growth.

Variable costs items consist of concentrates, veterinary services, and miscellaneous costs including transport and forage costs. A relationship exists between forage and concentrate costs; expenditure on fertilizer and seeds for grass and forage production is a base requirement for producing a high quantity and quality of home-grown food and thus reducing the requirements of purchased concentrates; stocking rate per hectare is also directly related to the quantity of fertilizer applied, particularly nitrogen.

In addition to variable costs other fixed costs are incurred in sheep production. Table 13.2 shows some estimated per ha farm fixed costs which are attributable to the sheep enterprise. These figures need to be viewed with extreme caution since fixed costs vary widely from one farm to another; also it is extremely difficult to apportion whole-farm fixed costs to enterprises. Fixed costs are appreciable and net margin figures inclusive or otherwise of family labour are appreciably lower than gross margin figures.

In most farm situations any reduction in fixed costs is difficult to achieve. There is a close relationship between gross and net margin figures and any improved management which increases gross margin performance will be reflected in an improved net margin figure.

Table 13.2. Physical and financial results for a lowland flock of 300 ewes selling most lambs off grass in summer and autumn (1980 prices)

(a) Gross margin

	Flock			Per ewe	
	Quantity	Price/Unit	£	Quantity	£
Lambs sold finished	210	£36.75	7 718	1.37	46.50
Value of store lambs	201	£31	6 231		
Wool fleeces sold	300	£2.72	816	1	2.72
			14 765		49.22
Replacement costs (depreciation)					
Sale of cull ewes	60	£27	+1 620	⅕th	−6.60
Purchase of replacement ewes	60	£60	−3 600		
Sale of cull rams	2.5	£20	+50		
Purchase of replacement rams	2.5	£175	−438		−1.29
			12 397		41.33
ENTERPRISE OUTPUT					
less Variable costs:					
Concentrates	21 t	£108/t	2 268	70 kg	−7.56
Vet and medicines			525		−1.75
Miscellaneous costs + transport			510		−1.70
Forage costs (fertilizer and seeds)	on 30.3 ha	£95.84/ha	2 904	on 0.10 ha	−9.68
			6 190		20.64

GROSS MARGIN

Physical results
Per 100 ewes to tup

		Stocking rate (ewes/ha)	
No. of empty ewes	7	Summer grazing	12.7
No. of dead ewes	5	Overall grass	10.4
No. of ewes lambed	91	Overall grass and forage	9.9
No. lambs born dead	12	kg N/ha	138
No. lambs born alive	147		
No. lambs dead after birth	10		
No. lambs reared	137		
No. lambs sold finished	70		
No. store lambs at end of year	67		

GROSS MARGIN PER HECTARE = £6190 ÷ 30.3 = £204.30 = 20.64 × 9.9

(b) *Net margin*

	£	£
Gross margin per ha		204.30
Estimated fixed costs:		
Rent and buildings	43	
Machinery and power	46	
Hired labour	41	
Family labour	35	
Others	27	
		192.00
Estimated net margin		£12.30
Estimated net margin excluding family labour		£47.30

NUTRIENT REQUIREMENTS IN THE BREEDING CYCLE OF THE EWE

The sheep is a ruminant and like the cow has a 'four-compartmented stomach' which digests bulky fibrous foods. The ewes are fed as a flock because it is impractical to feed them individually and their nutrient requirements at any one time are very similar.

The nutrient needs of the ewe are closely linked with its breeding cycle consisting of five months gestation, four months lactation and three months dry period; this is summarized in Fig. 13.1.

The daily pattern of metabolizable energy and protein requirements can be appreciated by referring to Fig. 13.2. In this representation it is assumed that a dry 70 kg ewe can ingest 0.57 kg (100%) daily of indigestible organic matter – this intake reduces to 80% in late pregnancy and reaches a peak during lactation; the voluntary intake of silage is 15% below these figures; the

daily metabolizable energy and protein requirements closely match one another, peaking before tupping and again during late pregnancy and lactation; thus high-quality food is required during these peak periods for effective metabolism and production. The quality of herbage required is shown in Fig. 13.3 and Table 13.3.

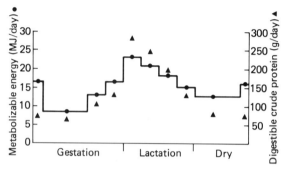

Fig. 13.2 The metabolizable energy (ME) and digestible crude protein requirements of a 70 kg ewe rearing twin lambs (source: Dr. R. J. Wilkins, Grassland Research Institute, Hurley).

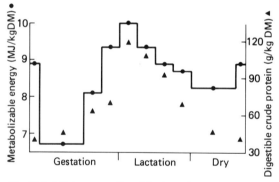

Fig. 13.3 Minimum quality of food requirement for a 70 kg ewe rearing twin lambs (source: Dr. R. J. Wilkins, Grassland Research Institute, Hurley).

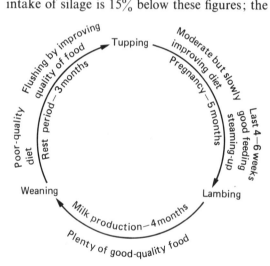

Fig. 13.1 The feeding of the ewe flock in relation to its breeding cycle.

Table 13.3. Daily indigestible organic matter intake possible, metabolizable energy requirement and quality of herbage required for a ewe weighing 70 kg and bearing twin lambs (source: Dr. R. J. Wilkins, Grassland Research Institute, Hurley)

Months:		*Gestation*					*Lactation*				*Dry*		
		1	2	3	4	5	1	2	3	4	1	2	3
Indigestible organic matter intake*	kg:	0.57	0.57	0.57	0.57	0.46	0.63	0.74	0.74	0.63	0.57	0.57	0.57
	%:	100	100	100	100	80	110	130	130	110	100	100	100
Metabolizable energy (MJ/day):		8	8	8	12	16	23	21	18	15	12	12	16
Metabolizable energy (MJ/kg DM):		6.5	6.5	6.5	8.0	9.3	10	9.3	8.9	8.6	8.1	8.1	8.9

* This is 15% lower with silage intake.

Flushing

About 6–8 weeks before tupping the quality of the ewe's diet is gradually improved. This is called flushing and it stimulates egg production, thus increasing the number of twins born. Body condition scoring (see p. 182) is often carried out so as to separate fat ewes with a score of say 4 from those with a score of 2 or less. Ewes with low body-score can thus be batched and fed on a good quality diet so as to increase body weight.

Gestation Period

During the early stages of pregnancy the developing embryo does not draw heavily on its mother's food supply and care needs to be taken that the ewe is adequately nourished so as to maintain condition but not to become overfat.

During the last 2 months of pregnancy the growing embryo makes increasing demands on the ewe's food supply so that a plentiful supply of good quality food must be provided, particularly during the last month.

Whatever the quality of home-grown food, some concentrate needs to be fed during the last 4–6 weeks. An initial 0.2 kg per head per day of crushed cereals can be gradually increased to 0.5 kg; during the last 4 weeks a half of this ration could consist of ewe nuts for the supply of adequate protein. The use of mineral licks with traces of cobalt and copper helps to prevent ailments such as sway-back and pining in young lambs. Correct feeding through pregnancy is also the only way to prevent twin-lamb disease.

Lactation

The young lamb is completely dependent on its mother's milk for the first 3 weeks of its life; between 3 and 6 weeks the lamb's stomach develops sufficiently to enable it to feed on herbage in addition to milk. The energy and protein requirements of the ewe are at their peak during this period and to ensure rapid growth of lambs it is essential that she receives ample supplies of the best quality food.

Dry or Scavenging Period

After the lambs have been weaned, usually at 12–14 weeks of age, the ewe enters her dry period. It is essential that she is not allowed to get overfat since this will impair egg production. Adequate nutrients need to be provided, however, so that her body condition can be gradually improved after the rigour of 8 to 9 months pregnancy and suckling. In the first 2 months of this period the ewes can be used as scavengers to clean up poor and overgrown pastures, banks and stubble; on highly fertile lowland farms with rich pastures it may be difficult to provide them with winter keep.

TIME OF LAMBING AND CROPPING EFFECTS

Table 13.4 broadly illustrates how the natural growth curve of grass is differentially utilized by flocks lambing at different times; reference also to Fig. 13.4 shows the grass growth curve and the nutrient demand of sheep throughout their productive cycle.

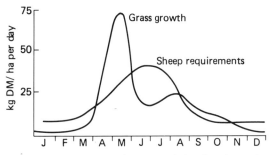

Fig. 13.4 The grass growth curve and the sheep's requirements measured as kg DM/ha per day.

With mid-lambing flocks the grazing pressure, i.e. number of animals relative to amount of grass, is closely related to grass growth so that liveweight gain is achieved virtually by grazing grass alone. The main problem is the finishing of lambs left over on low grass production in the July/August period.

With early lambing there is high grazing pressure during the February to May period; although plentiful supplies of highly nutritious grass are available during April/May for the heavy demand of growing and fattening lambs fodder of high quality is necessary for the late pregnancy and lactation stages from November to March. The advantage of the system is that there is no pressing feed requirement during the difficult July/August period and consequently conserved hay or silage is normally made during this period.

Table 13.4. How seasonal grass growth is differentially utilized by early, mid and late lambing flocks

Times of lambing	Jan.	Feb.	Mar.	April	May	June	July	Aug.	Sept.	Oct.	Nov.	Dec.
Early		↓ Lambing		Lamb sales→|					↓ Tupping			
		←High grazing pressure——————→|				←No pressure on grass – silage can be conserved——→					←Silage or hay and concs supplement→	
	←Silage or hay and concs supplement——→|			←Highly nutritious grass for lamb growth——→								
Mid				↓ Lambing		Lamb sales→|			↓ Tupping			
		←Silage or hay and concs supplement——→|		←Grazing pressure closely related to grass growth→|								
						←Finishing of lambs on grass is difficult ——→						
Late				↓ Lambing							↓ Tupping	
		←Winter months correspond with first 3 months of pregnancy→|	←High quality grass growth maximal during last 2 months pregnancy and first month of lactation. Grazing pressure low because of high quality of grass——————→|			←Animal nutrient demand high on low grass growth resulting in store lambs——→		←Lambs suitable to graze stubble turnips and rape for finishing——→				
				←Quality silage possible——→|								

With late lambing the winter months coincide with the first 3 months of pregnancy and grass growth and quality are maximal during the last 2 months of pregnancy and first month of lactation; grazing pressure is also at its lowest because of abundant grass if stocking rates are kept at reasonable levels. The limitation of the system is the nutritive demand of heavier lambs during the August to September period of limited grass growth, resulting in store lambs which can only be finished in the following autumn on forage crops.

It needs to be remembered that whilst the relative advantages of early, mid and late lambing can be described in this way the lambing policy on most lowland farms is dictated by the area of arable crops grown and the grazing demands of the main livestock enterprise on the farm; the sheep enterprise on most lowland farms is a subsidiary one which has to 'fit in'.

Forage Crops

Forage crops which can be grown to supplement grazed grass are many and their quality as measured by metabolizable energy in MJ/kg dry matter and protein content needs to be reasonably high. Physical data concerning such crops are shown in Table 13.5.

For Autumn flushing of ewes and finishing of lambs, crops such as Italian ryegrass, aftermath of hay, a rested sward, maiden seed sown in spring, stubble turnips or rape can be grown. With winter pregnancy, good quality hay and to a lesser extent good quality silage could satisfy the ewe's nutrient needs when supplemented by concentrates in the fourth and fifth month of pregnancy (see p. 172). A winter lactation period could be met by crops of swedes, kale, good hay and silage with perhaps early grass during the later stages; concentrates would also be required for maximum milk production.

Lamb can be fattened on good quality hay (> 8.0 MJ/kg DM) and weight gain will increase directly as the quality of the hay improves. With silage feeding there is a tendency to produce high fat content carcasses and this is probably due to the inefficient use of protein. Grass, lucerne and maize silages can be fed provided their MJ/kg DM is over 8.5.

Table 13.5. Forage crops – physical data (source: Agricultural Budgeting and Costing Book No. 10 – Agro Business Consultants Ltd.)

Per ha	Kale		Rape	Stubble turnips	2–3 cuts silage and aftermath	1 hay cut and aftermath	Grazing		Grass establishment	
	Ploughed/ drilled	Direct drilled					Inten- sive	Aver- age	Perma- nent ley	Tem- porary ley
Seed rate (kg)	2–4	2–4	2–4	0.5–4					34	30
Nitrogen (kg)	125	175	100	100	370	190	375	300	60	60
Phosphate (sol.) (kg)	60	60	25	50	77	40	30	30	160*	50
Potash (kg)	60	60	65	65	77	75	30	30	60	60
Desmetryne (litres)	1.5	1.5								
Paraquat (litres)		4.5								
Slug pellets (kg)		15								
Lime (tonne)									6.25	
Yield (tonne)	50	60	33	45	40	12				
%DM	14	14	14	12	20	85	20	20	20	20
DM/ha (kg)	7000	8400	4620	5400	8000	10 200				
ME (MJ/kg DM)	11	11	9.5	11.2	8.8	8.4				
DCP (g/kg DM)	114	114	144	73	102	40				

* Includes 100 kg insoluble phosphate.

STOCKING RATE

The stocking rate is dependent on the amount of grass grown, the size of the ewe and the number of lambs reared at pasture. The generalized relationship between optimum stocking rate for 65 kg ewes with 1.8 lambs and the amount of grass grown is shown in Fig. 13.5, as worked out by a computer model. The number of ewes and lambs per hectare carried varies directly according to the amount of grass grown and this in turn depends on the quantity of fertilizer, particularly nitrogen, applied and the grazing management adopted to equalize grazing pressure according to seasonal quantities of grass.

The voluntary intake of dry matter per day by ewes and lambs is directly proportional to their size. Table 13.6 illustrates this point where the number of small Welsh Mountain ewes kept is double that of the larger Masham ewes; the productive output in terms of kg meat/ha is virtually the same and the gross margin/ha would have been comparable if the Welsh Mountain fleece had been more valuable. Stocking density is often expressed as livestock units/ha, a livestock unit being equivalent to the energy requirements of a dairy cow for one year. Cattle and sheep of different weights and energy requirements can be converted into grazing livestock units by using livestock unit factors. Thus a heavy lowland ewe has a livestock unit factor of 0.11 and this implies that her energy

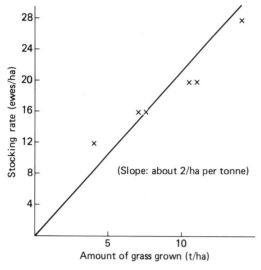

Fig. 13.5 Optimal stocking rate versus amount of grass grown (source: J. E. Newton, Grassland Research Institute, Hurley).

Table 13.6 Lamb production from temporary grassland (1975) (source: J. E. Newton, Grassland Research Station, Hurley)

	Large ewe	*Small ewe*
Ewe size	70 kg	32 kg
Ewe breed	Masham	Welsh Mountain
Date of lambing	March	March
Selling %	199	91
Stocking rate (per ha)	17.5	35
Sward	PRG S24	PRG S24
Nitrogen (kg/ha)	250	250
Grazing management	8 paddocks with forward creep	4 paddocks
Carcass output (kg meat per ha)	459	448
GM per ewe	£10.22	£4.66
GM per ha	£179	£165

requirements in one year are eleven hundredths of the energy requirements of a cow; the livestock unit factors for different sheep are shown in Table 9.4. Example 1 on p. 115 illustrates how this method operates.

Grazing Systems

It is becoming economically necessary on some lowland farms to keep as many sheep as possible per hectare. A stocking rate of at least 15–17 ewes and lambs per hectare is an accepted target but a stocking rate of 22 ewes and 35 lambs per hectare seems a practical possibility.

At these high stocking rates two things are of major importance:

(a) the provision of adequate quantities of leafy, nutritious grass for the growing lambs as well as to stimulate milk production by the ewes;
(b) to reduce the uptake of intestinal worms by the young lambs.

The number of worms on pastures increases enormously (see p. 240) particularly by late July and August, if ewe stocking density is high. The young lambs graze more as they get older and consequently pick up large numbers of worms which will seriously reduce their growth rate.

It is possible to provide adequate quantities of grass by the use of fields containing good grasses and clovers and applying increased quantities of fertilizers; between 185 and 250 kg per hectare of nitrogen together with appropriate quantities of phosphate, potash and lime can be applied. Grazing management must also be of a high standard to maintain the grass in a leafy condition. In addition grazing systems can be used to reduce the number of worms eaten by the young lambs. The various systems of grazing in use for fat lamb production are:

(i) Set stocking

This is still the most common system of grazing. Its success depends on the practical experience of the farmer who decides how many ewes and lambs are needed on each field so as to keep the grass in a leafy nutritious condition and yet avoid overgrazing which reduces the amount of food available. The stock remain on the same land until the lambs are sold off fat. As the lambs go off, this automatically reduces the stocking rate as the quality and quantity of grass decreases.

(ii) Rotational grazing

The land required for the summer grazing is divided into about 8 equal sized paddocks. The ewes and lambs are moved forward into a fresh paddock every few days when the shepherd decides that fresh grass is needed. Surplus growth of grass in early summer can be conserved as light crops of silage or hay; this has the additional advantage that these paddocks will produce young leafy aftermath, free of worms, during mid-summer. The grass on paddocks which are not used for hay or silage is kept leafy in mid-summer by topping over.

(iii) *Mixed grazing*

When cattle and sheep are grazing together each benefits the other. The cattle improve lamb growth by eating the coarser grass (thus stimulating leafier growth) whilst at the same time consuming and destroying a large number of worm larvae. Cattle can be incorporated into either of the above systems. On rotationally grazed plots a stocking rate of 3.6 cattle and 10.5 ewes per ha can be attained.

(iv) *Creep grazing*

There are two systems of creep grazing (Fig. 13.6). The intention is to give the lambs first choice of the young leafy grass, and also to

(a) Rotational creep grazing

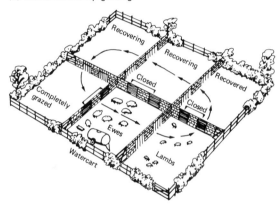

The lambs have access to each paddock ahead of the ewes. This gives them first pick at the best grass. The ewes follow behind as scavengers

(b) Sideways creep grazing

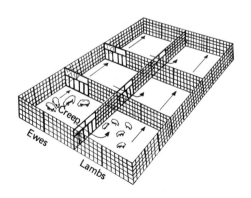

Only the lambs enter one set of paddocks. Worm build-up in the lambs' paddocks is kept to a minimum

Fig. 13.6 Two systems of creep grazing (from *The Farmers Weekly*): (a) rotational creep grazing; (b) sideways creep grazing.

reduce the number of worm larvae eaten by the lambs. It seems that a higher proportion of store lambs are produced on this system as compared with the other systems.

Disposal of Lambs

It should be the intention on all systems to sell off as many as possible of the lambs fat when prices are favourable; finished lambs can be selected for sale before they become overfat; they command a better price because of carcass quality rating and their sale also reduces pressure on the available land. Those which are not ready for slaughter may either be sold as stores or moved to a fresh aftermath for fattening.

Whatever system the farmer employs, he must guard against such diseases as navel-ill, lamb dysentery and pulpy kidney (p. 237). Once lambs start grazing they may pick up nematodirus worms, which can kill, and other stomach worms (see p. 241), which can markedly slow down their rate of growth. The lambs will, therefore, have to be drenched and given the appropriate injections.

Castration

Most of the male lambs will have to be castrated. Nowadays the two most popular methods are the Burdizzo bloodless method and the Elastrator method (see p. 155); the latter must by law be used before the lamb is seven days old. Castrating with the Burdizzo method at 5–6 weeks often checks their growth rate.

Tailing or Docking

This is also very important when the lambs are grazing on lush grass in summer. Dirty tails and hind-quarters will attract the maggot fly.

There are two methods of tailing:

1. The tails of lambs under 3 weeks old are cut off by means of a sharp knife or by the use of the bloodless castrator.
2. Rubber rings, as used for castration, are slipped on the base of the tails. This can be done before the lambs are 3 weeks old.

Castration and tailing are unnecessary when lambs are disposed of early in the season.

Age and Dentition

Sheep have two sets of teeth. The first or milk teeth are 20 in number, and the second set or permanent teeth number 32. These latter consist of eight incisors, twelve premolars and twelve molars. The age of a sheep can be determined from its incisor teeth as follows:

8 temporary incisors	6–10 months
2 permanent	10–14 months
6 temporary incisors	(2 toothed)
4 permanent	around 2 years old
4 temporary incisors	(4 toothed)
6 permanent	around 3 years old
2 temporary incisors	(6 toothed)
8 permanent	around 4 years old
0 temporary incisors	(full mouthed)

In order to obtain a quick growth rate and not lose many lambs, the farmer must manage his flock competently, provide ample food and keep them as free as possible from disease. To do this successfully he must rely on his experience as a shepherd as well as using to the full the latest techniques of management and disease prevention.

The ewe lambs destined to be used as flock replacements will, of course, not be fattened and sold. They will follow their mothers on to the scavenging diet and some may be mated in the following autumn (see p. 172). The choice of ewe-lambs as flock replacement is described on p. 11.

THE FEEDING OF HILL SHEEP

Hill sheep must rely on natural vegetation to provide their food throughout the year.

On the hills the soil is poor, lacking in both depth and fertility. The climate is very severe in winter and cool and wet during the summer.

Under these conditions the growth of grass and other plants is never very abundant. Grass starts growing late in spring, grows fairly quickly during late May and June, and then fades away early in the autumn. The quality of this herbage is also rather poor, and at most times the ewes have to walk considerable distances to find sufficient food for their maintenance.

The breeding cycle of the hill flock is thus dependent on this natural cycle of herbage production (see Fig. 13.7).

Mating

Tupping usually occurs from mid to late November, and lambing will thus commence from mid to late April.

The ewes are *not* flushed because under these conditions they are only able to carry and suckle a single lamb.

Early Pregnancy

During this period the ewes must rely on whatever herbage they can find. The available food varies with the type of season. If the winter is very hard and much snow falls, the ewes will have to search hard for food, and the tips of heather plants may form an important source of nutrition. If, on the other hand, the winter is milder, the food supply will not be so desperately short, but even in the mildest of winters, the grazing is never adequate. Fortunately, however, the developing foetus does not make very heavy demands on the ewes during early pregnancy.

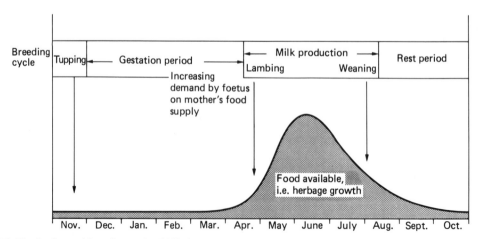

Fig. 13.7 The feeding and breeding cycle of hill sheep.

Late Pregnancy

The developing lamb makes increasing demands on its mother and usually the ewes have to draw on the reserves of foodstuffs stored in their body to feed it.

During this period the ewes are very much at the mercy of the season. If it has been a very hard winter and the spring is late, the food supply will be at a dangerously low level, and indeed many ewes may die.

If the spring is early, however, the herbage may start growing before lambing and this will help the ewes to produce a fairly strong lamb, and to be in a reasonable condition themselves. Under these conditions the lambing percentage may be around 85%, but it can be as low as 50% in a hard winter.

Supplementary Feeding

There has been a reluctance to feed mountain ewes, because the view was held that it reduced their willingness to search for grazing. Hay was, and often still is, only fed in the severest of seasons.

In recent years, however, a self-help system of feeding has been developed. This consists of solid blocks of food, which can contain energy supplying foods (e.g. cereals), protein (often urea), minerals and vitamins. These blocks are weatherproof and need only to be distributed every one or two weeks. The ewes nibble at these blocks; a 25 kg block is sufficient for 25–30 ewes per week. They are well scattered on the areas of the mountains where the sheep usually graze during the winter. This improved nutrition can raise the lambing percentage by as much as 20%.

Milk Production

During the period when the lambs' milk requirements are increasing, the ewes will be feeding on the freshly growing grass. This will stimulate milk production, especially during the first 8 weeks of the lamb's life. However, the food available is never sufficient in quantity nor sufficiently satisfactory in quality to produce enough milk to fatten the lambs. Consequently,

after weaning in August, the lambs are taken down to the lowland for fattening.

The Rest Period

By weaning time the amount and quality of herbage is already declining and during the autumn the ewes again have to search diligently to obtain enough food to finish rebuilding their bodies and udders in readiness for the next breeding season.

Drafting

Hill ewes are normally drafted at four years of age to lowland farms. Although they still have another few years of good productive life left, they are sent to lower land, usually because their teeth are badly worn and they would be unable to fend properly for themselves on the hills. On the lowland farms where the grass is more plentiful and climate less severe, these ewes do well.

Feeding on Hill Sheep Farms with Enclosed Land

Many hill sheep farms, particularly in Wales, have some areas of enclosed land on the lower and more sheltered hillsides (*ffridd*) together with a few sheltered fields suitable for growing conserved forage crops. The grass in the *ffridd* is much better in quantity and quality than on the open hill, particularly in early spring, because there is greater control of grazing.

The 3–4 year-old ewes are out-wintered on the hills and the two-year-olds are out-wintered in the *ffridd*; this provides the latter with better keep for their body growth and first lambing.

The ewes are brought down from the hillsides to the enclosed land about 5 weeks before lambing is due to commence. The better herbage provides them with more food when the unborn lamb is making heavy demands on their bodies and, consequently, both the lambs and ewes are much stronger at lambing time. Lambing can also commence earlier during late March under this improved feeding regime.

The ewes and lambs return to the hillsides in late April when the herbage has started growing.

ARTIFICIAL REARING OF LAMBS

The artificial rearing of orphan lambs has been a practice for a very long time. Today, however, large-scale artificial rearing is now being consid-

ered as a possible means of increasing the output of lambs from lowland flocks. It is considerably more expensive than natural rearing, however, and its main application seems to be for rearing the extra lambs produced by prolific ewes which they cannot rear themselves. In practice, this means that each ewe should be able to rear two good lambs herself and lambs produced over and above these can be reared artificially. Other possibilities are being investigated, however, such as its value for rearing the lambs of ewes which can produce 5–6 lambs per year in two crops.

There are a few systems of artificial rearing in use, and this account will be devoted to the general principles involved, and will not attempt to describe any one system in detail.

Removal of Lambs

Many factors are taken into consideration in deciding which lambs to remove from the ewes for artificial rearing. It is sound practice to select two fairly evenly matched lambs for the mother to suckle; the remainder can be artificially reared.

Feeding

The lambs are left with their mothers for between 6 and 24 hours to receive colostrum (see p. 11).

After removal they are fed on an appropriate substitute for at least three weeks because they can make very little use of solid food during this period; the milk substitute used can be either full creamed dried milk reconstituted in water, or dried skimmed milk with added fat. Cows milk is seldom used because it is too expensive.

The feeding is either on an *ad lib.* basis (a supply of milk being constantly available), or on a restricted basis, when each lamb is given 0.5 litre of milk 3 or 4 times daily. The former system is less laborious but more milk substitute is used.

There are various types of self-feed equipment available to cut down the work load. Machines are available which will automatically mix the substitute, whilst other less expensive models have to be hand-filled with the required amount. Fig. 13.8 shows some types of equipment used. It is essential to keep all feeders clean to avoid the multiplication of germs which cause digestive upsets.

Hay, water and weaner concentrates are made available to lambs to encourage them to start eating solid food.

Weaning

If lambs are to be sold when prices are high it is economic to feed milk substitute until they are

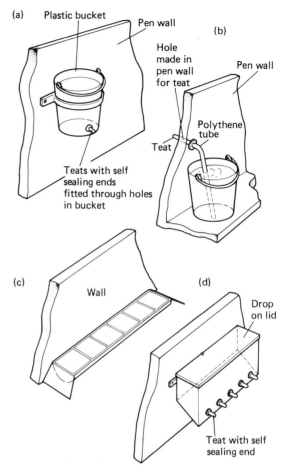

Fig. 13.8 Some equipment used for self-feeding by lambs: (a) bucket for feeding milk; (b) simple equipment for feeding reconstituted milk substitute; (c) trough suitable for restricted feeding of warm milk to lambs 1 to 4 weeks old; (d) simple tank used for feeding lambs cold milk-substitute.

sold. Under other marketing conditions, however, it is important to wean them from milk substitute on to less expensive solid foods. This is usually done at 3–4 weeks of age when the young lambs are consuming sufficient quantities of weaner concentrates. Such concentrates are highly palatable and nutritious and can either be purchased ready-mixed or home-mixed from barley, wheat offals and extracted oil cakes.

After weaning less expensive concentrates can be used until slaughter. There are many types available, the following mixture being one example:

Rolled barley	83%
Soya bean meal	10%
White fish meal	5%
Vitamin mineral mixture	2%

These concentrates are fed *ad lib.* and the lambs consume 3–3.5 kg per kilogram of liveweight gain. Lambs usually put on 0.25–0.35 kg liveweight gain daily.

Lambs kept indoors are fed on these concentrates together with hay and water until fat. In summer, young leafy grass free of worms can be used to replace part of the concentrate ration up to weaning and the whole of the concentrate ration from 6 to 7 weeks onwards.

Place of Rearing

During winter and early spring artificial rearing is practised indoors. The types of buildings used vary but they must be draught-free and well ventilated. For ease of management the lambs are separated into groups of 6–12.

In spring and summer the lambs may be reared out-of-doors on pasture, especially after they have been trained to feed themselves. Shelter should be provided; straw bales are quite suitable.

WINTER HOUSING

Housing can be used to in-winter:

(a) the whole or part of lowland flocks usually from December to lambing time;
(b) upland and hill ewe lambs instead of tacking them away on lowland farms; evidence suggests that such in-wintering does not measure up to good tack when available;
(c) upland and hill draft ewes for another year after which time they are usually sold with lambs at foot to lowland farms; this practice reduces the number of ewe lambs which used to be kept as replacements.

The effect of such in-wintering is to increase the stocking density of the farm by alleviating poaching and overgrazing in winter and thus increasing the availability of spring and summer grass; the disadvantage of housing is its cost.

Housing

Unused cattle yards and pole barns can be used. Buildings need to be constructed cheaply on level, well-drained sites using wood, concrete blocks, corrugated iron or straw bales as cladding. The inside must be dry but temperature and ventilation should be similar to outside. Each ewe on straw requires 1.5 m² of floor area and 1.0–1.2 m² when lodged on slatted floors. A simple indoor pen is shown in Fig. 13.9.

Feeding

1.0–1.5 kg hay or 3–4 kg silage of good quality forms the main part of the daily ration. Eight weeks before lambing this diet is supplemented with concentrates consisting possibly of barley, oats and dried sugar-beet pulp plus a mineral mixture; if only medium quality forage is available it is advisable to include 1 part high protein cake to 12 parts cereals; concentrate is fed at 0.1 kg per head per day at the start and increased to 0.5 at lambing time. Adequate trough space of 450 mm per ewe is vital. An unfailing supply of clean water, preferably running water, must be available.

Unless the weather is bad, each ewe and lamb is turned out to pasture within 48 hours after birth and feeding is continued until there is sufficient grass thus lessening risk of disease.

(a) Simple outdoor pen

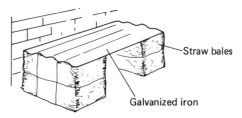

Straw bales

Galvanized iron

(b)

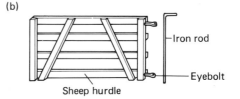

Iron rod

Eyebolt

Sheep hurdle

(c) Simple indoor ewe and lamb pens

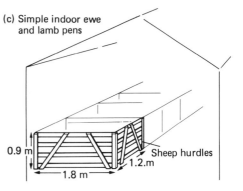

0.9 m

1.8 m

1.2 m

Sheep hurdles

Fig. 13.9 Sheep pens (source: *Sheep Management and Production*, Derick H. Goodwin; published by Hutchinson).

CONDITION SCORING

The body condition of ewes at tupping affects the number of barren ewes in the flock and the number of lambs born per fertile ewe. The Meat and Livestock Commission has developed condition scoring as a convenient handling method of determining condition. Lowland ewes should have a condition score of 3.5 at tupping but most flocks contain ewes with scores ranging from 1.5 to 4.

Flocks should be scored six to eight weeks before tupping. Ewes scoring 2 or below can be drawn out of flock and batched to be given the best available grazing, or fed supplementary concentrate if required. An improvement from condition score 2 to 4 is equivalent to a gain of about 12 kg live weight. Ewes scoring 5 can also be grouped and fed on a scavenging diet in the hope of reducing their fatness to a score level of 3.5 to 4.

During early pregnancy many ewes lose weight and a reduction to a score of 2.5 is acceptable. Ewes need to be scored again, however, some eight weeks before lambing so that feeding can be adjusted in the important last two months of pregnancy. All lowland ewes will normally require supplementary feeding at this time but those with scores below 2.5 should be drawn out for special treatment.

Scoring

Condition is assessed by finger pressure along the top and sides of the backbone in the loin area immediately behind the last rib and above the kidneys. The MLC list the following points for assessment in order:

i) the sharpness or roundness of the spinous processes of the lumbar vertebrae (the bony points rising upwards from the back);

ii) the prominence and degree of cover of the transverse processes of the vertebrae (the bone protruding from each side of the backbone);

iii) the extent of muscular and fatty tissues underneath the transverse processes (judged by the ease with which the fingers pass under the ends of the bones);

iv) the fullness and fat cover of the eye muscle (judged by pressing between the spinous and transverse processes).

Scoring System

The standardized system of body condition scoring as developed by the Hill Farming Research organization is based on a six point scale from 0 to 5. Most ewes score between 1.5 and 4.5 and scoring is made to 0.5 point accuracy. The condition scores are described by them as follows:

0. Extremely emaciated and on the point of death. It is not possible to detect any muscular or fatty tissue between the skin and the bone.

1. The spinous processes are prominent and sharp; the transverse processes are also sharp, the fingers pass easily under the ends, and it is possible to feel between each process; the loin muscles are shallow with no fat cover.

2. The spinous processes are prominent but smooth, individual processes can be felt only as fine corrugations; the transverse processes are smooth and rounder, and it is possible to pass the fingers under the ends with a little pressure; the loin muscles are of moderate depth, but have little fat cover.

3. The spinous processes have only a small elevation, are smooth and rounded, and individual bones can be felt only with pressure; the transverse processes are smooth and well covered, and firm pressure is required to feel over the ends; the loin muscles are full, and have a moderate degree of fat cover.

4. The spinous processes can just be detected with pressure as a hard line; the ends of the transverse processes cannot be felt; the loin muscles are full and have a thick covering of fat.

5. The spinous processes cannot be detected even with firm pressure; there is a depression between the layers of fat where the spinous processes would normally be felt; the transverse processes cannot be detected; the loin muscles are very full with very thick fat cover.

Fig. 13.10 Diagnostic flow diagram for the gross margin analysis of a sheep flock's performance.

ANALYSIS OF A FLOCK'S PERFORMANCE

As shown in Table 13.2, per ewe and per ha gross margins can be calculated from a flock's annual physical and financial data.

Fig. 13.10 shows a diagnostic flow diagram which relates all the factors responsible for the ultimate efficiency measure of gross margin. Analysis involves comparing the figures for the farm either with the farm figures of past years or with standard or target figures for a group of farms which practise the same flock management system; the latter are compiled by central government and private agencies possessing data collected from a wide range of farms; the Meat and Livestock Commission in particular publish extensive data on different sheep production systems. Each farm figure which is unsatisfactory compared with a standard figure pinpoints a cause of low gross margin performance; comparison with target figures highlights the managerial levels of performance required to equal the best.

When analysing by means of the flow diagram, the farm and average figure should be inserted, where possible, under each factor listed; logical analysis should start on the extreme left with the gross margin figure and then move systematically to the right of the diagram; in this way the factors responsible for low performance can be marked; it is these factors which need to be examined and corrective action taken to improve their performance. This exercise highlights the importance of keeping simple but effective records of the flock's performance.

A particular difficulty which may arise in many lowland farm situations where sheep are not kept exclusively on a block of land but graze the farmland with other livestock is estimating the area of farmland used by the sheep in order to arrive at a GM/ha figure. One method of approximately estimating the land used by the sheep is as shown on p. 115, Example 1.

14

Feeding and Management of Pigs

The farmers of the United Kingdom produce between 70 and 75% of the nation's total annual consumption of pig meat. Additionally, there is a small export trade in meat and also in live animals. In 1980 the export of live animals totalled nearly 300 000 and this was largely from Northern Ireland to the Irish Republic. With regard to home produced bacon and ham it amounts to slightly over 40% of the total consumption. The main exporter of pig meat to Britain is Denmark, with smaller contributions from a number of other countries, from both within and outside the European Economic Community (Fig. 14.1).

Pig production in this country can be sub-divided into two main activities – breeding and fattening. Some producers undertake both activities and others specialize in one or the other. For the fattener there is a further choice whether to produce porkers, cutters, baconers or heavy hogs. The decision is influenced by factors such as personal preference, local marketing facilities, the range and size of building accommodation and available capital. Pork and cutter production is less specialized than bacon production. Food rationing is not so critical, providing the genetic potential is adequate, because the pigs are slaughtered at relatively light weights.

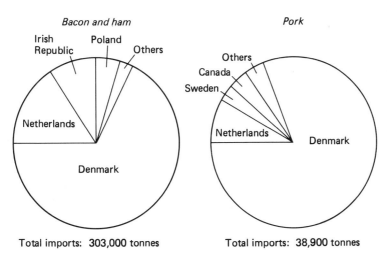

Fig. 14.1 Sources of pig meat imports (source: Meat & Livestock Commission, 1980).

ENTERPRISE NET MARGIN

Gross Margins

Gross margins for the main methods of production have to be considered individually.

Breeding Herd

Table 14.1 shows physical and gross margin figures for the breeding herd. The gross margin is the difference between output made up from the sale of weaner pigs less sow and boar depreciation, minus the total variable costs. The variable costs are made up from cost of feed (for sow, boar and weaners), veterinary services, medicines and miscellaneous items. By far the most important single item of variable costs is feed, making up around 90% of the total.

Important factors that contribute to the gross margin figures are:

i) litters per sow per year;
ii) pigs born alive per litter;
iii) pigs reared per litter;
iv) pigs reared per sow per year;
v) feed usage.

Meat and Livestock Commission figures giving average, top-third and bottom-third figures are shown in Table 14.2. There are striking differences in sow performance between the top and bottom thirds. Additionally there are differences in food usage and the top-third herds consume less feed per pig due mainly to better sow productivity.

Table 14.1. Physical and financial results for a herd of 100 breeding sows selling weaners

	Herd			Per sow	
	Quantity	Price per unit (£)	£	Quantity	£
Weaners sold	1820	26	47 320	18.2	473.20
Replacement costs (depreciation)					
Sale of cull sows	33	70	+2 310 ⎫	⅓rd	−9.90
Purchase of replacement gilts	33	100	−3 300 ⎭		
Sale of cull boars	2	70	+140		
Purchase of replacement boars	2	220	−440		−3.00
Enterprise output			46 030		460.30
less Variable costs:					
Sow meal	130 t	148	19 240	1.300 t	192.40
Creep feed	25.5 t	192	4 896	0.255 t	48.96
Growers ration	45.5 t	160	7 280	0.455 t	72.80
Vet & medicine			900		9.00
Bedding			600		6.00
Sundries			1 400		14.00
Gross margin			11 714		117.14

Physical results

Litters per sow per year (No.)	2.0	Feed use:	
Live pigs born per litter (No.)	10.6	Sow meal (sow, boar, gilt) (kg)	1300
Piglet mortality (%)	14.0	Creep feed (kg)	255
Weaners per litter (No.)	9.1	Grower's ration (kg)	455
Weaners sold per sow per annum (No.)	18.2	Total feed per sow	
Age at weaning (days)	42	per annum (kg)	2010
Age at sale/transfer (days)	77	Feed per pig reared (kg)	110
Live weight at weaning (kg)	13		
Live weight at sale/transfer (kg)	27		
Sow:boar ratio	20:1		
Proportion of sows replaced annually (%)	33		
Proportion of boars replaced annually (%)	40		

Table 14.2. Breeding herd results (source: MLC, 1980)

	Average	Top-third	Bottom-third
Sow performance			
Litters per sow per year	2.2	2.3	2.0
Pigs born per litter:			
live	10.4	10.7	10.0
dead	0.7	0.8	0.8
total	11.1	11.5	10.8
Mortality of pigs born alive (%)	12.8	11.0	14.8
Pigs reared per sow per year	19.8	22.3	17.1
Weight of pigs produced (kg)	18	18	18
Feed usage			
Feed per sow per year (tonnes)			
sow feed	1.26	1.20	1.28
pig feed	0.45	0.51	0.41
Total	1.71	1.71	1.69
Feed per pig reared (kg)			
sow feed	63	54	75
pig feed	23	23	24
total	86	77	99

Feeding Herd

Table 14.3 shows the gross margins figures for four types of systems. The tables provide figures at one level of food conversion ratio for each system, this being the amount of food (kg) required to put on 1 kg liveweight gain. The gross margin per head is the difference between output made up of the sale of the finished animal less weaner cost and an allowance for mortality minus the variable costs; the variable costs consist of feed and miscellaneous items. The feed costs again form the highest single item of variable costs, amounting to some 90 to 95% of the total. The single most important factor contributing to an above average gross margin figure is the sale weight for the end product together with the price received per kilogram. The second most important factor is the feed conversion ratio achieved.

Fixed Costs

These are the annual charges incurred for labour, buildings and rent, machinery and equipment,

Table 14.3. Physical and financial results for fattening pigs

	Per head			
	Pork	Cutter	Bacon	Heavy
Sale value	48.23	61.00	68.34	81.90
less Weaner cost (£26) less mortality (3%)	26.78	26.78	26.78	26.78
Enterprise output	21.45	34.22	41.56	55.12
less Variable costs:				
Feed: rearing meal (18% CP) at £160 t	6.40	6.40	6.40	6.40
rearing meal (16% CP) at £148 t	11.54	22.64	26.20	23.83
rearing meal (14% CP) at £142 t	—	—	—	21.30
Vet & medicines	0.08	0.10	0.10	0.11
Sundries	1.55	1.85	2.00	2.10
Gross margins	1.88	3.23	6.86	1.38
Physical results				
Live weight: at purchase/transfer (kg)	27	27	27	27
at slaughter (kg)	64	82	89	118
Dead weight at slaughter	45.5	61	67	91
Killing out (%)	71	74	75	77
Price per kg dead weight (p)	106	100	102	90
Feed: rearing meal (18% CP) (kg)	40	40	40	40
rearing meal (16% CP) (kg)	78	153	177	161
rearing meal (14% CP) (kg)	—	—	—	150
Total feed (kg)	118	193	217	351
Feed conversion ratio	3.2:1	3.5:1	3.5:1	3.9:1
Feed period (days)	80	105	126	147
Mortality (%)	3	3	3	3

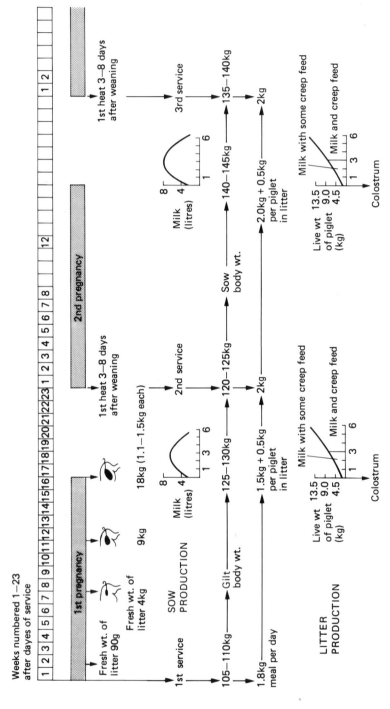

Fig. 14.2 The productive cycle of the sow (weaning at six weeks).

finance charges and insurance, and general overheads. Table 14.4 shows the result of a survey carried out by the Meat and Livestock Commission on breeding and feeding farms mostly producing baconers. This survey shows that 76% of the total is made up of labour, building and rent charges.

Table 14.4. Fixed cost survey (source: MLC 1980)

	Average fixed costs	
	£ per pig	% of total fixed costs
Labour	4.27	40
Building and rent	3.81	36
Machinery and equipment	0.91	9
Finance charges and insurance	0.13	1
Sundries	1.46	14
Total	10.58	100

Net Margins

The net margin is calculated by subtracting the fixed costs (labour, housing, and depreciation) from the gross margins.

Productive Cycle of the Sow

Part of the productive cycle of the mothering sow is illustrated in Fig. 14.2.

First Pregnancy

Young gilts normally come on heat for the first time at about 6 months of age but are not served until the second or third heat. At the time of service they will therefore be between 7 and 8 months old and should weigh at least 105 kg live-weight. They farrow at between 11 and 12 months of age. During the 16 weeks pregnancy the gilt's live-weight increases by between 40

and 45 kg. Part of this gain is due to the developing litter and individual piglets should weigh at least 1.1 kg at birth. Piglets weighing below 0.68 kg 24 hours after birth seldom make satisfactory progress. The greatest increase in litter weight occurs during the last 8 weeks of pregnancy. The quantities of food fed to the gilt need to be gradually increased in order to supply the nutrients required for this increase in foetal weight. The gilt, however, must be kept lean and fit. The level of feeding during pregnancy can affect birth-weight, size of litter and gilt body-weight. Litter size is only influenced by very low and very high levels of feeding. Birth-weight increases with increased feeding but the cost of improving weights above a level where the piglets are viable is uneconomic. With regard to gilts, and also sows, if allowed to become overfat there can be problems during farrowing followed by a reduced appetite during lactation. If grossly underfed the reproductive performance can be severely depressed.

Suckling Period

The sow suckles her piglets for up to 6 weeks after farrowing. During the first 3 weeks of this period the main source of food available to the growing pigs is the sow's milk. The graph in Fig. 14.3 shows that milk production gradually increases during this period so that around 7 litres per day is produced during the peak period. To encourage milk production the sow must be fed on a ration over and above her maintenance needs. Target weights for the piglets are:

1 week old   –   2.7 kg
2 weeks old   –   4.5 kg
3 weeks old   –   5.9 kg
4 weeks old   –   8.2 kg
5 weeks old   –   11.3 kg
6 weeks old   –   13.0 kg

Weaning can take place as early as three days or as late as eight weeks. In practice the most popular time for weaning is when the pigs are between 3 and 5 weeks old. Available evidence suggests that the number of pigs reared per sow per year falls with increased age at weaning. Weaning at an early age requires high standards of management.

Second Service and Pregnancy

The period from weaning to conception needs to be as short as possible if a high annual number of weaners are produced and this is one of the

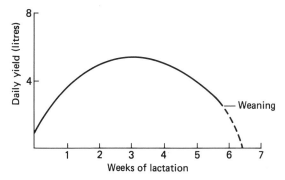

Fig. 14.3 A lactation curve for a sow.

key factors in the profitability of the breeding herd. Some 2–8 days after weaning, the absorption of milk helps to stimulate the onset of a heat period. Another important factor in bringing on heat is the close proximity of an active boar. The ideal situation is nose to nose contact through a gate or pen division. The weaning to heat interval increases as lactation length is reduced below 42 days. The sow is normally served during the first heat after weaning and therefore gets little rest between pregnancies. At weaning the sow tends to be down in condition due to the litter's heavy demand for milk during the suckling period. Since the amount of foetal growth during the early stages of the gestation period is very limited the sow is able to build up

her body reserves provided the level of feeding is adequate. This reserve will be required to meet the heavy demands made on her during the later stages of pregnancy. It is recommended that sows are double served and that each service is supervised. Eighteen to 21 days later the sow should be carefully watched to note any signs of return to service. When sows are safely in-pig they can be moved to the accommodation for dry sows. The 'average number of empty days' for the herd, i.e. the average number of days from weaning to effective service, is an important factor in maintaining a good farrowing index. How to record and then lower empty days is shown in Table 14.5.

Table 14.5. How to record and lower empty days (source: Big Farm Management)

(a) How to record empty days

Sows' No.	Date weaned (or gilts first service)	Date served (or removed from breeding herd)	Boar identity	Empty days
G 132	4/6	4/6	1 and 2	0
84	31/5	5/6	2 and 2	5
35	1/4	6/6	Removed	67
6	31/5	8/6	3 and 4	8
105	31/5	7/6	4 and 3	6
G 98	21/5	12/6	1 and 1	22
18	7/6	12/6	2 and 2	5
65	7/6	13/6	3 and 3	6
8				119

$$\frac{\text{Average no. of}}{\text{empty days}} = \frac{\text{Total no. of empty days}}{\text{Total no. sows served or gilts re-served}} = \frac{119}{7} = 17$$

G = Gilt.
Note how just two service 'failures' (Sow 35 and Gilt 98) raise the empty day average and lower profits.

Do this monthly and transfer to a progress chart with target or action levels.

(With acknowledgement to ADAS.)

(b) Lowering empty days

- Improve on your skills in detecting weaned, non-served sows within a shorter time, say 7–10 days.
- Use a pregnancy detector as routine.
- Clearly mark sows which are served but which are not in-pig.
- Give stockmen time to do the remating job properly.
- Cull boldly and decisively.
- Record properly and use the interference-level monitoring technique with monthly roll-over average graphs to give advance warning of trends.

The farrowing index of the herd is calculated as follows:

$$\frac{365}{\text{Average gestation period} + \text{average suckling period} + \text{average empty days}}$$

and e.g. in a herd weaning at three weeks with an average of 7 empty days the farrowing index is

$$\frac{365}{115 + 21 + 7} = \frac{365}{143} = 2.55$$

Table 14.6 shows the effect of empty days on weaner production per annum.

Table 14.6. The effect of empty days in a herd weaning at 35 days

Number of empty days	Litters per sow per year	Pigs reared per sow, per year at 9.5 pig per litter	Gross margin in a 100 sow herd at £6.50 per weaner (£)
8	2.31	21.95	14 267.50
16	2.20	20.89	13 578.50
24	2.10	19.93	12 954.50

FEEDING (GENERAL CONSIDERATIONS)

Pigs, unlike cattle and sheep, have a simple stomach and are less able to digest fibrous foods. They must therefore be fed on concentrated and highly digestible foods. These foods are expensive and correct feeding practices therefore have a marked effect on the profitability of the enterprise. There is a daily requirement for energy, proteins, minerals and vitamins, and rations need to be formulated on a least-cost basis consistent with the needs of the animal.

Energy-giving foods are the most important part of the ration and the energy value of the ration is stated in terms of digestible energy (DE) which is expressed as megajoules (MJ) per kilogram of feed. The main source of energy in the ration is carbohydrate, derived largely from the inclusion of cereals, chiefly barley. This part of the diet is required for maintenance, and any surplus is converted into fat and stored.

Proteins are needed for maintenance, the production of lean meat, and, in breeding sows, the developing foetuses and milk production. The level of protein in the diet is expressed as the percentage Crude Protein (CP). Proteins are made up of amino acids, and protein quality depends on the amount and availability of the different amino acids present in the rations; two that are particularly important are lysine and methionine.

Additionally, the ration must include minerals and vitamins. The major minerals that normally need to be added to the ration are calcium and sodium, but when the animal protein is replaced by vegetable protein, e.g. extracted soya bean meal, phosphorus is also required. The only trace elements normally required are copper, iron and zinc. When the animal protein level is below 2.5% there may also be a need for iodine and selenium. Most rations need to be supplemented with vitamins A, D and B. Vitamins and trace elements can normally be purchased mixed together in proprietary supplements. Ready mixed rations containing all essential nutrients in the correct balance are available as either meal or nuts. It is also possible to use proprietary concentrates for mixing with home-grown cereals or to home-mix using straights.

It also needs to be recognized that the efficiency of food use is related to other factors such as genetic potential, disease levels and the general environment.

FEEDING AND MANAGEMENT DURING THE PRODUCTIVE CYCLE

First Pregnancy

Gilts for breeding should be selected at approximately 80 kg live-weight and fed at the rate of 2.5 kg per day. With gilts being served during their second or third heat periods, flushing is possible for the last 10 days before service and during this period the feed should be increased to 3.5 kg per day. Flushing for this period of time increases the ovulation rate and this can improve the litter size by one or two piglets. This level of feeding is maintained for 2 days after service to ensure that ovulation is completed. The level of feeding can then be reduced to 1.8 kg per day and continued until the later stages of pregnancy if individually fed. With group feeding an extra 0.5 kg is provided to avoid the underfeeding of timid sows. Since gilts and sows which have had less than four litters are growing animals, their condition should be checked and the ration adjusted where necessary. Table 14.7 provides a guide for feeding during pregnancy. The ration fed should have the following analysis:

Digestible energy (MJ/kg) – 12.50
Crude protein (%)   – 12.90
Lysine (%)   – 0.55

During the last 30 days, when most of the foetal growth occurs, the ration can be increased by 0.4 kg.

It is usual to dose animals with de-worming agents about two weeks prior to farrowing. Where swine erysipelas is a problem, a vaccination programme is necessary and breeding stock are normally vaccinated every 6 months. This is carried out during pregnancy.

Table 14.7. A guide to feeding during pregnancy (source: Ministry of Agriculture, Fisheries and Food)

Weight of animal (kg)	Feed allowance per day (kg)
Up to 140	1.8
180	2.0
230	2.5

Farrowing

It is advisable to move animals to their farrowing quarters some 4 days before they are due to farrow. Before entering the quarters, washing with a suitable parasiticide is advised in order to remove external parasites and their eggs.

The farrowing house should be draught free and the temperature maintained at between 15°C and 18°C, and the creep area for the first week at 29°C. This can then be reduced by 2°C per week until it reaches 20°C, at which level it is maintained. A protected creep area for the piglets is essential to minimize losses.

Suckling Period

The ration is reduced by half on the day before farrowing, the bulk being supplemented by the addition of bran and then gradually increased, according to the appetite, up to the maximum allowance. If constipation is a problem a mash made up of 1.36 kg bran plus 1.36 kg meal is fed to overcome the problem. Within 24 hours of

birth the eight sharp teeth of the piglets are cut to prevent teat damage as this can cause infections and also savaging due to the sow becoming irritable. The sow's milk is deficient in iron and to meet the needs of the piglets a supplement is required to prevent anaemia. This can be administered at 3 days of age as either an intra-muscular injection or fed orally as a paste.

Within seven days of farrowing the sow should be on full ration and this is related to her general condition and the number of pigs in the litter.

The recommended rates of feeding per day are:

For light sows (below 135 kg live-weight) – 1.5 kg plus 0.5 kg per piglet
For heavier sows (above 135 kg live-weight) – 2 kg plus 0.5 kg per piglet

Examples
1. A sow weighing 130 kg LW with a litter of 9 pigs:

Daily ration = 1.5 + (0.5 × 9)
= 1.5 + 4.5 = 6 kg

2. A sow weighing 180 kg LW with a litter of 11 pigs:

Daily ration = 2.0 + (0.5 × 11)
= 2.0 + 5.5 = 7.5 kg

The ration fed should have the following analysis:

Digestible energy (MJ/kg) – 12.50
Crude protein (%)   – 15.00
Lysine (%)   – 0.68.

Table 14.8 gives an example of a mixture that would meet this requirement.

From one week onwards all piglets need to be earmarked with a number which is entered on the litter-recording charts. Male pigs, not designated for breeding, are castrated as the presence of the testes renders the carcass unacceptable to some meat traders.

Creep feeding is introduced to the piglets at 5 days of age to supplement the milk supply. The creep feed needs to be palatable, easily digestible and in pellet form. At the start only small quantities need be offered and any not eaten removed after 24 hours and replaced by a fresh supply. As feed intake increases so does the quantity until *ad lib.* feeding is practised.

The creep ration should have the following analysis:

Digestible energy (MJ/kg) – 13.70
Crude protein (%)   – 19.00
Lysine (%)   – 1.04

Table 14.8 gives an example of a mixture that can meet these requirements.

Table 14.8. Example diets (source: Ministry of Agriculture, Fisheries and Food)

Ingredients	PIGLETS Creep (5 week weaning) (kg*)	GROWERS Weaning to 50–65 kg. Porkers to slaughter (kg)	GROWERS (kg*)	FINISHERS Baconers 50 kg to slaughter (kg)	FINISHERS Baconers (kg*)	FINISHERS Heavy hog 65 kg to slaughter (kg)	FINISHERS Heavy hog (kg*)	SOWS Pregnancy (kg)	SOWS Lactating (5 week weaning) (kg)
Barley	250	660	310	670	340	900	395	755	705
Wheat	200		500		495		500		
Wheat middlings	75	183		200				200	200
Flaked	250								
Fish meal	85	50	60					15	15
Soya bean meal	90	95	130	110	165	82	105	30	80
Dried skim milk	50								
Dicalcium phosphate					4	4	5		
Limestone				4	3	2	2	6	6
Mineral/vitamin supplement†	12	12.5	12.5	12.5	12.5	12.5	12.5	12.5	12.5
Calculated analysis:									
Digestible energy (MJ/kg)	13.7	12.5	13.6	12.3	13.5	12.8	13.6	12.5	12.6
Crude protein (%)	19	16.9	18.4	14.7	16.3	12.5	14.3	12.9	15
Lysine (%)	1.04	0.85	0.91	0.69	0.76	0.56	0.6	0.55	0.68
Calcium (%)	1	0.8	0.8	0.57	0.61	0.56	0.59	0.74	0.75
Phosphorus (%)	0.7	0.7	0.6	0.5	0.5	0.45	0.49	0.51	0.55

* High energy diets, 9 kg equivalent to 10 kg barley based diet.

† The mineral/vitamin supplement is assumed to contain 28% calcium. 12.5 kg should supply at least six million IU vitamin A, 1.5 million IU vitamin D_3 and 10 g vitamin E. It should also contain an adequate level of the B group vitamins.

Weaning takes place by removing the sow; she should be individually housed if single suckling has been in operation or remain in her familiar group if multi-suckling has been practised. This will minimize stress at this particular time. Food is reduced on the day of weaning to 1.8–2.0 kg, increasing to approximately 4 kg the following day, and remaining at this level for up to two days after service.

Second and Subsequent Pregnancies

The pregnant sow is fed on the same basis as the pregnant gilt (Table 14.7). However, adjustments may be necessary depending on the condition of the sow. The average net gain per cycle should be about 14 kg. This would mean that on a five-week weaning system the liveweight gain during pregnancy would be approximately 45 kg; 22 kg of this will be lost during farrowing and an additional 9 kg during the lactation period.

Table 14.9 shows the recommended adjustments to the normal daily allowance.

Table 14.9. Recommended adjustments to the normal daily allowance of the pregnant sow (source: Ministry of Agriculture, Fisheries and Food)

Sow weight change during cycles 1–4	Feed adjustment for the next pregnancy	Sow weight change during cycle 5 and after
Up to 8 kg gain	+ 0.5 kg per day	More than 5 kg loss
Up to 20 kg gain	0	5 kg loss to 5 kg gain
Over 20 kg gain	− 0.5 kg per day	Over 5 kg gain

MANAGEMENT SYSTEMS FOR THE BREEDING HERD

A wide range of management, housing and feeding systems are used for the breeding herd. Table 14.10 gives an indication of this range and the relative popularity of each system.

Condition Scoring of Sows

The regular weighing of sows is not widely practised by commercial farmers and for such figures to be meaningful weighing should take place at the same time in each cycle. Condition scoring provides an easier and quicker way of assessing the sow's condition.

The system employs six categories (0 to 5) and the most important body sites for assessing condition are the edges of the transverse processes in the loin regions and the protrusions on either side of the vulva (Fig. 14.4). The range of

Table 14.10. Percentage of recorded breeding herds using various management, housing and feeding systems (source: MLC)

HOUSING

Dry sow accommodation				Farrowing accommodation				Weaner accommodation			
Tethered	30	Paddocks	3	Fully enclosed, purpose-built, fan-ventilated	42	One stage	42	Verandah type	23	Solid floors	44
Untethered	65	Solid floor stalls	23			Two or more stages	49	Tiered cages	7	Partially slatted or perforated floors	30
Combination	5	Slatted or perforated floor stalls	20	Individual, purpose-built	5	Weaners not kept in breeding herd	39	Flat decks	21		
	100	Cubicles and other individual housing	9	Other purpose-built	13		100	Weaner pools	41	Fully slatted or perforated floors	25
		Yarded, not individually housed	29	Converted accommodation	33			Others and combinations	8	Others and combinations	1
		Others and combinations	16	Others and combinations	7				100		100
			100		100						

FEEDING

Dry sow feeding				Lactating sow feeding		Weaner feeding			
Individually fed	83	Wet meal	9	Restricted	72	Ad lib.	55	Dry pellets	77
Group fed	17	Dry meal	30	To appetite	22	To appetite	15	Dry meal	18
	100	Wet pellets	3 } 84	Others and combinations	6	Restricted	11	Others	5
		Dry pellets	54		100	Others and combinations	22		100
		Others	4				100		
			100						

MANAGEMENT

Sow service management		Weaner management			
Served once only	2	Grouped by sex	93	Weaners per pen:	
Served twice and supervised	66	Not grouped by sex	7	Under 11	15
Served twice, not supervised	3		100	11–20	26
Served more than twice	21			21–30	30
Others and combinations	8			31–50	21
	100			Over 50	3
				Variable	5
					100

condition scores are shown in 14.5; Table 14.11 gives details of condition scoring. It is generally considered that at weaning the score condition should not be less than 2.5, and not more than 3.5 at farrowing.

Feeding of Fattening Stock

After weaning, the pigs are normally vaccinated against swine erysipelas and swine fever, and also treated against parasitic worms.

There are four possible end-products of the fattening process – porkers, cutters, baconers and heavy hogs.

Economic levels of feeding are a compromise between maximum liveweight gain, efficient food conversion and acceptable carcass quality.

Target feed efficiencies are shown in Table 14.12.

Food is required by the growing pig to provide for maintenance in the first instance and any surplus is used for the growth of bone, lean meat and fat tissues. Lean meat contains around 22% protein and 78% water, and body fat 90% fat and 10% water. The production of lean meat therefore requires less food input than fat production; roughly 1.2 kg of feed to produce 1 kg lean, and 4 kg feed for 1 kg of fat. In order to prevent pigs from becoming overfat, food is rationed in order to restrict energy intake. Although this produces a leaner carcass the food needed for maintenance is increased because of a longer finishing period and the food conversion efficiency adversely affected. The feed conversion deteriorates from

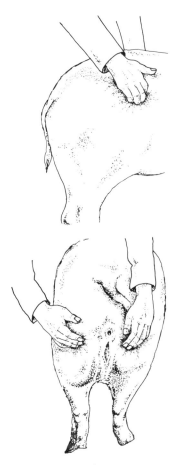

1. THIN:
    Hollow tailhead,
    prominent pinbones,
    ribs and backbone.

2. MODERATE:
    Backbone still
    visible and ribs
    covered but easily
    felt

3. GOOD:
    Satisfactory cover
    over pinbones,
    backbone and ribs.

Fig. 14.4 Body sites for assessing condition (source: Ministry of Agriculture).

2:1 or better at about 20 kg live-weight to 4:1 or worse at a live-weight of 90 kg. The feeding must therefore be generous for the young pigs, to encourage fast growth and to maximize lean tissue production, and to ration the later stage in order to restrict the fat tissues and to produce a carcass of acceptable quality at minimum cost.

Feeding Systems

In practice three types of feeding systems are used for growing pigs.

1. *Ad lib. feeding*
This method can be used when carcass quality is not of prime importance. *Ad lib.* feeding will generally cause a deterioration of some 5% in feed conversion efficiency, increase feed intake by 17% and lead to a 10 to 12% faster rate of liveweight gain.

4. OVERFIT:
    Pinbones, backbone
    and ribs cannot be
    felt.

5. FAT:
    Heavy deposits of
    fat on tailhead,
    back and over ribs.

Fig. 14.5 Sow condition score (source: BOCM Silcock).

2. *Restricted feeding*
With this system, feed allowances are linked to either the liveweight or the age of the animals. Table 14.13 gives the daily feed allowances based on various weights and ages.

Table 14.11. Condition Scoring for sows (scheme devised by J. Deering, ADAS, Reading)

Score	Condition	Pin bones and tail setting	Loin	Backbone	Ribs
0	Emaciated about to die	Pin bones very prominent. Deep cavity around tail setting.	Loin very narrow Sharp edge on transverse spinal processes. Flank very hollow.	Vertebrae prominent and sharp throughout length of backbone.	Individual ribs very apparent
1	Poor	Pin bones obvious, but some slight cover. Cavity around tail setting.	Loin narrow. Only very slight cover to edge of transverse spinal processes. Flank rather hollow.	Vertebrae prominent.	Rib cage less apparent. Difficulty in seeing individual ribs.
2	Moderate	Pin bones covered.	Edge of transverse spinal processes covered and rounded.	Vertebrae visible over shoulder. Some cover further back.	Ribs covered but can be felt.
3	Good	Pin bones only felt with firm pressure. No cavity around tail.	Edge of transverse spinal processes only felt with firm pressure. Flank full.	Vertebrae only felt with firm pressure.	Rib cage not visible. Very difficult to feel any ribs.
4	Fat	Pin bones impossible to feel. Root of tail set deep in surrounding fat.	Impossible to feel bones. Flank full and rounded.	Impossible to feel vertebrae.	Ribs impossible to feel.
5	Grossly fat	Further deposition of fat impossible.	Further deposition of fat impossible.	Mid line appears as slight hollow between rolls of fat.	Thick fat cover.

Table 14.12. Production systems and target feed efficiencies (source: Ministry of Agriculture, Fisheries and Food)

	Liveweight range (kg)	Food conversion efficiency
Weaner production (weaned at 3 weeks)	6–20	1.5
Porker production	20–63	2.8
Bacon production	20–90	3.1
Heavy hog production	20–118	3.6

Restricted feeding is best suited to methods of production where payment is made according to carcass quality, e.g. bacon production.

In the larger pig units the gilts and castrates should be separated at 20–25 kg live-weight as gilts at similar feed intakes will grow faster, convert food more efficiently and produce leaner carcasses. If the pigs are then separated Table 14.13 shows the modified feed allowances for each type.

3. Ad lib. and restricted feeding
This system is in common use for both bacon and pork production. The pigs are fed *ad lib.* at an early age but when feed intake has reached a certain level, restricted feeding is then introduced. This system increases growth rate in the

Table 14.13. Daily feed requirements for growing pigs (medium energy diet) (source: Ministry of Agriculture, Fisheries and Food)

(a) Liveweight (kg)	Approx. daily gain	
	0.6 kg Ration in kg	0.7 kg Ration in kg
20	1.00	1.00
30	1.50	1.50
40	1.75	1.95
50	1.95	2.15
60	2.05	2.25
70	2.15	2.40
80	2.30	2.50
90	2.40	2.60

(b) Age (weeks)	Improved strains and gilts (kg)	Gilts/ castrates (kg)	Castrates (kg)
9	1.00	1.00	1.00
11	1.35	1.35	1.35
13	1.75	1.60	1.50
15	2.05	1.80	1.62
17	2.20	1.95	1.74
19	2.35	2.05	1.85
21	2.45	2.15	1.94
23	2.55	2.25	2.02
25	2.65	2.35	2.11
27	—	2.45	2.20
29	—	—	2.30

early stages without seriously affecting food conversion efficiency or carcass quality.

Pork production – slaughtered at 35–63 kg live weight at between 14 and 20 weeks

There are strains of pigs which are capable of growing rapidly from weaning to slaughter weights and whose carcasses possess a maximum of lean meat. This growth is stimulated by *ad lib.* feeding and this can be carried out until slaughter at the lighter weights. If the animals are carried beyond 35–40 kg live weight then most pigs need to be fed on a restricted diet.

The ration should have the following analysis:

	Medium energy diet	High energy diet
Digestible energy (MJ/kg)	12.50	13.60
Crude protein (%)	16.90	18.40
Lysine (%)	0.85	0.91

Table 14.8 gives examples of mixtures that can meet these requirements and Table 14.13 provides details of daily feed requirements.

Cutter production – slaughtered at 64–81 kg live weight at between 20 and 24 weeks

Cutters are fed in a similar way to the heavier pork pigs. The quality of the ration again is the same as for pork production. Table 14.13 provides details of daily feed requirements.

Bacon production – slaughtered at 82 to 90 kg live weight at between 24 and 26 weeks

The system of feeding is again the same as for the heavier porkers but from 50 kg live weight to slaughter the ration is changed to one with the following analysis:

	Medium energy diet	High energy diet
Digestible energy (MJ/kg)	12.30	13.50
Crude protein (%)	14.70	16.30
Lysine (%)	0.69	0.76

Table 14.8 gives examples of mixtures that can meet these requirements and Table 14.13 provides details of daily feed requirements.

Heavy hog production – slaughtered at over 90 kg live weight

These are strains of pigs which are usually fed *ad lib.* until slaughter. They are fed on rations of the same quality as for porkers until 65 kg live

weight and then the ration is changed to one with the following analysis:

	Medium energy diet	High energy diet
Digestible energy (MJ/kg)	12.80	13.60
Crude protein (%)	12.50	14.30
Lysine (%)	0.56	0.60

Table 14.8 gives examples of mixtures that can meet these requirements.

Feeding Methods

Once-daily feeding of pigs on restricted systems is as effective as feeding twice daily, and wet feeding generally gives better results than dry feeding. If the floor system of feeding is adopted then cubes are more effective than meal.

Water Requirements

It has been estimated that the daily water requirements for breeding stock are as follows:

Non-pregnant sows – 5 litres
Pregnant sows – 5–8 litres
Lactating sows – 15–30 litres
(Agricultural Research Council)

It is advisable to provide free access to water for animals in the breeding herd. For growing pigs it is estimated that at 20 kg live weight the water requirement is 2 kg and that at 90 kg live weight the need is 6 kg. With wet and pipe-line feeding the mixture is made up of about 2.5–3.5 kg water and 1 kg meal and this is considered to be adequate for normal water requirements. Where pigs are 'wet fed' once a day it is advisable to offer additional water to that supplied in the feed.

Management Systems for the Feeding Herd

A wide combination of management, housing and feeding systems are used by pig farmers. Table 14.10 indicates the variety of systems used and their level of adoption.

Feeding and Management of Boars

Young boars are normally ready for service at around 7 months of age and to start with they should be used for a single service once or twice a week. For mature boars four or five services evenly spread per week is probably the ideal number. When farrowings are evenly spread over the year a suitable sow to boar ratio is 20:1

for a three to four week weaning system, and 25:1 when weaning is at four to five weeks. For the average sized boar the daily feed requirement is between 2.4 to 3.0 kg of the meal used for lactating sows. Under-feeding can reduce the boar's fertility and over-feeding will increase live weight and reduce its libido. Lameness is a major cause of culling and thus regular foot treatment can reduce this problem. Boars should be included in any form of routine treatment designed to reduce disease, e.g. worming, external parasites.

ANALYSIS OF PERFORMANCE

The average gross margin per head is a reflection of the annual performance and can be used to analyse possible weaknesses in the enterprise. Figs. 14.6 and 14.7 show diagnostic flow charts for the breeding and feeding herds and relate factors responsible for the gross margin per head achieved. Analysis involves comparing the figures for the farm with standard or target figures and each figure which is unsatisfactory when compared with the standard or target pinpoints a cause which adversely affects the gross margin figure.

Food Costs per £100 Enterprise Output

This provides a quick check on the performance of the enterprise. It is an efficiency measure incorporating the enterprise output on the one hand and the largest single item of variable costs on the other. In general the lower the figure the greater the eventual gross margin. If this figure is unsatisfactory when compared with standards, further investigations should proceed in the same way as for the gross margin system of analysis.

Controlling Performance

Analysis of the enterprise performance indicates weaknesses which have occurred during the previous year. These faults need to be corrected but once corrected the enterprise's performance

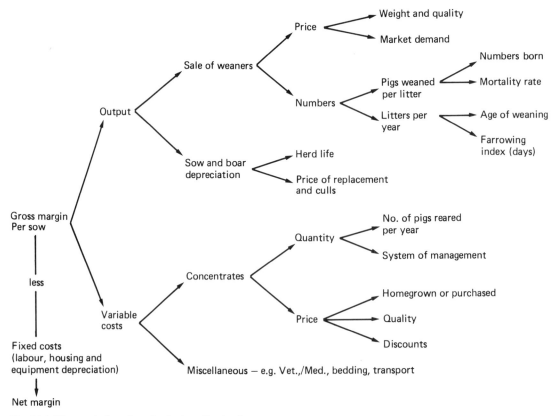

Fig. 14.6 Diagnostic flow chart for the breeding herd.

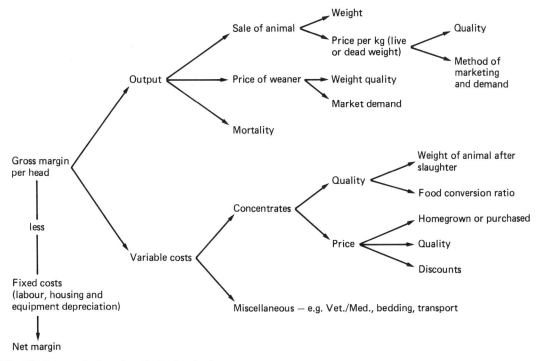

Fig. 14.7 Diagnostic flow chart for feeding herd.

needs to be controlled so that the overall situation at the end of the year can be forecasted with some degree of accuracy. This managerial control of events is part of a continuous process and is described on p. 131.

Recording

In order to obtain satisfactory results for the enterprise a system of efficient recording is essential. Many agencies provide recording and consultancy services, e.g. Ministry of Agriculture (A.D.A.S.), Meat and Livestock Commission and certain commercial firms. The recording system outlined is that of the Meat and Livestock Commission's Pigplan. This covers both the breeding and the feeding herds and can also be extended to cover the Rearing herd, i.e. from weaning to sale or transfer out of weaners. 'Pigplan' is available to all pig producers irrespective of the size of the enterprise. The scheme can be extended to provide information on specific areas of management such as cash flows and production forecasts.

Breeding Herd Recording

The essential breeding herd records can be subdivided into three main sections.

1. *Individual performance records*
These are a service register, litter record cards and sow and boar performance records. In order to make efficient recording possible both sow and piglets must be easily identified. Tattooing is the most common method used but the ear-tagging of sows is recommended as an additional measure.

2. *Management records*
These show when sows have been served, the possible return dates, expected farrowing and weaning dates.

3. *Feed and costing records*
Such records are needed to monitor the financial position of the unit. Fig. 14.8 shows the stock details and Fig. 14.9 the feed details the farmer needs to complete. The information is processed by computer and the results giving efficiency measures together with comparative figures are returned to the farmer. The results are divided into four sections – herd structures, sow performance factors, litter performance .factors and pig performance factors. Table 14.14 gives the format of the Breeding Herd Report.

PIGPLAN

Recording and Costing

STOCK DETAILS

PP2

THIS IS A COMPUTER DOCUMENT
PLEASE WRITE CLEARLY TO AVOID ERRORS

Name ....

Start date of period / /

STOCK DETAILS	BREEDING HERD							REARING HERD			FEEDING HERD		
	Sows, Gilts		Boars		Piglets								
	1 Number	2 Value (£)	3 Number	4 Value (£)	5 Number	6 Weight (Kg)	7 Value (£)	8 Number	9 Weight (Kg)	10 Value (£)	11 Number	12 Weight (Kg)	13 Value (£)
NUMBER AT BEGINNING OF PERIOD A													
BOUGHT B													
TRANSFERS IN C					Born alive								
TOTAL (A+B+C) D													
SALES E													
TRANSFERS OUT F													
DEATHS G													
TOTAL (E+F+G) H													
END OF PERIOD TOTAL (D–H) I													

OTHER STOCK DETAILS J	Number of unserved gilts	Start of period	End of period	Total number of sows and gilts served		Total number of litters born		Total piglets born dead		Average weaning age (days)	
		1	2		3		4		5		6

DEADWEIGHT SALES: FEEDING HERD

SALES OUTLETS		Outlet code	GRADING number First	Second	Third	Other	Total number Sold	Total Carcase Weight (Kg)	Total Net Value (£)	Probe method 1.2.2.A.	Average probe (mm)	Killing out %
			1	2	3	4	5	6	7	8	9	10
I	K											
II	L											
III	M											
IV	N											
V	P											

LIVEWEIGHT SALES – FEEDING HERD

Liveweight Type	Number Sold	Total Liveweight (Kg)	Total Net Value (£)
11	12	13	14
Boars & Gilts Q			
Outlet 1 R			
Outlet 2 S			

OFFICE USE ONLY

	Member No.	day	month	year	DNA
PP2					

Fig. 14.8 Pigplan – stock details (source: Meat & Livestock Commission).

PP3

PIGPLAN

FEED DETAILS

Recording and Costing

Name ....

Start date of period ...... / ...... / ......

THIS IS A COMPUTER DOCUMENT
PLEASE WRITE CLEARLY TO AVOID ERRORS

FEED DETAILS	Delete as applicable		Unit e.g. tonne, kg, litres	Unit price (£)	Total quantity	Total Cost (£)
SOWS – GILTS – BOARS			BREEDING HERD			
	HOME MIX	PURCHASED COMPOUND				
	HOME MIX	PURCHASED COMPOUND				
	HOME MIX	PURCHASED COMPOUND				
	HOME MIX	PURCHASED COMPOUND				
	HOME MIX	PURCHASED COMPOUND				
PIGLETS	HOME MIX	PURCHASED COMPOUND				
	HOME MIX	PURCHASED COMPOUND				
	HOME MIX	PURCHASED COMPOUND				
WEANERS			REARING HERD			
	HOME MIX	PURCHASED COMPOUND				
	HOME MIX	PURCHASED COMPOUND				
	HOME MIX	PURCHASED COMPOUND				
	HOME MIX	PURCHASED COMPOUND				
	HOME MIX	PURCHASED COMPOUND				
	HOME MIX	PURCHASED COMPOUND				
GROWERS/FINISHERS			FEEDING HERD			
	HOME MIX	PURCHASED COMPOUND				
	HOME MIX	PURCHASED COMPOUND				
	HOME MIX	PURCHASED COMPOUND				
	HOME MIX	PURCHASED COMPOUND				
	HOME MIX	PURCHASED COMPOUND				
	HOME MIX	PURCHASED COMPOUND				
	HOME MIX	PURCHASED COMPOUND				

VARIABLE COSTS (£)

Veterinary	
Medicine	
Transport	
Electricity and gas	
Water	
Straw & Bedding	
Miscellaneous	

FIXED COSTS (£)

Labour	
Buildings & Rent	
Machinery & Equip	
Finance charges	
Insurance	
Sundries	

CREDITS (£)

Other credits	

FOR OFFICE USE ONLY

	Weight	Cost £
11		
12		
13		
21		
22		
31		
32		
33		
41		
42		
43		

OFFICE USE ONLY

Member No	day	month	year	DNA
PP3				

Fig. 14.9 Pigplan – feed details (source: Meat & Livestock Commission).

Table 14.14. Breeding Herd Report (source: MLC)

	CURRENT YEAR			PREVIOUS YEAR			MLC
	Period ended Sep. 80	Period ended Mar. 81	Year ended Mar. 81	Period ended Sep. 79	Period ended Mar. 80	Year ended Mar. 80	Top third
HERD STRUCTURE							
1. Ave. No of sows and gilts in the herd	265	274	270	277	281	279	170
2. Ave. No. of unserved gilts	16						9
3. Ave. No. of productive sows	249						161
4. Ave. No. of sows and gilts per boar	22						22
SOW PERFORMANCE FACTORS							
5. Percentage breeding sow replacements	42			RELEVANT DATA IN THESE			37
6. Percentage breeding sow sales and deaths	37			COLUMNS			36
7. Percentage breeding sow deaths	3						2
8. Percentage successful services	92						96
9. Ave. No. of litters per sow and gilt per year	2.39						2.37
10. Ave. No. of pigs weaned per sow and gilt per year	21.88						22.63
11. Qty of sow and boar feed per sow and gilt per year (kg)	1.095						1.090
12. Cost of sow and boar feed per sow and gilt per year (£)	148						129
13. Cost per tonne of sow and boar feed (£)	135						118
LITTER PERFORMANCE FACTORS							
14. Ave. No. of pigs born per litter ALIVE	10.26						10.70
15. DEAD	0.63						0.78
16. TOTAL	10.89						11.48
17. Ave. No. of pigs reared per litter	9.14						9.56
PIG PERFORMANCE FACTORS							
18. Percentage mortality of pigs born alive	10.9						10.6
19. Total qty of feed per pig reared (kg)	55						52
20. Total feed cost per pig reared (£)	7.54						6.32
21. Qty of piglet feed per pig reared (kg)	1						1
22. Cost of piglet feed per pig reared (£)	0.25						0.29
23. Cost per tonne of piglet feed (£)	250						290
24. Ave. weight of pigs weaned (kg)	5.6						5.6
25. Total feed consumption per kg pig weaned (kg)	9.86						9.50
26. Total feed cost per kg pig weaned (p)	138						114
27. Overall cost per tonne of feed (£)	137.3						122.8
28. Ave. weaning age (days)	23						22

Rearing and Feeding Herd Recording

The stock and feed details shown in Figs. 14.8 and 14.9 have to be completed by the farmer. The results monitoring the most important economic factors – total liveweight gain, feed conversion efficiency and feed costs per kg liveweight gain – are included in the reports. Tables 14.15 and 14.16 give the format of Rearing and Feeding Herd Reports.

Table 14.15. Rearing Herd Report (source: MLC)

	CURRENT YEAR			PREVIOUS YEAR			MLC
	Period ended Sep. 80	Period ended Mar. 81	Year ended Mar. 81	Period ended Sep. 79	Period ended Mar. 80	Year ended Mar. 80	Top third
1. Ave. No. of pigs in herd	535	380	397	400	330	365	250
2. No. of pigs sold/transferred	1872						875
3. Ave. weight of pigs entering herd (kg)	5.6						5.6
4. Ave. weight of pigs leaving herd (kg)	16.5						18.3
5. Total weight gain (kg)	20 405		RELEVANT DATA IN THESE				—
6. Ave. weight gain per pig (kg)	10.9		COLUMNS				12.7
7. Ave. daily live weight gain (g)	290						325
8. Ave. feed fed per pig per day (kg)	0.44						0.50
9. Ave. feed conversion ratio (kg feed per kg LWG)	1.50						1.54
10. Feed cost per kg LWG (p)	45.45						42.16
11. Feed cost per pig produced (£)	4.95						5.35
12. Cost per tonne of meal (£)	303						274
13. Overall cost per tonne of feed (£)	303						274
14. Percentage mortality	1.6						2.0

Table 14.16. Feeding Herd Report (source: MLC)

	CURRENT YEAR			PREVIOUS YEAR			MLC
	Period ended Sep. 80	Period ended Mar. 81	Year ended Mar. 81	Period ended Sep. 79	Period ended Mar. 80	Year ended Mar. 80	Top third
1. Ave. No. of pigs in herd	1635	1670	1652	1493	1560	1542	928
2. Ave. No. of pigs sold	3270						1765
3. Ave. weight of pigs entering herd (kg)	16.5						17.6
4. Ave. weight of pigs leaving herd (kg)	81.7						85.3
5. Total weight gain (kg)	106 602		RELEVANT DATA IN THESE				—
6. Ave. weight gain per pig (kg)	65.2		COLUMNS				67.7
7. Ave. daily live weight gain (g)	540						550
8. Ave. feed per pig per day (kg)	1.49						1.81
9. Feed conversion ratio (kg feed per kg LWG)	2.75						3.17
10. Feed cost per kg LWG (p)	35.75						40.58
11. Feed cost per pig produced (£)	23.31						27.47
12. Cost per tonne of meal (£)	130						128
13. Overall cost per tonne of feed (£)	130						128
14. Percentage mortality	3.7						3.3
15. Ave. carcass weight (kg)	60.5						64.0
16. Ave. sale value (£)	53.24						55.68
17. Ave. price per kg dead weight (p)	88						87
18. Ave. price per kg live weight (p)	—						64

SECTION C

Health and Disease in Farm Livestock

15

Principles Governing Health and Disease

How does one tell or diagnose whether an animal is healthy or unhealthy? Health is commonly defined as being 'free from disease'. If there are no signs or symptoms of ill health, then one can assume that the animal is healthy. There are a number of clues or symptoms to be looked for by the stockman in assessing the health of his animals.

1. *Food*
This is the main product taken in by the animal. If it refuses food, is unable to swallow or salivates abnormally when eating then the animal is unwell.

2. *Faeces*
The appearance of the faeces is an indication of what is happening in the true stomach and intestines of the animal. Food is digested and soluble foodstuffs and water are absorbed into the blood in these organs. If the absorption of water is interfered with, then the animal will scour and the faeces will be loose and watery. As a result of continued scouring, the food does not remain in the stomach and intestines long enough to be properly digested and loss of weight may result.

On the other hand, the animal may be constipated and the faeces become hard and dry. This indicates that undigested food has been in the intestine too long and as a result too much water has been absorbed into the blood.

3. *Urine*
Normal urine is pale and straw-coloured and has a distinct smell. Abnormal urines include those that are:

(a) cloudy and smoky: turpentine poisoning causing serious damage to the kidneys;

(b) brown: bleeding in bladder and kidneys due to bracken poisoning;
(c) very yellow: jaundice caused by ragwort poisoning or inflammation of the liver;
(d) red or port-wine colour with no sediment: red water fever;
(e) red or blue sediments on standing: inflammation of the kidneys;
(f) sweet smelling: may indicate acetonaemia.

4. *Milk*
One of the very first signs of disease in mothering animals is a drop in milk yield. This is one very important reason why milking cows in particular should be milk recorded. Pain in the udder, clots in 'the milk or thinner milk in one or more quarters indicate mastitis.

5. *Body temperature, pulse rate and respiratory rate*
A rise or fall in body temperature sometimes means that the animal is heading for or already has a disease. Any excitement, especially in hot weather, can raise the body temperature; it should return to normal rapidly in a healthy animal.

Examples of abnormal temperatures in cattle are as follows:

40–40.5°C Fever, e.g., acute mastitis, pneumonia
   41.6°C Could be magnesium deficiency
   42.0°C Sunstroke; it implies damage to the heat regulatory centre in the brain
Below This subnormal temperature indi-
  37.6°C cates falling resistance to disease.

6. *Posture and movement*
When an animal is incapable of walking, lying down and getting up properly, then something is obviously wrong. An animal may be lame for

many reasons – its hoof may be overgrown, a joint or a muscle may have been strained; examine the foot for nails and stones before sending for the veterinary surgeon. Sometimes an animal may walk with an unsteady gait; this may be due to the nearness of calving or may be a symptom of some disease; arched backs or inability to get up are all indications that something is amiss.

7. *Carriage and appearance*

An animal carrying its head high, with a clear eye and a moist nose, shows every indication of well-being. Running noses and eyes, dull and dejected appearance are indications that all is not well within the animal. To examine the eye, press the top eyelid on to the eyeball; this everts the lower eyelid and allows you to see the colour of the conjunctiva.

Swelling between the jaws may be a sign of wooden tongue, when it is accompanied by abnormal salivation. A soft, fluctuating swelling (bottle jaw) may be due to starvation, liver fluke, Johne's disease or heart disorder.

8. *Coat*

A dry, clean coat with a sheen is again an indication of health. If an animal is running a temperature it may sweat profusely. Lice and mites may be the cause of baldness on part of the animal's coat. A staring, scurfy coat may indicate that the animal is not being fed properly and may be particularly short of vitamins and minerals. Any circular scabs or ringworm should be noted.

9. *Coughing*

This is the animal's way of trying to remove an irritation from its lungs or bronchial tubes. Continuous or intermittent coughing clearly shows that something is causing such irritation, e.g. huskworm.

10. *Pain*

Groans, grunts, grinding of teeth, arching of back, show that the animal is suffering some kind of pain. It could indicate the presence of a foreign body in the reticulum. By placing the hand on the left flank, about three contractions per minute will be felt; when the rumen contracts alone there will be an audible belch; when the rumen and reticulum contract together there is no belching; if there is a foreign body in the stomach, a grunt will be heard at the time of this contraction.

11. *Reproduction*

When an animal is fertile and gives birth to healthy offspring with no calving difficulties, then the animal's reproductive system is functioning normally.

PREVENTING DISEASE

A thriving animal has a higher resistance to disease than an unhealthy animal. Part of the stockman's task is to keep his animals healthy and to prevent the occurrence of disease by maintaining certain essential rules of stock management. Attention to the following factors will go a long way towards the maintenance of health in farm animals.

Feeding

When an animal receives a varied diet of green food, roughages and concentrates most of the foodstuffs required by the animal are supplied to it. Table 8.1 shows the foodstuffs contained in most farm crops. Obedience to the rules of feeding described in previous chapters will ensure a balance between energy-giving foods and proteins and also enable the stockman to alter feeding according to the particular requirements during the animal's productive cycle.

Adequate vitamin supplement should be given to young growing animals. Too much cod-liver oil destroys vitamin E and leads to muscular dystrophy in young calves. It is better to inject vitamins because some lose potency when added to foods. Too much vitamin D can cause loss of calcium from the long bones and its deposition in the skull resulting in calves with short legs and huge heads.

It is important to emphasize once more that ruminant animals must have a minimum quantity of roughage if the rumen is to function properly.

One of the most common causes of digestive upsets, particularly in young stocks, is the use of dirty feeding utensils. Stale food may accumulate in the corners and crevices of food troughs, buckets, etc. These deposits of stale food make ideal breeding-grounds for bacteria, which cause so many diseases. Therefore feeding utensils should always be kept scrupulously clean.

Fresh Air

When animals are kept indoors it is important that they receive an adequate and steady supply of fresh air. When ventilation is poor, carbon dioxide and water vapour accumulate in the air and prevent the animals breathing properly. Dampness also encourages the growth of bacteria and moulds. Good ventilation, but without draughts, will ensure the healthy breathing and metabolism of the animal. Since hot air is lighter than cold air, convection currents of warm air move upwards from the floor to roof level. To facilitate this movement of air and to introduce continuous fresh air, hopper windows are normally installed above floor level. The escape of warm moist air from the roofs of the building is usually achieved by a controlled chimney or ridge vent. Buildings such as piggeries which are kept at high temperatures are occasionally supplied with extractor fans to remove the hot stale air. It has been estimated that each pig being fattened for bacon requires 5.66–11.33 cubic metres of fresh air per hour.

Use of dusty hay and straw should be avoided since it can cause abortion as well as pneumonia.

Adequate Temperature

The buildings in which most mature farm animals are housed are heated by the heat given off from the animals themselves. This means that part of the animals' food is being used to heat the building. Although it is important to keep most mature animals hardy, buildings which are not too cold will improve their production of meat or milk.

The question of warmth is particularly important with young or rapidly growing animals. Piglets, and sometimes young calves, are kept warm by infra-red lamps, and clean litter; rapid-growing animals such as fattening pigs require a room temperature of at least 15.5°C to improve their food conversion ratio. Pigs lodged in cold draughty piggeries have low conversion ratios since they are using a large proportion of their food to keep themselves warm.

In all farm buildings, the main method of maintaining room temperature is by insulating floors, walls and roofs of buildings. Since air is a poor conductor of heat the materials usually used for insulation are porous so as to trap large quantities of air. Straw bales, hollow blocks, pipes and hardcore are some of the materials used.

To prevent dampness rising from the ground through the floor and walls into the building, a damp-proof course, normally consisting of felting or strip metal, is constructed above soil level. Buildings which are damp are invariably cold.

Regular Exercise and Welfare Codes

With the exception of rapidly fattening animals such as pigs, regular daily exercise is important for stock. It keeps their feet in trim, prevents joints and muscles from stiffening and stimulates the activities of internal organs, particularly the heart, lungs and digestive organs. The farmer should consult Welfare Codes for Animals; they are the official recommendations regarding the welfare of farm animals, particularly in the field of intensive production.

Disposal of Urine and Dung

Decomposing urine and dung are breeding grounds for bacteria and other disease-causing organisms. Ammonia and other gases are formed also which give rise to bronchitis and pneumonia. When animals are kept in deep-litter systems, abundant straw is provided to absorb urine and introduce air into the heap. Drainage must also be adequate so that liquids can drain away from the heap. Under these dry, aerated conditions dung breaks down into harmless, useful humus and there is little or no danger of disease.

Where drainage is inadequate and too little straw laid down, pathogenic (disease-causing) bacteria thrive in such heaps of dung and urine and are a source of contamination to animals and milk. They are also excellent breeding-grounds for flies and parasites.

When animals are kept in buildings, dung must be cleaned out regularly and efficient drainage systems provided to allow stagnant water and urine to flow away.

Rotation of Land Usage

Where stock graze on the same field year after year, disease organisms, particularly worms and parasites, multiply. Ploughing followed by re-seeding prevents the build-up of disease organisms. Crop rotations reduce the incidence of animal diseases, as well as plant diseases.

Performance Records

Records of service, birth, milk yield and live-weight gains are invaluable when diagnosing the cause of disease. The onset of infertility and disease can invariably be detected by a close study of such records. Examining the herd for pregnancy every three months or so is useful in detecting early infertility, cystic ovaries, etc.

Prevention of Physical Injury

As far as possible, the stockman must ensure that animals do not injure themselves. Nails or pieces of wire in a feed can cause injury to the stomach; points, sharp edges, awkward posts can result in eye injuries, skin cuts and abrasions and damage to joints and limbs; slippery floors are a hazard to man and beast alike. When milk routines are not properly organized, overmilking frequently results in injury to the cow's teats and mastitis may set it. Damage to the animals at calving can often be averted if the stockman keeps a distant but regular eye on animals giving birth.

Physical injury causes the animal considerable discomfort and a possible drop in production standards. Since many disease organisms enter the body through cuts and abrasions, this is yet another reason why animals should, as far as possible, be prevented from causing themselves physical damage or injury. Cattle are also naturally curious and they will lick up nails, staples, etc., left on window ledges, etc.

Clean Coats

When skins of animals are irritated by lice, mites, warble flies and other parasites, they invariably get agitated and lose condition. Brushing the coats and washing them clean from dirt and dung will help to reduce the incidence of such skin disorders. Prompt treatment of any skin disease will also avert annoyance and suffering.

WHAT IS DISEASE?

Disease may be broadly defined as some disturbance in the normal life processes which affects either a particular organ or the entire animal and which sometimes leads to premature death. When an animal is suffering from a disease, it shows certain signs or symptoms, e.g., lameness, inability to eat, high temperature, laboured breathing and many others. The symptoms of the more common diseases of farm stock are listed under the specific diseases described in later chapters. A disease may be in a mild form or an acute form. With the latter, clinical symptoms such as those mentioned above are shown.

Diseases are caused by six main agencies: bacteria, viruses, fungi, parasites, metabolic upsets and poisons.

Most diseases can now be effectively treated by administering drugs, antibiotics, vaccines or by operating on the animal. Although these effective treatments are available for most diseases, the stockman's main task is to attempt, by efficient husbandry, to prevent the occurrence of such diseases.

If the stockman understands the behaviour of disease-causing agencies, then he will be in a better position to take preventive measures.

BACTERIA

Size and Form

Bacteria constitute a very important group of plants. They are one-celled organisms extremely small in size; some bacteria can hardly be seen with the most powerful microscope. They are measured in micrometres (μm), i.e., 1/1000th of a millimetre. The largest such as the anthrax bacillus are about 4–8 μm long; the smallest coccus is about 1 μm.

Bacteria may be either rod-shaped (bacilli), spherical (cocci) or spiral-shaped (spirella). Bacilli may be arranged end-to-end as filaments,

cocci bacteria may occur in chains (streptococcus), in irregular clusters (staphylococcus) or in a Chinese lettering arrangement (corynebacteria). Some are capable of movement because they possess whip-like flagella, either singly or in tufts on points of their bodies. Fig. 15.1 illustrates a few of the many bacteria which exist.

Bacteria survive adverse conditions such as extreme temperature changes by forming rounded, thick-walled resting spores. When conditions become favourable, these spores burst and a new bacterium is formed.

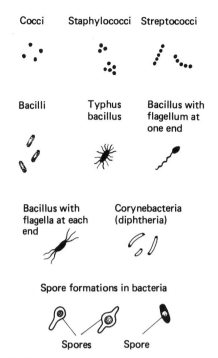

Cocci   Staphylococci   Streptococci

Bacilli   Typhus bacillus   Bacillus with flagellum at one end

Bacillus with flagella at each end   Corynebacteria (diphtheria)

Spore formations in bacteria

Spores   Spore

Fig. 15.1 Some forms of bacteria (magnified approx. ×1500).

Chemical Changes

In order to supply themselves with energy for growth and reproduction, bacteria bring about a number of chemical changes. Some of these chemical changes are beneficial to the farmer. Soil bacteria, for example, are responsible for the decay of dung, slurry and vegetation ploughed into the soil. Other soil bacteria are capable of chemically altering nitrogenous salts added to the soil so as to produce nitrate salt, the only salt which can be absorbed by plant roots. Such changes as these are summarized below:

 i) urine is converted into ammonium salts;
 ii) nitrite bacteria oxidize ammonium salts into nitrite salts;
 iii) *Nitrobacter* bacteria oxidize nitrite salts into nitrate salts;
 iv) other bacteria present in the root nodules of legumes are capable of fixing atmospheric nitrogen by converting the nitrogen gas into nitrate salts.

A large number of bacteria obtain energy by fermenting foodstuffs. The vinegar bacteria ferment alcohol into acetic acid or vinegar. Milk turns sour because certain bacteria feed on the lactose present in milk, changing it into sour-smelling lactic acid. Other bacteria decompose protein; cut meat can decompose in this way if left in the open air.

Pathogenic bacteria, which cause disease, usually break down proteins into poisonous substances called toxins. Some of these toxins are the most powerful poisonous chemicals known. When a disease is caused by a bacterium, it is these toxins in the animal's bloodstream which give rise to the symptoms of the disease.

Reproduction and Changes of Form

Most bacteria can be grown in the laboratory on a jelly-like substance called *agar* in which extracts of food such as milk, meat or fruit juices, etc., have been dissolved. Under suitable temperatures, a single bacterium multiplies rapidly forming colonies of bacteria visible to the naked eye.

They reproduce simply. One bacterium grows in size and splits into two new bacteria. By this method of multiplication, a few bacteria can very quickly form a colony of many million bacteria. They also have the ability to change their form rapidly. Many forms of bacteria which were killed with an antibiotic have now changed their form, so that strains or forms of bacteria resistant to it now exist. To avoid this, the prescribed course and dosage of antibiotic for a specific disease should be strictly adhered to, and any antibiotic left over destroyed.

Conditions Ideal for Bacterial Growth

Certain conditions are ideal for the growth and multiplication of bacteria.

1. *Temperature*
At or around body temperature, 31–38°C, bacteria multiply rapidly. Most of them can, however, be killed by boiling or steam sterilizing at temperatures of 98.8–100°C. Below 3.3–4.4°C, bacterial activity is reduced appreciably and very little multiplication in numbers occurs.

2. *Food supply*
Bacteria will not grow unless there is a source of food. Proteins, carbohydrates, fats, alcohol and many other forms of organic material constitute the food supply of bacteria.

3. *Moisture*
Bacteria cannot live under absolutely dry conditions. A thin film of moisture is all that they require to enable them to absorb digested food into their bodies.

4. *Oxygen*

Some bacteria require oxygen to feed and are called *aerobes*. Nitrifying bacteria are examples of this type. Other bacteria, however, can live without oxygen and are called *anaerobes*. Unfortunately, some of the worst forms of disease, e.g., braxy, lamb dysentery and blackleg, are caused by these anaerobes; their spores are capable of living in soil for many years.

Control of Bacteria

Bacteria are so small that they can be carried or transmitted in any material. They live in air, water, soil, food and dung.

Animals usually pick up bacterial infection by:

i) Feeding on infected food;
ii) Breathing in infected air;
iii) Wounds and abrasions being exposed to infected air or being rubbed against infected surfaces; some bacteria such as *Brucella* penetrate intact skin.
iv) The introduction of infectious material into the eye, teats, vagina, navel, rectum or mouth.

The stockman can reduce and sometimes eliminate harmful bacteria by introducing the following measures where appropriate into his farm practice:

1. *Scrubbing and washing*

Bacteria can only survive where deposits of food are left behind in receptacles such as milking utensils, feeding troughs and buckets. Thorough scrubbing, with the help of detergents to remove oil films, will eliminate most sources of infection.

2. *Boiling and steam sterilizing*

Bacteria will not survive in boiling water or steam. Boiling and sterilizing are undoubtedly the most effective methods of killing bacteria.

3. *Use of disinfectant*

Disinfectants kill or inactivate most bacteria. Hypochlorites, used to sterilize milking utensils, set free chlorine which acts as an oxidizing agent. Washing soda, carbolic acid, formalin, potassium permanganate and iodine form the bases of some disinfectants; approved disinfectants are listed by the Ministry of Agriculture, Fisheries and Food.

4. *Drying*

Dry utensils are much less likely to harbour bacteria than wet utensils.

5. *Cooling*

It is necessary to cool milk after it has been taken from the cow. The more effective the cooling the greater the reduction of bacterial activities. Most difficulties are experienced in summer-time when the temperature of mains or well-water is above 4°C. Many farmers have introduced refrigerated tanks.

6. *Removal of dung*

It is normal practice to remove dung from cow sheds and pig-fattening pens daily. This eliminates a possible source of bacterial infection. Under deep-litter methods, water and urine are drained away and bacteria, harmless to livestock, quickly decompose the dry dung.

7. *Injections of vaccines and sera*

When bacteria infect an animal, toxins are formed. The animal body quickly reacts to infection conditions and attempts to combat the pathogenic bacteria. White corpuscles in the bloodstream ingest or eat up bacteria and powerful antibodies are produced to set up a resistance against the invading bacteria. Such antibodies can be produced in the body artificially by introducing specially treated dead bacteria into the blood-stream; such a preparation is called a *vaccine*. In this way an active immunity to the disease is set up in the body. Vaccines to counteract such diseases as pulpy kidney and swine erysipelas are widely used. Vaccines injected or fed orally confer on the animal a high degree of resistance against any possible infection by living bacteria.

Sometimes, antibodies and not dead bacteria are injected into an animal. A preparation of such antibodies is called a *serum*. This injection confers on the animal a short-lived passive immunity to a disease.

Immunity from a disease can also occur naturally. Antibodies from colostrum confer on the young animal a passive immunity to certain diseases. Immunity can also be inherited in some cases; horses are immune to foot-and-mouth disease, whilst cows are immune to glanders. When an animal has a mild attack of a disease, it may confer on that animal an immunity against any future infections by that particular causative bacterium.

8. *Use of antibiotics*

Professor Alexander Fleming discovered the first antibiotic, penicillin, and Sir Arthur Florey extracted it from the blue fungal mould *Penicillium notatum*. The antibiotic, when injected, taken orally or smeared on to wounds and cuts, kills certain forms of bacteria. The high acidity produced by the antibiotic makes it impossible for bacteria to live. Other antibiotics such as streptomycin, auromycin and many others have since been extracted from other fungi. It is now possible for scientists to synthesize these chemicals in the laboratory without having to grow vast colonies of fungi. Widespread use of antibiotics often kills only sensitive bacteria with the result that resistant varieties such as the staphylococcus have assumed serious importance, e.g., mastitis caused by this organism has over-shadowed the old familiar streptococcal type.

9. *Use of drugs*

Sulphanilamide and many other sulpha drugs are extremely effective against certain streptococcal bacteria. Derivatives of these drugs and their combinations with antibiotics are important in controlling many diseases.

VIRUSES

Viruses are the smallest known disease-causing agents. Until comparatively recently, the cause of such diseases as the common cold, poliomyelitis, foot-and-mouth disease, fowl pest and many others was unknown. It was realized that some agency caused the disease but it required the development of the electron microscope to show scientists the shape and size of the viruses which cause these diseases.

Form and Behaviour

When looked at under the electron microscope (Fig. 15.2) viruses look like crystals; some of them are rod-like, hexagonal or cubic in shape. It is now known that viruses are made of proteins closely resembling the protein constituting the nuclei of living cells. Because it is possible to filter these viruses from cell juices and to crystallize them, some of them resemble certain dead chemical compounds.

Unlike chemicals, however, they are able to grow and multiply within the cells of plants and animals. They can only perform these functions within living cells.

As with bacteria, they are able to change their forms rapidly thus creating many new strains of viruses.

They feed by extracting basic foodstuffs from the living cells and building them up into their own type of protein. As a result of these chemical changes, symptoms of a disease appear in their animal hosts.

Control of Virus Diseases

Viruses are mainly transmitted in dust, food, air and water. Certain viruses causing disease in man and animal are transmitted by biting flies and parasites, e.g., yellow fever in man is carried

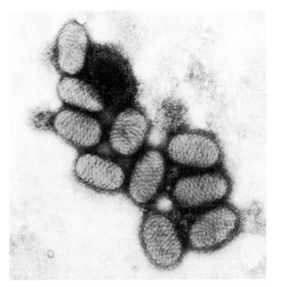
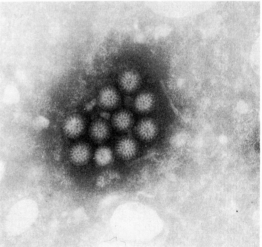

Fig. 15.2 (Top) Parapoxvirus – orf. × 50 000. (Bottom) Rotavirus. × 100 000. (Photographs provided by the Central Veterinary Laboratory, Weybridge Department of Virology, Electron Microscopy Section. Crown Copyright.)

by the mosquito; tick-borne fever in cattle is carried by ticks as the name implies. The rabies virus is known to be transmitted through the bite of the vampire bat. It is also believed that birds can carry the virus of foot-and-mouth disease on their feet and beaks. More is discovered concerning the transmission of virus diseases as research progresses.

Like bacteria, viruses thrive at body temperatures and where there are ample food supplies, i.e., the cells of animals. Most of the measures described to prevent the incidence of bacteria will also control the spread and multiplication of viruses. Until recently it was not possible to produce a pure virus vaccine to immunize an animal effectively against certain virus diseases. Many forms of foot-and-mouth disease can now be controlled by vaccination; orf vaccine in sheep is applied to a scratch made on the skin.

FUNGI

As with all groups of lower plants and animals, some of them are beneficial and others harmful to animals and man. The fungi are no exception to this rule. Mushrooms make a tasty meal, fungi such as *Penicillium* supply us with antibiotics. Some toadstools, however, are poisonous to eat; ergot fungus causes abortion in animals and some fungi cause ringworm disease in animals and man.

Form

Fungi are colourless plants of varied form. The yeast used for fermenting beer and bread is made of a single cell. Moulds such as *Mucor* and *Penicillium*, commonly formed on stale wet bread and dung, consist of a loose network of thin, white, multi-celled threads. In the higher forms of fungi these threads are organized into distinct structures; in toadstools and mushrooms the below-ground threads or mycelium form an above-ground fruiting structure consisting of a stalk and an umbrella-like head (Fig. 15.3).

Feeding

Fungi can be divided into two distinct classes:

1. *Saprophytes*
These fungi feed on dead organic matter such as bread, dung, soil humus, milk and wood, etc. Fungi and bacteria are jointly responsible for the breakdown of vegetation and dung into humus in the soil. They are thus largely responsible for improving soil fertility.

2. *Parasites*
These fungi feed on living matter and cause considerable inconvenience to plants and animals. Enzymes produced from the tips of the white threads normally digest foodstuffs and absorb them into the body of the fungus. The

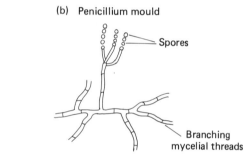

(a) Single yeast cell

Multiplication of yeast by budding

(b) Penicillium mould

Spores

Branching mycelial threads

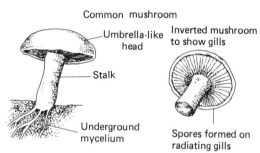

Common mushroom

Umbrella-like head

Stalk

Underground mycelium

Inverted mushroom to show gills

Spores formed on radiating gills

Fig. 15.3 Some forms of fungi (magnified approx. × 250).

usual metabolic processes occur within the threads and the fungus grows in size.

Reproduction

Most fungi reproduce by forming minute spores. Under warm, damp conditions, these spores germinate and a single white thread grows out from each spore. Plentiful supplies of food enable this thread to digest and absorb food; each thread lengthens and divides until a new fungus plant is formed.

Control of Fungi

Because fungi are colourless plants they can survive without light. Moist, damp, dark conditions are ideal for the growth and multiplication of fungi.

Clean, well-lighted, well-ventilated buildings will, to a large extent, prevent the uninhibited growth of most fungi. Chemical fungicidal sprays and certain disinfectants can be used. Woodwork infected with fungi must inevitably be either burnt or scraped, scorched, disinfected and painted with creosote.

PARASITES

There are a number of small organisms, visible to the naked eye, which spend the whole or part of their lives on or inside the bodies of farm animals. Parasites such as lice, mites, ticks, flies, flukes, worms, etc., cause farm animals a great deal of annoyance; most slow down the growth and milk production of an animal; some carry other disease organisms; others, if in sufficient numbers, cause anaemia; some parasites cause death.

These parasites cannot be grouped together as one class of animal. They form a motley collection; some of them are insects, others are flat worms, many are simple worms called *nematodes*.

Broadly speaking, they can be divided into two groups:

i) *External parasites*, which complete their life cycles on or outside the body of the animal, e.g., lice and ticks;
ii) *Internal parasites*, which live for part of their life cycle within the body of the animal; the remaining part of the life cycle is completed outside the body of the host animal.

Life Cycles

In the more highly developed insect types (e.g., the warble-fly), the parasite passes through four distinct stages of development (see Fig. 16.1): adult fly, egg, larva, pupa. This division of the animal's life cycle into four stages is associated with specialized functions for each stage. Adult flies are highly mobile and are able to lay eggs in suitable places. Eggs develop in the presence of plentiful supplies of food into larvae. Larvae feed voraciously so as to increase rapidly in size. It is the larva which normally causes the host animal the most trouble. Pupae are resting larvae shrouded with thick protective coats which enable them to survive the rigours of adverse wintery conditions.

Some other parasites have no pupal stage, e.g., the lungworm. Most stomach or intestinal worms lay eggs which are passed out in the faeces and mature into larvae before they can be infective. Others encyst in the gut wall and lay eggs there. Other parasites such as the liver fluke (see Fig. 17.3) have extremely complicated life histories and require the presence of a secondary host such as the snail to complete it; the dog tapeworm has to spend part of its life as a cyst usually in the sheep or ox where it causes gid. Reference to the life histories of parasites described in later chapters will better illustrate the range of life cycles that exist among these parasitic organisms.

Feeding

Parasites living in the digestive tracts of animals invariably feed on the digested foodstuffs of the host. When an animal is badly infected with worms of this kind, part of the food is being used to feed the worms and not the animal. Other internal parasites such as the warble fly, lung-worms and liver fluke feed on the foodstuffs present in the body cells of the host; these often damage the tissues they infest, e.g., pneumonia following husk worm, and enteritis due to bowel worms. External parasites such as ticks often feed by sucking blood from the animal.

Although these parasites produce excretory waste products, they are seldom produced in such quantity as to render them toxic to the host animal. Such parasites merely sap the animal of its necessary food and energy supply; the host invariably becomes dull and lethargic.

Control of Parasites

1. *Rotations*
Since most parasites reproduce by passing out their eggs or larvae in the dung of their hosts, a continuously stocked strip of land will inevitably

become densely populated with breeding parasites. Thus the most effective way of controlling the build-up of parasites is to plough and reseed heavily infected land. Young stock are particularly susceptible to parasitic attacks – they should always precede and not follow older cattle when grazing and should invariably be turned out on to clean, reseeded pastures.

2. *Removal of dung*
Dung should always be regularly removed from buildings, and in particular from the buildings housing young stock, as dung piles contain the deposited parasites.

3. *Destruction of secondary hosts*
When a parasite such as liver fluke lives for part of its life in the body of a snail, one method of preventing the disease is to attempt to destroy the secondary host. Land which is well drained rarely harbours snails; a dressing of copper sulphate or one of the modern molluscides will also help to kill any snails present on the land.

4. *Use of drugs and insecticides*
Having faeces analysed at the Ministry labora-

tory will save time and money. The type of parasite dictates which drug to use. There are excellent drugs to cure liver fluke and worms and with the laboratory report and veterinary advice the correct drug can be used. Insecticides are available for external parasites and warble fly infestation can be cured by systemic drugs.

5. *Premunition*
This is the resistance of an animal to internal parasites. Resistance depends on the presence of some of these parasites in the body, e.g., animals reared on farms infected with red water fever seldom succumb to it although parasites are present in their blood; new arrivals, however, invariably develop the disease.

Young cattle let out very early in the year pick up a few husk worms and develop immunity to further infection. This is the basis of the vaccination against husk. The larva of the worm is subjected to X-rays and its development is arrested. When the live vaccine is given by the mouth to the animal the larvae migrate only as far as the mesenteric lymph glands. Their presence in the body prevents husk infection by creating antibodies in the blood.

METABOLIC DISEASES

Some diseases are not caused by an invading organism. The metabolic processes in the body occasionally fail to function properly and a diseased condition manifests itself. Milk fever, hypomagnesaemia, acetonaemia, trace-element diseases, bloat, etc., are examples of such metabolic upsets. In this book, an attempt has been made to describe the functions of the animal body as simply as possible. It must be remembered, however, that such functions are extremely complicated, and delicate balances in the amounts of foodstuffs contained in the blood and body cells must be constantly maintained. With many of these metabolic disorders, the exact cause of the disease is unknown and a great deal more research work will have to be undertaken to find the correct answers. It is known, however, that minerals and vitamins play an essential role in maintaining the balances required for the proper functioning of metabolic processes.

A biochemical analysis carried out on blood can indicate the content of calcium, magnesium, phosphorus, some trace elements, glucose and other components in the blood; this is known as a metabolic profile. It can show which deficien-

cies exist and help to avoid conditions such as milk fever, hypomagnesaemia, and infertility. It is often carried out when herd problems manifest themselves; this is also done on many farms as a regular routine.

Minerals
Minerals constitute some 3% of the total food eaten by an animal. Minimum quantities of these are essential, however, for the proper functioning of the body.

Phosphorus, calcium, magnesium, sodium, potassium, chlorine and sulphur are required in small amounts; elements such as iron, copper, cobalt, manganese, zinc, iodine and many others are required in minute quantities. They are often referred to as trace elements. In all, some twelve elements are essential for normal nutrition.

The functions of these elements within the body are summarized in Table 7.1, p. 78. Many of these elements are stored in parts of the body, e.g., calcium and phosphorus are stored in bone. In a high-yielding cow, considerable quantities of calcium are extracted from bone and transferred via the bloodstream to the udder for milk production. Similarly, varying amounts of other mineral elements are being constantly transferred in the bloodstream from one part of the body to another.

Metabolic diseases associated with mineral elements generally result from two main causes:

1. *General deficiency of a mineral element in the body*. Diseases such as rickets, sway-back and pining in lambs are the results of such deficiencies.

2. *Deficiency of available mineral elements present in the bloodstream when required by the animal*. Milk fever and hypomagnesaemia are notable examples of these upsets. Hormones produced by the glands of the body play an important part in controlling the amounts of minerals passed into and absorbed from the bloodstream. It is thought by some that the basic cause of milk fever is a temporary inactivity of some of the hormone-producing glands resulting in a deficiency of calcium in the bloodstream. Some forms of shock often stimulate these glands into reactivity; a cow may avoid milk fever after the shock of a difficult calving.

Although most of these diseases are caused by mineral deficiency, it must be remembered that certain of these elements are harmful when fed in excess of the animal's requirements. It is known that arsenic is extremely toxic and that copper is harmful except in minute amounts; in the United States, selenium has been found harmful to animals and excessive amounts may cause 'blind staggers' in cattle. Such cattle have depraved appetites, defective vision, paralysis and may die. Copper deficiency, which can be discovered by a blood test in cattle, causes unthriftiness in calves and breeding difficulties in heifers.

It is thus necessary for stock to receive not only the correct amount of minerals but also a balance of all minerals.

Vitamins

Vitamins are required in small quantities for normal health. It is known that farm animals require vitamins A, B complex, C, D and E; other vitamins have been discovered but little is known of their functions in the nutrition of farm animals. The sources of supply and functions of vitamins within the animal body are summarized in Table 7.1, p. 78.

Ruminant animals seldom suffer from deficiencies of vitamins B and C since these are manufactured in their rumens. The bacteria present in the rumen break down plant fibre and multiply rapidly. During this process they also synthesize vitamins B_{12} and C; it seems that cobalt must be present in minute quantities in the food for the synthesis of B_{12}.

Vitamin D is manufactured in the skin of animals which are exposed to sunlight. Farm animals living out of doors will seldom suffer from deficiencies of this vitamin.

Vitamin E and selenium are inter-related in metabolism. They protect muscle tissue against damage during activity. Grass and green food are full of vitamin E. Trouble arises when vitamin E is limited as in old hay or totally absent as in roots. Animals which become unthrifty benefit from dosing with selenium and vitamin E.

Vitamins undoubtedly play a large part in the synthesis of enzymes and hormones in the body. Deficiencies hinder the formation of these essential chemical compounds and affect the health of animals.

Abnormal Rumination

Health in ruminants depends, to a large extent, on proper rumen activity; rumen bacteria are essential to cows and sheep. They break down roughages and synthesize vitamins. Gases are produced as waste products in this process and are normally expelled from the rumen by belching.

Occasionally, when ruminants are turned out to graze fresh pastures in spring, the normal rumination process is upset and large volumes of waste gases are produced. If the animal is unable to release these gases, the rumen swells; such swelling can be seen on the left side of the animal above the level of the last rib and front edge of the pelvis. Such a disease condition is known as bloat.

Cattle grazing on succulent herbage occasionally get bloat. Fermentation occurs with rapid accumulation of gases within the rumen. Milder cases recover themselves or can be relieved by injections.

On some pastures, particularly some types of clover, hydrocyanic acid is formed in the rumen, which kills certain bacteria concerned with ruminal function. This upsets the sequence of digestion in the rumen and leads to frothy bloat which can be so rapid as to be fatal within minutes of it starting.

Severe frothy bloat is relieved by puncturing the rumen in the left flank. It might be necessary to open the rumen at this site in order to allow the escape of the frothy stomach contents. Unless the condition is relieved quickly the pressure within the abdomen paralyses the heart and lungs.

Cattle grazing fresh spring grass or lush aftermath should be inspected several times a day in case of bloat.

Control of Metabolic Disorders

Certain general practices can be implemented in an attempt to prevent metabolic disorders. Detailed preventive measures are enumerated under specific diseases described in later chapters.

1. A varied diet of food will supply most of the minerals and vitamins required. An animal fed on too much of one crop may develop metabolic trouble. Excess feeding of brassica crops may induce thyroid trouble and cause abortions or birth of full-developed dead calves; cows deprived of concentrates in spring and summer may suffer from magnesium deficiency.

2. Young growing stock and heavy-yielding cattle can receive a supplement of essential minerals and vitamins by supplying mineral licks or injections.

3. Home-grown, well-manured crops are invariably rich in phosphorus, potassium and calcium. Occasionally when excessive lime is applied to fields, mineral elements such as copper, cobalt, manganese and iodine become 'locked up' and are unavailable to crops. Animals fed on such crops may suffer from deficiencies of these elements. Stock fed on crops heavily dressed with nitrogen may also suffer from a deficiency of magnesium.

Where pastures are known to be deficient in a particular minor element, two remedies are usually possible:

i) The animal can be given the appropriate element by feeding licks or by injection;
ii) The pastures themselves can be dressed with small quantities of the appropriate salt.

4. Sensible management of stock during their first spring grazing may reduce the incidence of bloat and hypomagnesaemia. Rationing of fresh, young grass coupled with a ready supply of fibrous hay or straw may help in this respect.

5. Particular attention is needed with the management of high-yielding cows consuming large quantities of concentrates. Availability of minerals will offset the heavy drain of minerals from the cow's body. Adequate rations of good-quality hay will ensure proper working of the rumen; molasses added to steaming-up and other calving rations may also hinder such troubles as acetonaemia. Regular exercise will also help to keep such 'heavily taxed' animals fit and resistant to many metabolic upsets.

POISONS

Certain chemicals are highly toxic to farm animals and generally cause bowel disorders. Care must be taken that stock do not come into contact with the following poisonous materials:

1. *Plants:* bracken, ragwort, acorn, woody nightshade, bryony, dog's mercury, horsetail, laburnum, foxgloves, deadly nightshade, rhododendrons, yew;

2. *Chemicals:* arsenic, lead, molybdenum, zinc, mercury, herbicides, insecticides and rat poisons.

NOTIFIABLE DISEASES

There are certain animal diseases which are so highly infectious that they are a danger to the animal population in general. If an outbreak of any of these diseases is suspected it must immediately be reported to the police authorities, and control is placed in the hands of Ministry veterinary surgeons. Steps are taken immediately to isolate farms on which outbreaks occur, and all the susceptible animals on the particular farms are slaughtered and burned. Farmers must keep a record of all movements of stock on to and away from their farms. Such records enable the authorities to trace any possible spread of infection and take appropriate measures.

The following diseases are notifiable:

Foot-and-mouth	in cattle, pigs and sheep
Anthrax	in all animals
Sheep scab	in sheep
Swine vesicular disease	in pigs
Certain forms of tuberculosis	

In addition to the diseases mentioned above the full list includes rabies in all animals, cattle plague*, glanders*, epizootic lymphangitis*, sheep pox, parasitic mange of horses, asses and mules (except leg mange), and fowl pest in poultry.

*Have not been known in Great Britain for many years.

Movement of Animals Register

All stock owners are bound by law to keep a written record of movement of animals on to and off their farms. This involves in the case of cattle their identification numbers as well.

The police can ask to see the register at any time; failure to produce it can lead to prosecution.

LEGAL REQUIREMENTS

Protection of Animals (Anaesthetics) Act

The Act states that a suitable anaesthetic must be used for all operations on sensitive tissues or bones of animals to prevent pain.

Exceptions are:

i) infections;
ii) first aid or emergency saving of life or relieving pain;
iii) authorized experiments;
iv) docking of dogs and amputation of dew claws before their eyes are open;
v) castration of a bull before it is 3 months old, a sheep before it is 3 months old, a goat before it is 2 months old, a pig before it is 2 months old; a rubber ring or bloodless castrator must be used before the animal is a week old;
vi) minor operations performed by a veterinary surgeon which are customarily performed without anaesthetic by reason of their quickness and painlessness;
vii) a minor operation not normally performed by a veterinary surgeon;
viii) disbudding of calves except by chemical cauterization.

In addition it is well to know that a person under 16 years of age cannot legally perform an operation.

It is illegal for anyone other than a veterinary surgeon to castrate the following over the age specified:

Bull	– 2 months
Goat	– 3 months
Sheep	– 3 months
Pig	– 3 months
Cat	– 6 months
Dog	– 6 months

Only veterinary surgeons may castrate horses, ponies, asses and mules, and dehorn sheep and goats.

Medicines Act 1968

This and other subsequent acts govern the use of certain drugs such as antibiotics and hormones. Controlled drugs such as morphia, opium, etc., are strictly for administration by veterinary surgeons only; they are available only under licence to the profession.

Antibiotics may be dispensed only by a veterinary surgeon or on his prescription. Possession of antibiotics not obtained legally is an offence.

Other Regulations

Other regulations related to the presence of drugs in milk and meat exist and are being constantly added to or amended, thus increasing the amount of legislation governing the ownership of animals.

16

Health and Disease in Cattle

The first part of this chapter considers what to look for and what to do in the feeding and management of (a) mature dairy cattle through their productive cycles, (b) growing calves and (c) young stock. The last part of the chapter describes the symptoms, cause, prevention and treatment of the more common diseases which attack cattle.

PREVENTION OF DISEASE DURING THE PRODUCTIVE CYCLE OF THE DAIRY COW

This cycle can be conveniently divided into eight stages:

 i) heat and service;
 ii) pregnancy;
 iii) before calving;
 iv) calving;
 v) after calving;
 vi) period of rising milk production;
 vii) remainder of lactation;
 viii) dry period.

Points of stock husbandry which need to be practised during this cycle are summarized in Table 16.1.

Heat and Service

On p. 7 the mechanism controlling the onset and duration of heat periods was described. It often happens that a cow fails to come on heat, or that her heat periods are irregular or that she fails to conceive after being served. All these upsets indicate that there is something wrong with the cow's reproductive system and inevitably result in sterility or temporary infertility.

The causes of infertility are many. They can be broadly classified as follows:

1. *Failure of the reproductive mechanism*
The yellow body may fail to disappear from the ovary and consequently the animal does not return to heat. In addition the egg or ovum may not be shed from the ovary where it forms a cyst. When the ovary is cysted in this way, heat periods become frequent and irregular. Absence of heat may also be due to a shortage of the hormone which induces heat. An injection of the hormone may correct the trouble.

2. *Infections*
Bacterial infections frequently cause inflammation of and discharges from the fallopian tubes, uterus, cervix and vagina (see pregnancy, p. 3).

Immediate attention must be given to a cow when discharges are seen. Discharges may contain infective bacteria or viruses and swabs should be taken from them for examination. The veterinary surgeon will do this and irrigate the womb or take any other measures that are necessary.

3. *Anatomical deformities*
Any part of the reproductive system may not be properly formed or may be sited in an incorrect position. A vagina may be 'slack' and thus obstruct the penis of the bull. The cervix may be inclined downwards against the vaginal wall preventing sperm from entering the uterus. Artificial insemination has proved to be effective in serving some cows who could not conceive with normal bull service. This is due to the fact that semen is deposited inside the uterus during artificial insemination whilst it is deposited in

Table 16.1. Prevention of disease during the productive cycle of the dairy cow.

Disease	Prevention of disease by:			Disease
	Management	Period	Feeding	
Infertility	Immediate attention paid to discharges	Heat and service	Correct balance of foodstuffs during growth and development	Infertility
Abortion	Careful handling. Practice a self-contained breeding policy	Pregnancy	Avoid mouldy hay and straw as fodder or bedding	Abortion
			Adequate quantities of vitamin A, manganese and iodine in diet	
		Before calving	Reduce protein intake and increase carbohydrates a few weeks before calving	Milk fever
			Phosphate and calcium supplements	
			Doses of vitamin D_3	
Womb infection	Strict hygiene	Calving		
Johne's disease: infection of calf	Immediate removal of calf	After calving		
Eversion of uterus	Veterinary attention required			
Milk fever	Complete milking-out delayed for 24–48 hours			
Milk fever	Close watch kept on cows prone to milk fever	Rising milk production	Avoid over-feeding of concs. too soon after calving	Indigestion
			Correct balance of energy and protein. Minimum of 2.7 kg hay daily to high yielders	Acetonaemia
Mastitis	Good milking routine	Remainder of lactation	Rationing of lush grass	Bloat
			Feeding of roughages	
			In spring and cold months feed magnesium-rich concentrates	Hypo-magnesaemia
			Dress pastures with calcined magnesite in spring	
			Correct fertilizer policy	
Summer mastitis	Use dry cow antibiotics as prescribed by veterinary surgeon	Dry period		
	Daily examination of dry udders			

the vagina by the bull. Damage caused to the uterus and vagina during calving may also prevent a cow from getting into calf.

Most cows who have deformities of this type are usually fattened and slaughtered.

4. Faulty feeding and management

In this respect the farmer can play a decisive part in the prevention of infertility. Broadly speaking an animal fed and managed sensibly seldom suffers from these troubles.

It appears that fertility depends mainly on the balance of foodstuffs. In particular it depends on the correct balance of:

i) protein, carbohydrates and fats in the maintenance and production rations;

ii) calcium, phosphorus, manganese and other trace elements;

iii) vitamins E and D.

Undernourished animals receiving insufficient protein and energy-giving foodstuffs are often infertile. Proper rationing of food during the animal's productive cycle helps to ensure the correct functioning of the reproductive organs and also raises the resistance of the animal to diseases affecting these organs.

Mineral balance is very difficult to achieve in practice. Over-liming has certainly locked up elements such as phosphorus, manganese, copper and iodine, deficiencies of which cause sterility. Feeding of mineralized licks and powders will most certainly help where farm soils have tended to become too alkaline.

Vitamin E is closely associated with fertility; apparently it indirectly promotes a healthy lining for the uterus. Vitamin D is closely associated with the mechanism controlling the availability of calcium and phorphorus in the bloodstream. In winter-time when cattle are not exposed to the sun's rays they are liable to suffer from a deficiency of vitamin D.

Pregnancy

With the virtual elimination of brucellosis, abortions have become less frequent.

The fungus from 'dusty' hay and straw causes abortion and is found on aborted calves and on the afterbirth. It is the most common of the known causes of abortion. It is wise therefore to avoid the use of infected hay and straw either as fodder or bedding. It is also a danger to human health.

Ergot fungus which grows in the flowering heads of some grasses and cereals, especially rye, can cause abortion.

The venereal diseases trichomoniasis and vibrio have been largely eliminated. Some abortions are due to *Salmonella* or to lesser known organisms.

It is also important to remember that mechanical injury to a pregnant cow will often result in abortion. Such animals should be handled carefully and not frightened, beaten by sticks, or driven through deep mud. Butting by other cows may also cause abortion.

Cows which have aborted must be reported to the veterinary surgeon. He will take specimens to be tested under the Brucellosis Scheme.

Where a breeding problem is suspected, the Veterinary Surgeon should be consulted.

Before Calving

Six to eight weeks before calving a cow will receive a steaming-up ration; for the last fortnight or so of pregnancy the protein factor should be reduced and more carbohydrate given.

The following measures need to be noted:

1. An injection of Vitamin D_3 between 8 and 2 days before calving benefits the calf and may help to avoid milk fever.
2. Regular mineral supplements suitable for pregnant cows are beneficial.

If the udder becomes too full of milk before calving it may be necessary to ease off such udder pressure. However, if this practice is undertaken the calf will either be deprived of its quota of colostrum or the colostrum will have to be drawn away and stored in a refrigerator.

Calving

Scrupulously clean conditions will prevent infection. It has already been emphasized that calving boxes should be thoroughly cleaned and disinfected before the cow is brought in for calving. Clean litter on the floor is also essential.

Internal examination of the cow by the cowman should be minimal. Veterinary assistance should be sought if trouble is suspected.

It is essential that the ropes used to draw the calf should be sterilized and the hands of those assisting should be clean. It must be emphasized that most cows calve normally and should be given plenty of time. Also refer to the section on calving on p. 5.

After Calving

A calf should suckle its mother after calving. The first feed is the important one and the calf should have its fill. Antibiotics, etc., are absorbed easily at this stage; 12 hours later absorption capacity diminishes.

On some farms where Johne's disease has occurred the calf is frequently taken away from its dam immediately. It is believed that some calves are infected during suckling; the bacterium remains dormant in the growing calf but becomes active in the older animal and symptoms of the disease occur. Calves can be inoculated if the Ministry consents and they will need injections of the vitamins of which they were deprived by not having the colostrum.

Occasionally a cow may be unable to stop straining after the birth of the calf. Pressure with the nails of the finger and thumb to either side of the backbone may stop this straining; failing this a rope can be passed around the body of the animal and tightened to exert a steady pressure. If this straining cannot be stopped there is a possibility that the womb will be prolapsed out of the body through the vagina; this can occur during milk fever. If it does the veterinary surgeon must be consulted as soon as possible.

In some cases the cow may show paralysis of the hind limbs. This may be due to damage of the nerves or limbs resulting from calving or milk fever. The veterinary surgeon should be called and the cow should not be drenched.

The placenta may be retained as a result of milk fever or a difficult calving; if it is not expelled in 3 or 4 days veterinary advice should be sought.

Complete milking out should be delayed until 24–48 hours after calving. This will help to prevent milk fever.

Period of Rising Milk Production

A close watch must be kept on cows known to be prone to milk fever, especially for the first few days after calving. Any cows showing the recognized symptoms should be given an injection of calcium borogluconate.

Acetonaemia and acute indigestion are upsets likely to occur during this period. The former mainly occurs in high-yielding cows; feeding a minimum of 2.7 kg of hay per day and particular attention paid to the balance between protein and starch will help to offset this disease condition.

Acute indigestion can arise by feeding too much concentrates too soon after calving. A sensible procedure is to feed some 0.9–1.4 kg of concentrates night and morning on the second and third days after calving. This can gradually be increased until the full production ration is being fed on the tenth day.

Remainder of Lactation

With cows feeding on spring and summer grass, bloat and hypomagnesaemia are likely diseases to occur. In chapter 15 the main causes of two of these diseases were described. Strict rationing of fresh grass supplementing with hay or straw will help to prevent bloat.

Hypomagnesaemia occurs all the year round but more frequently on fresh spring grass and lush aftermath. Heavy applications of potash and nitrogenous manures predispose to it.

The main form of prevention is the feeding of magnesium (p. 228) during the critical times of the year, i.e. in spring and during extremely cold months. Calcined magnesite in small amounts is often applied to spring pastures so that it can be eaten by the animal when grazing.

With milking cows, one of the most common and costly diseases is mastitis. Seventy-five per cent of reported cases of mastitis could have been prevented by proper milking routine methods on the farm (p. 226).

Dry Period

Cows which have been dried off in summer months are susceptible to summer mastitis. This is usually caused by the germ *Corynebacterium pyogenes*. Since this disease invariably results in a useless quarter and often in the death of the animal, any preventive action which can be taken is important (p. 226).

PREVENTION OF DISEASE IN CALVES UP TO SIX MONTHS OF AGE

The first six months of a calf's life is often described as the baby calf period. During this period particular attention must be paid to housing, feeding and hygiene, so as to prevent the possible occurrence of disease (see Table 16.2).

Housing

Calves should preferably be housed singly in pens built of solid walls. Three or four calves at the most should occupy one pen. The building should be well insulated, well ventilated, free from draughts, particularly down-draughts, well lighted and well drained. Such housing will keep the calves warm and contented.

Feeding

When a calf is born it has but one functional stomach and no resistance to disease. Bearing these facts in mind a sound feeding routine involves:

1. *Feeding colostrum* during first 2 days when antibodies can be absorbed. This substance is rich in protein, minerals and antibodies. It is the ideal food for the yet untried digestive system of the animal. It confers on the calf a high level of immunity against disease to which it is susceptible.

2. *Milk feeding*. Since the calf is susceptible to digestive disorders, particularly stomach clotting and scouring, milk should be fed:

i) at body temperature, i.e. 35–37.7°C;
ii) as three feeds per day evenly spaced;
iii) as slowly as possible;
iv) preferably diluted with up to 25% of its volume of water.

3. *Supplying vitamins A, D and E* either by adding to the food or by injection. This will prevent rickets, eye weaknesses and muscle wasting.

Hygiene

It is particularly important to ensure that the surroundings of young calves are scrupulously clean and free from bacteria.

Such conditions can be promoted by ensuring that:

i) calving takes place in clean, disinfected, well-littered calving pens;
ii) the umbilical cord is sprayed with an antibiotic dressing and inspected daily for 10 days;
iii) calf pens are clean, disinfected and littered with clean straw before each new batch of calves is installed;
iv) Feeding utensils are kept scrupulously clean by daily scrubbing and sterilizing with boiling water or steam;
v) old, flaked paintwork is removed from doors and internal fittings (paints with lead bases cause poisoning);
vi) drainage of pens is adequate and dung is removed regularly. Care should also be taken that no twine or plastic bags are left in the bedding as these will be eaten by the calves and string balls formed in the stomach;
vii) the quarters are well ventilated to prevent pneumonia.

PREVENTION OF DISEASE IN YOUNG STOCK

After 6 months of age the main purpose of feeding and management is to produce sturdy, well grown, disease-resistant heifers which are not too fat (Table 16.2). Careful observance of the following guiding rules will help considerably in this respect.

Feeding

1. Ensure that the drinking water is always fresh and clean.
2. Encourage calves to eat concentrates and hay as early as possible.
3. Feed silage, kale or roots together with a synthetic supplement so as to supply animals with vitamins A and D.
4. Provide ample mineral supplies in the forms of licks, powders or mineralized milk substitutes.
5. So as to prevent infertility and calving difficulties in heifers, feed:

i) balanced maintenance ration of good hay or silage;
ii) silage or kale rich in vitamins;
iii) 0.4–0.9 kg of dairy concentrates.

Housing

1. House in well-lighted, airy and clean buildings.
2. Remove dung and disinfect buildings before a new batch of young calves are turned in.
3. Scrape down old woodwork and scorch with blowlamp so as to avoid ringworm, salmonella; purpose-built sheds with metal fittings are easier to disinfect.

Grazing

1. Do not turn out on to continuously used calf paddocks; calf paddocks should be regularly ploughed and reseeded.
2. Turn out calves when a month old if adequate milk, fresh concentrates and hay are fed. Such exercise will prove invaluable to calves and keep them healthy.
3. Dose 6-month old calves for worms a month after they have been turned out on to the grass. This will kill any stomach or intestinal worms they have picked up during grazing.
4. Never allow young stock to graze on pastures which have just carried adult stock unless they have been vaccinated against husk. This will reduce the incidence of husk amongst young stock.
5. Allow the dew to rise from herbage before allowing calves out to graze; bring them in to buildings before the dew drops in the evening. This prevents the calves from picking up the free-swimming larval stages of parasites.

Table 16.2. Prevention of disease in calves and young stock.

Disease	Disease prevention by:			Disease
	Management	Period	Feeding	
White scour	Clean and disinfect pen	Birth	Colostrum	White scour
Johne's disease	Remove from dam and vaccinate			
Navel or joint ill	Disinfect navel. Treat calf			
Pneumonia	Good, warm, well-ventilated, clean housing	Up to six months old	Good feeding routine and clean utensils	Digestive upsets and scours
Colds			Small quantities of vitamins in food, adequate calcium and phosphorus	Rickets, eye weakness, muscle atrophy
Ringworm				
		Six months	Fresh pastures, not grazed by adult stock. Kept inside until dew rises	Husk
Ringworm	House in well-lighted, airy, clean buildings. Scrape old woodwork, burn with blow-lamp. Treat with spray and/or oral dosing	Onwards – young growing stock	Fresh pastures not grazed by adult stock. 1 dose of worm medicine	Stomach and intestinal worms
			Ponds etc. fenced off. Segregated from adult stock. Uncontaminated food	Johne's disease
			Adequate supplies of vitamins A and D and minerals	Lack of good strong growth
			Good balanced rations	Infertility
Summer mastitis	Check teats frequently for sores and treat. Apply fly repellent. Practice Dry Cow therapy	1st Service onwards		

Other Measures

1. Observe the preventive measures described under Johne's disease (p. 231).

2. Vaccinate against salmonella if necessary; vaccines for general bacterial infections are available.

DISEASES MAINLY AFFECTING ADULT ANIMALS

Bacterial Diseases

Tuberculosis

This disease has been largely eradicated from cattle in Great Britain.

It is a disease that can affect all parts of the body, and can be transmitted to human beings via the milk. Some wild animals, such as badgers in some areas, are reservoirs of infection. Humans occasionally transmit it to cattle.

Most cattle are subjected to an intra-dermal test every two or three years according to the ruling of the Ministry of Agriculture. This is done by injecting into the skin a small amount of tuberculin. This is produced from the tuberculosis bacillus. Positive reactions show a swelling at the site of injection. Because the disease is now very rare in this country, tuberculin testing is reviewed periodically.

Brucellosis

This has been virtually eliminated from the U.K. Its features were premature calving generally at 5–7 months of pregnancy with subsequent serious infertility problems. It is infectious and affects humans.

By law all abortions have to be reported to a veterinary surgeon. He will then send swabs of blood and milk to the Veterinary Investigation Laboratory.

The suspected case has to be kept in isolation until the test is completed. If negative, the cow is again tested after a period; if positive, she is slaughtered, and the whole herd tested twice.

Mastitis

There are five main forms of this disease – streptococcal, staphylococcal, summer mastitis, *E. coli* mastitis and gangrenous mastitis.

Streptococcal
Caused by *S. agalactiae* or *S. dysgalactiae*.
   Symptoms:
   i) Swollen udder and quarter.
   ii) Milk yield may drop.
   iii) Milk may be watery with clots.

Treatment: Penicillin is generally effective, either as an injection or as an insertion into the udder.

Staphylococcal
Caused by several types of staphylococci, especially when accompanied by stress resulting from liver fluke, cold conditions, bad milking techniques, etc.
   Symptoms:
   i) Generally more severe than streptococcal mastitis.
   ii) One or more quarters swollen and painful.
   iii) Milk watery or yellow and sometimes large clots.
   iv) High temperature – 38.5°C.
   v) Symptoms may be so severe that the cow stops feeding, collapses and dies in a few hours.

Treatment: A broad spectrum antibiotic should be used promptly in a severe case.

Prevention and control: Where a mastitis problem exists a veterinary surgeon should be consulted; knowing which organism is responsible is essential in deciding the correct course of action.

   i) Organize a proper milking routine.
   ii) Avoid overmilking.
   iii) Check vacuum pressure and pulsation rates.
   iv) Renew teat liners frequently.
   v) Treat sores promptly.
   vi) Wear rubber gloves and dip in disinfectant solution frequently.
   vii) Use strip cup or other mastitis detector.
   viii) Adopt a strict hygiene standard.
   ix) Dip clusters between milking in water at 85°C for 5 seconds or better still sterilize them.
   x) Use teat dip containing an emollient.
   xi) Do not hurry cows with dogs.
   xii) De-horn all cows.
   xiii) Insert Dry Cow antibiotic into the quarters for the dry period.
   xiv) Keep up to date through the many publications available on the new approaches to the problem of mastitis.

Summer mastitis
Caused by the pus-producing *Corynebacterium pyogenes*.
   Treatment: Can be cured by antibiotics in the earliest stage. The bacteria destroy the udder tissues so that full recovery is rare.

Treatment is aimed at saving the animal's life and avoiding a premature calving; it should be under veterinary direction.
   Prevention:
   i) Examine dry cows daily and treat all sores.
   ii) Insert penicillin tube in each quarter of the udder once monthly.
   iii) Isolate affected cows.
   iv) Seal teats with plastic solution when they are turned out dry.
   v) Apply fly repellent to dry cows and heifers in summer.

E. coli mastitis
This is caused by a combination of stress and filthy conditions in cubicles and sheds; it is usually very acute and can cause rapid death.

Gangrenous mastitis
   Symptoms:
   i) May begin as a staphylococcal mastitis.
   ii) Cow becomes very ill.
   iii) Udder becomes blue and cold.
   iv) If the cow lives, the udder or affected quarter drops off.

   Treatment:
   i) Isolate cow.
   ii) Immediate antibiotic injections when symptoms are seen.

Retained Afterbirth

   Causes:
   i) Interference at calving.
   ii) Premature calving.
   iii) Brucellosis.
   iv) Milk fever.
   v) *Vibrio foetus.*
   vi) Calving fatigue following a twin birth.

Treatment:
i) Isolate cow.
ii) If off her food or straining, inform the veterinary surgeon.
iii) Remove afterbirth – this should be done by a veterinary surgeon.

Foul-of-the-Foot

Cause: Damage to cleft of hoof and invasion by a germ, *Fusiformis necrophorus*. Mud, particularly in gateways, is a breeding-ground for it.

Symptoms:
i) Severe lameness.
ii) Foot is swollen up to fetlock or futher.
iii) Examination of the cleft shows an angry, evil-smelling ulceration. A stone or other foreign body may be lodged there.

Treatment:
i) Remove cause, e.g. stone, etc.
ii) Injection of antibiotics or sulphonamides.
iii) Keep the animal in clean box while recovering.

Prevention:
i) Keep treated animals in until recovered to avoid spreading infection.
ii) Dress infected gateways, etc., with lime.
iii) Keep cattle from infected pasture for three weeks if possible. The germ should die out in that time.
iv) Keep clean yards.
v) Supply footbath at entrance of milking parlour; it will wash away dirt and stones from the feet.

Salmonellosis in Adult Cattle

Salmonella dublin. Occurs particularly in South Wales; *S. typhimurium* and other varieties occur in many parts of Britain. Since these organisms cause food poisoning in man and are difficult to kill by cooking and processing, the disease is a serious menace to public health.

Salmonella is the commonest cause of scouring in calves but once they recover they do not usually remain carriers. Adult cattle are believed to remain carriers as long as they live.

Symptoms:
i) Off food, high temperature.
ii) Severe diarrhoea with blood clots in it.
iii) Collapse and death within about four days.
iv) Many cases of aborting with no apparent illness are due to *S. dublin*.

Treatment:
i) Isolate the animal.
ii) Use disinfectant liberally and dip boots, etc., after leaving the animal.
iii) Wear disposable gloves and protective clothing when handling the sick animal.
iv) Injections and oral dosing of various suitable antibiotics.

Prevention:
i) The wisest precaution is to get rid of any infected animal, recovered or not.
ii) Infection is often carried by pollution of rivers and streams; fence off all rivers, streams and ponds.
iii) Vaccination, which should only be carried out under veterinary supervision, since it can rekindle a latent infection and cause further spread.

Infectious bovine rhinotracheitis (I.B.R.)

This is a respiratory infection of cattle. It is widespread in Britain.

Symptoms: Severe difficulty in breathing with nasal and eye discharges. This occurs particularly during transit of a large number of animals with stress and lack of air. Most cases have mild attacks and mortality is low.

Treatment:
i) Administer antibiotics to prevent bacterial complications.
ii) A live vaccine may be administered but it is very expensive.
iii) Allow plenty of fresh air and tranquil environment.

Virus Diseases

Foot-and-Mouth Disease

Symptoms:
i) Reduced milk yield and appetite.
ii) Dribbling from mouth and reluctance to stand on feet.
iii) Blisters on the inside of the mouth and later sores on the top of hooves.
iv) High temperature.
v) Disease spreads rapidly.

Preventative action:
i) Restrict movements of stock and notify the local police of suspected outbreak.
ii) When foot-and-mouth disease is confirmed, all animals with cloven hooves on the farm are shot and burnt. Buildings are thoroughly

cleaned with disinfectant before allowing new stock to inhabit the farm.

External Parasitic Diseases

Warble Fly (Fig. 16.1)

Treatment: Any warble infection in the herd has to be reported to the Divisional Veterinary Officer. If it is confirmed, all the cattle over 12 weeks old are treated. It is compulsory also for a second treatment in the autumn where spring infection has been detected.

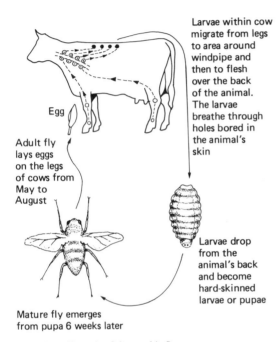

Larvae within cow migrate from legs to area around windpipe and then to flesh over the back of the animal. The larvae breathe through holes bored in the animal's skin

Egg

Adult fly lays eggs on the legs of cows from May to August

Larvae drop from the animal's back and become hard-skinned larvae or pupae

Mature fly emerges from pupa 6 weeks later

Fig. 16.1 Life cycle of the warble fly.

It is advisable to dress the cattle in the autumn voluntarily. It is hoped that this policy will result in the eventual extinction of the warble fly.

Ticks

Cause and symptoms: Oval insect-like organisms found adhering to the armpits and inside of thighs. They sometimes carry red-water fever and other diseases.

Treatment: Rub fat or goose-grease over them to block their breathing vents. They then drop off.

Lice

Cause and symptoms: Lice are much smaller than ticks and they are highly mobile. A severe infestation leads to loss of condition, wasting and anaemia.

Treatment: Dust affected areas with derris.

Metabolic Diseases

Milk Fever

This generally occurs during the three days after calving. It can, however, be seen before calving and late in the lactation.

Symptoms:
i) The cow loses interest in the calf and in food.
ii) Paddles stiffly with her hind legs.
iii) Constipation.
iv) Subnormal temperature.
v) She sways drunkenly on moving, and finally collapses.
vi) When down, the head is turned back resting on the shoulder.
vii) In extreme cases the cow becomes completely unconscious and dies.

Cause: A temporary lowering of the calcium content of the blood due to some hormonal upset, leading to a disorder of the brain. It occurs usually in cows after the third calving onwards, but is occasionally seen in first and second calves. High-yielders are the most susceptible.

Prevention:
i) Ensure adequate mineral supplement to the diet.
ii) Inject vitamin D_3 during pregnancy as directed.
iii) Reduce the protein content of food and replace with extra carbohydrates two weeks before calving. Leave off 'steaming up' a few days before calving.
iv) Do not strip the udder completely for three days after calving.
v) Inject cow with calcium borogluconate after calving.

Treatment:
i) Inject calcium borogluconate subcutaneously or intravenously. The latter needs skill and should be left to the veterinary surgeon.
ii) Do not drench or you may choke the animal.
iii) A cow that is liable to have milk fever should either be in a loose-box or tied with a halter. If she is tethered in her standing she might collapse and strangle herself.

Hypomagnesaemia

Symptoms:
i) Acute excitement which often results in death within a few minutes.

ii) In less acute cases, muscular tremors, flickering eyelids and increased excitability occur.

iii) When the disease is milder and prolonged, it results in loss of condition and a drop in milk yield.

Cause: A sudden drop in the magnesium content of the blood. It occurs mainly in spring shortly after the cows have been turned out to graze. In beef and dry dairy cattle, outbreaks usually occur in the cold months of the year. It often occurs in cattle which graze on pastures heavily dressed with nitrogenous fertilizers. It is also seen in cows suckling calves on a sudden flush of aftermath which is deficient in magnesium.

Prevention:

i) Feed 50 g calcined magnesite daily; as this compound is unpalatable, it is often mixed with moist sugar-beet pulp. The response is wholly satisfactory in some cases; *or*

ii) Ensure that the cows have access to mineral mixtures containing magnesium all the year round and during the spring and autumn particularly; *or*

iii) Treat the herd with magnesium alloy bullets in spring and autumn. These are slowly eroded inside the animal's stomach over a period of about 6 weeks, thus ensuring sufficient magnesium for the duration of the worst period; *or*

iv) Feed magnesium cake.

v) See that cattle have enough food. Often the disease is seen on aftermath and spring grass which may be plentiful but of little nutrient value. The cows may be suckling one or more calves; they lose condition quickly due to starvation.

vi) Dress pasture with calcium magnesite (28 kg/ha).

Treatment: Inject a solution of 20% magnesium sulphate subcutaneously. Most cases do not recover because of brain and cardiac haemorrhages.

Acetonaemia

Symptoms:

i) Poor appetite and may refuse to eat cake.

ii) Cudding is infrequent.

iii) Dung hard, black and shiny.

iv) Cow walks unsteadily.

v) Milk yield drops gradually.

vi) Sweet-smelling milk and urine.

Cause: It usually occurs in high-yielding cattle feeding on too much cake rich in protein. There is a general deficiency of sugar in the diet which hinders the correct breakdown of fat. Ketones are produced and passed into the bloodstream. The disease often occurs 6 weeks after calving.

Prevention:

i) Feed adequate quantities of good-quality hay.

ii) Exercise high-yielding animals regularly.

iii) Add molasses to steaming-up ration.

Treatment: This involves injections or oral doses of cortisone by a veterinary surgeon. Small doses of potassium chlorate or potassium acetate also work well but require care in administration.

Bloat

Symptoms: This is a sudden swelling of the rumen seen on the left flank, rapidly filling the right flank as well. Breathing becomes laboured and finally the pressure of the stomach gases paralyses the heart and lungs and the animal collapses and dies.

Milder cases recover of their own accord.

Cause: See p. 217.

Prevention:

i) Feed daily rations of hay to cows before turning them out on to rich spring pastures.

ii) *Either* (a) control amount of succulent grass grazed by means of an electric fence, *or* (b) cut grass and allow to wilt before allowing stock to graze.

Treatment: In mild cases, drench with 20 ml of medicinal oil of turpentine in half a litre of milk or soapy water to emulsify the turpentine. In extreme cases, the rumen has to be punctured in the left flank to allow gases to escape. Unfortunately the gas is usually mixed with the ruminal contents forming a thick foam. The rumen should then be opened for 10–12 cm to allow the mass to escape and relieve the enormous pressure, thus saving the animal's life. The wound generally heals up in a few weeks.

Bloat can be so sudden that the stockman has to save the animal himself; the veterinary surgeon can advise beforehand the exact location for puncturing.

DISEASES MAINLY AFFECTING BABY CALVES

Bacterial Diseases

White Scour

Symptoms:
i) Scouring occurs a few hours or a few days after birth.
ii) Calf appears dull and dejected; it either refuses to suck or sucks listlessly.
iii) Greyish-white diarrhoea forms which has a sour smell.
iv) Calf may be so weak that it is unable to stand; its eyes are usually sunken.
v) Usually occurs between February and April.
vi) Blood appears in diarrhoea if the infection is due to salmonella.

Cause: Natural scouring is usually caused by chills or indigestion. White scour is caused by bacterial infection of the intestines. Two main types of bacteria cause the disease – coliform bacteria and salmonella.

Prevention:
i) Clean and disinfect pens before allowing access to calves.
ii) Isolate newly purchased calves until they become adjusted to their new surroundings.
iii) Ensure that feeding pails have been scrupulously scrubbed and sterilized.
iv) Ensure that colostrum is fed; calves deprived of colostrum are far more susceptible to scour.
v) Plan building layout so that a sensible system of calf-rearing can be adopted.
vi) Vaccinate with a suitable vaccine.

Treatment:
i) Isolate calves and keep them warm with straw bales, sacking or infra-red heat.
ii) Stop feeding milk and give a solution of electrolytes as per instruction of the veterinary surgeon.
iii) Treat with antibiotic and vitamin injections.
iv) Isolate calves whose body temperature readings are over 38.9°C.

Navel or Joint Ill

Symptoms:
i) Joints, particularly hocks and knees, are swollen and painful; navel is swollen and an abscess may have formed.
ii) Calf may grunt and groan and death may occur rapidly.

Cause: Infection by bacteria entering the body through the navel cord by contamination with dirt and sucking by other calves.

Prevention:
i) Provide scrupulously clean and disinfected calving pen and calf pens.
ii) Spray navel with antibiotic dressing.
iii) Place in single pens.
iv) Vaccinate new-born calves.

Treatment:
i) Injections of antibiotics.
ii) Send carcasses to veterinary investigation laboratory to identify the organism responsible. The disease is generally fatal or leaves the joints permanently damaged.

Metabolic Diseases

Vitamin A and D Deficiency

Symptoms:
i) Calves appear unthrifty and sometimes scour.
ii) Vision may be impaired; calves may bump into standing objects in dull light.
iii) Coats are scurfy and staring.
iv) Deficiency of these vitamins makes the calves less resistant to ringworm.

Cause: This is due to lack of vitamins A and D in the dam's milk. It is far more likely to occur when animals are kept indoors.

Prevention and treatment:
i) Ensure calves have colostrum.
ii) Inject vitamin mixture.

Miscellaneous Troubles

Lead Poisoning

Symptoms:
i) Fits and convulsions occur.
ii) Blindness.
iii) High temperature.
iv) Diarrhoea.
v) Unthriftiness.

Cause: Lead is highly toxic to animals. Young calves often lick paint which contains lead as a base and mortar from walls in areas of old lead mines. There is a great deal of containination of herbage by lead in these areas. Soft water can dissolve lead from pipes of that metal and cause poisoning.

Prevention:
i) Scrape down old, flaked paintwork.
ii) Cover doors of calf pens with zinc, aluminium, or asbestos sheet.
iii) Never paint anything in calf pens with lead paints.
iv) Supply a mineral lick.

Treatment: Lead poisoning can be acute or chronic and treatment varies accordingly.

To treat acute lead poisoning:
i) Drench with 15–30 g Epsom salts several times a day in order to precipitate the lead as lead sulphate.
ii) Remove cause of the poisoning.
iii) Inject vitamins and antibiotics.

Lead may be absorbed over a period and is stored in the bones, giving rise to chronic lead poisoning. Treatment involves drugs which extract it from the bones but not too quickly, because otherwise the concentration in the blood might become too high and acute poisoning occur. It is best carried out under veterinary direction.

Hair Balls

Symptoms:
i) Fits and convulsions occur.

ii) Calves may champ their jaws, froth and kick.
iii) Sight is slightly impaired and calves may run blindly around pens.

Cause: Any hair or fibrous matter eaten by the young calf forms a hair ball in the stomach which it is incapable of digesting. A calf picks up straw, twine and other material from its food or bedding; it may also lick areas of its hairy coat which are a source of irritation.

Prevention:
i) Ensure that no binder twine or plastic bags are left within the calf's reach.
ii) Treat all irritated areas of skin.
iii) Feed a little good-quality fresh hay to prevent straw eating.
iv) Muzzle calves with depraved appetites and correct with proper diet.
v) Provide individual calf pens or tie up calves during feeding time.

Cross-Suckling

This often results in damaged teats which may cause considerable trouble when the calf has grown and is producing milk. Cross-suckling can be prevented either by installing individual calf pens or by leaving calves tied up for half an hour after feeding.

DISEASES MAINLY AFFECTING YOUNG GROWING ANIMALS

Bacterial Diseases

Johne's Disease

Symptoms:
i) Animal quickly loses flesh although it eats well.
ii) Profuse scouring occurs and the dung sometimes contains bubbles.
iii) In advanced cases a swelling appears between the jaw bones, i.e. bottle jaw.

Cause: It is caused by *Mycobacterium johnei*, which is closely related to the tuberculosis bacillus. It lives and multiplies in the intestines causing thickening and corrugations of the intestinal wall. This impairs digestion and absorption of foodstuffs and starvation ensues. The bacterium can be picked up from the dam's teats by suckling calves. Contaminated ponds, ditches and streams are also a source of infection.

Prevention:
i) Fence off all streams, ponds and ditches.

ii) Set drinking troughs as high as possible to prevent contamination from animal dung.
iii) Ensure that indoor food is not splashed by dung.
iv) Segregate young stock from adult stock.
v) Where the disease is a serious menace, remove calf from dam at birth; such a calf should be vaccinated in the dewlap during its first few days of life; Ministry of Agriculture, Fisheries and Food permission has to be given for this to take place.

Treatment: None.

Fungal Diseases

Ringworm

Symptoms: Rounded, white, scurfy scabs all over the body but particularly on head and neck.
Cause: It is caused by a fungus. Spores are picked up from other animals or from dirty sheds, and rubbed into the skin. The spores

germinate and form a mycelium. The scab is flesh infected with such a mycelium. The fungus is highly contagious and can be handed on to persons handling such animals. It generally clears up when the cattle are turned out in summer.

Treatment:
i) Apply suitable fungicide, particularly round the edges of the lesions where the spores are active; fungicide sprays are available.
ii) Drench with systemic drugs or add to the feed.
iii) Inject vitamins A and D.
iv) Handler should wear protective clothing and gloves.
v) After treating infected animals clean out calf pens as follows:

(a) Burn all bedding.
(b) Scrape down walls and scrub with a hot soda solution.
(c) Flame all woodwork with a blowlamp and then apply creosote.

Internal Parasitic Diseases

Husk (Fig. 16.2)

Symptoms:
i) Paroxysms of coughing.
ii) Animal becomes thin – 'a bag of bones'.
iii) Pneumonia frequently sets in.
iv) Usually affects stock between 6 and 18 months old.

Prevention:
i) Plough, re-seed, and rotate calf pastures.
ii) Do not turn out young stock when dew is on the grass.
iii) Do not allow young stock to follow adult stock when grazing. Turn them out on to uncontaminated fresh pastures.
iv) Young stock turned out very early pick up a few worms and become resistant to further infection.
v) Give an oral vaccine. This is the larvae of the husk worm treated by X-rays thus

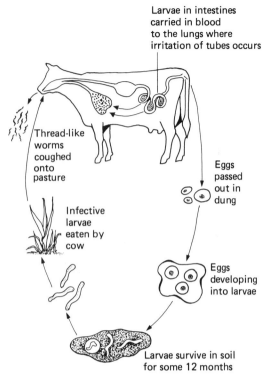

Fig. 16.2 Life cycle of the causative lungworm.

limiting their migration through the body. After drenching the larvae migrate to the mesenteric lymph glands and remain there stimulating the creation of antibodies in the blood. This prevents the development of husk in the animal.

Treatment:
i) Bring in to dry feeding.
ii) Treat with a suitable parasiticide.

Liver Fluke

This disease is described in chapter 17 (p. 239).

Stomach and Intestinal Worms

These are described in chapter 17 (p. 240).

17

Health and Disease in Sheep

In sheep farming, as well as in all other types of livestock farming, prevention of disease is much better and usually much cheaper than cure.

The most effective means of disease prevention is a sound system of husbandry. A well-fed, thriving sheep resists the onset of disease much more effectively than a weak, ill-fed sheep. Trouble from foot-rot, worms and pregnancy toxaemia, for example, can be greatly reduced by good husbandry. In addition, the sheep farmer has many vaccines, sera, and other medicines to help him in his task. It must be stressed, however, that the use of these is not an excuse for bad husbandry, and indeed without good husbandry, medicines alone could hardly keep the flock totally free from disease.

It is also being realized more and more that the greater the stocking density, the greater the likelihood of diseases such as foot-rot and stomach worms occurring. Heavy stocking leads to a 'build-up' of germs and parasites in the soil and, therefore, increases the risk of infection. Management techniques must, therefore, be designed to reduce the risk of infection and the spread of troubles such as these.

DISEASE PREVENTION IN THE MANAGEMENT CYCLE OF THE EWE FLOCK

In this section, the breeding cycle of sheep is described in relation to disease prevention (Table 17.1, p. 234). More detailed information on some of the most common diseases is given in the last part of this chapter.

Flushing and Tupping

Two weeks before flushing, ewes which are entering into their second breeding season can be given the first injection of a vaccine which gives immunity against lamb dysentery, pulpy kidney, struck, braxy, blackleg and post-parturient gangrene, black disease and tetanus.

As the flock is turned on to fresh pasture for flushing, measures can be taken to ensure that the sheep do not bring with them foot-rot bacteria and stomach worms.

In order to reduce the worm infestation, the ewes should be dosed with a suitable anthelmintic before they are turned on to the clean pasture. This will greatly reduce the number of worm eggs passed in the sheep droppings on to the new pastures.

In the case of foot-rot, the feet of ewes should be examined and trimmed if necessary. The flock should then be run through a foot-bath containing a 5% formalin solution before turning the sheep on to a clean pasture.

Great care should be taken to ensure that the ram does not introduce any disease into the flock. It is especially important to treat it for worms and foot-rot before it runs with the ewes.

Pregnancy

Maintaining the ewes in a 'store' condition during early pregnancy and then steaming up during the last 6 weeks before lambing helps to avoid twin-lamb disease occurring later on. It is essential, however, that the ewes do not lose condition during early pregnancy as this would lower their strength and hence their resistance to diseases in general.

Table 17.1. Prevention of disease during the breeding cycle of the ewe flock

Disease	Disease prevention by:				Disease
	Management			Feeding	
Worms	Dosing	Wks 3*	Dry period		
Pulpy kidney, tetanus, lamb dysentery, struck, braxy, blackleg, post-parturient gangrene, Black Disease	Vaccine	2			
Foot-rot	Foot inspection, paring, footbath	1			
Abortion	Segregation. Burn foetuses		Flushing, tupping	New pastures free from infection	Worms and foot-rot germs
Worms and liver fluke	Dosing				
Foot-rot	Foot inspection, paring, foot-bath		Early pregnancy	Moderate level of feeding	
Worms	Dosing	6†			Pregnancy toxaemia
		5			
		4			
		3	Late pregnancy	Increase concentrates	
Pulpy kidney, etc.	Inject and dose ewes	2			
		1		Dose with copper	Sway-back of lambs
Gas gangrene	Strict hygiene when assisting lambing; antibiotic injections		Lambing	New pasture free from infection	Worms, foot-rot germs, etc.
				Calcium borogluconate	Lambing sickness (milk fever)
Liver fluke	Dosing		Suckling period	Magnesium bullets or cake	Grass staggers
Worms	Dosing		Weaning		
Mastitis	Careful watch on udder				
Foot-rot	Foot inspection, paring, foot-bath, antibiotic applications		Dry period		
Blow-fly	Crutching and dipping				
Keds, lice, mites, ticks	Dipping				

* Before tupping.
† Before lambing.

Certain other routine preventative measures can also be carried out during pregnancy. A second dose of anthelmintic to get rid of worms could be given during early pregnancy. The feet of the flock could be examined for foot-rot and treated accordingly. Where fluke exists, measures could be taken at this time (p. 239).

In flocks liable to swayback, injections must be given during pregnancy.

Two weeks before lambing, the second of the two vaccinations against lamb dysentery, pulpy kidney, etc., should be administered.

When dosing and vaccinating ewes, especially during the latter stages of pregnancy, they must be handled very carefully. Mishandling and over-excitement could lead to injury and abortion, which would cause a greater loss than some of the diseases being guarded against.

Lambing

Young lambs are very susceptible to disease organisms. It is advisable for lambing to take place in different fields in consecutive years; lambing should not take place in fields which have been carrying sheep for many months prior to lambing.

Aborted and dead lambs, or other dead sheep, should be taken to the laboratory to verify cause of death and avoid further outbreaks.

The shepherd's hands should be clean before assisting a lambing. Internal examination of the ewe should be undertaken with great care and any acute difficulty with birth should be left to the veterinary surgeon to deal with. Any interference with the ewe should be followed by an antibiotic injection.

Before lambing hypocalcaemia may occur and afterwards hypomagnesaemia. The udder should be checked during the handling.

Suckling Period

It is important that the ewe should produce as much milk as possible during this period. Diseases such as worms, liver fluke, and foot-rot will certainly lower the milk production of the ewe; infected ewes are also ready sources of infection to the susceptible lambs.

If the dosing against liver fluke has not been carried out, a routine dosing in spring is always advisable.

Weaning and Rest Period

A routine dosing against worms is advisable at weaning time. Until the ewes dry up, signs of mastitis should be watched for.

Blow-fly is active during this summer period. Shearing away the wool from the hind-quarters ('crutching') will prevent the soiling of this body area with dung and urine, an attractive breeding-ground for the fly; a suitable fly repellent can be used. Sheep must be dipped for a full minute between June 14th and September 5th in the approved scab dip unless slaughtered during this period; this is also helpful in controlling blow-fly, keds, mites, lice and ticks. Ticks spread the diseases of tick-borne fever, louping ill and tick pyaemia; there is, therefore, an added advantage in destroying these.

The summer is also a suitable time for really intensified treatment of heavy worm and foot-rot infections, as outlined on pp. 240 and 238.

From April to September, the danger of possible infections by liver fluke can be reduced by draining wet patches and dressing ditches and other wet areas with copper sulphate or other molluscides, in order to reduce the number of snails, which are the intermediate hosts of the fluke.

Any scouring in the flock should be checked by taking a specimen of faeces to the veterinary surgeon. This may show the presence of some worm or other disease and the correct measure can be taken.

PREVENTION OF DISEASE IN YOUNG AND GROWING LAMBS

Lambs are born without a natural immunity to any disease organisms. They only obtain this immunity from the antibodies present in the mother's colostrum. Table 17.2 summarizes the prevention of disease in young and growing lambs.

Lambs are susceptible to lamb dysentery from 1 to 10 days of age and to pulpy kidney from 3 to 8 weeks of age. Since both these diseases are often fatal, it is very important to give the lambs immunity. This can be done by vaccinating the ewes as previously indicated or by injecting the new-born lambs with serum. This stimulates them to produce suitable antibodies which are transmitted to the lambs in the colostrum, thereby giving them protection.

Young lambs are also very susceptible to worm infestation. They pick up these worms as soon as they start nibbling at the grass. Once grass forms a major part of their diet, the pick-up of worms can be very heavy, especially with intensive stocking.

When this period arrives, it is wise to allow the lambs to graze on clean pastures. A system of 'creep' grazing on fresh, new leys, ensures that the lambs pick up very few worms. This prevents the ewes contaminating the lambs' grazings (see p. 177).

The lambs are moved forward to a new paddock every 3–4 days, i.e., before any eggs in their droppings reach the infective larval stage.

If such a system of grazing is not employed, dosing at 6 weeks of age, and subsequently every 3 weeks, will also keep the number of worms to a minimum; cake incorporating an anthelmintic can be fed.

Grazing the young lambs on a fresh first-year ley also ensures that the land is free from the

Table 17.2. Prevention of disease in young and growing lambs

Disease	Disease prevention by:				Disease
	Management	Wks*	*Lambing*	*Feeding*	
Navel ill / *Tetanus*	Antiseptic oil on cuts and disinfection of navel		*Lambing*	Clean lambing pastures	*Worms* / *Navel ill* / *Tetanus*
Sway-back, lamb dysentery, pulpy kidney	Adequate copper in ewe's diet; administer copper if necessary. Vaccination of ewe	1			
		2	*Suckling – grass intake increases*		
		3			
Worms	Dosing	4		New ley	*Nematodirus and other worms*
		5			
		6		Salt licks containing cobalt	*Pining*
		7			
		8			
		9		Creep grazing	*Worms*
		10			
		11			
		12	*Weaning*	Clean pasture	*Worms*
		13			
Foot-rot	Foot inspection, paring and foot-bath, antibiotic applications	14			
		15			
		16			
		17			
Blow-fly, etc.	Crutching and dipping	18			
		19			
		20			
		21			

* From birth.

eggs of the nematodirus worm. The unhatched eggs of this worm will survive in pastures in large numbers for up to 12 months. Heavy infestations of this worm bring rapid illness and many deaths.

All growing lambs are usually docked and the males castrated. Methods which do not provide wounds for entry of anaerobic germs are preferable, e.g., use of the elastrator. Docking and castration wounds often allow the entry of the bacterium responsible for tetanus or lock-jaw.

It is also wise to be on the look-out for such troubles as foot-rot, blow-fly, etc. This is even more necessary when lambs are not fattened off until mid or late summer.

Finally, it should be borne in mind that a flock of sheep will develop a certain amount of resistance to many disease organisms present in the sheep's environment. There is, therefore, always a danger when new sheep join the flock that they will introduce bacteria against which the home flock has a low natural resistance. On the other hand, the bought sheep might also have a lower natural resistance against the strains of bacteria present on the new farm; this might result in a flare-up of disease in these imported animals which might spread to the other sheep in the home flock.

SPECIFIC DISEASES

The remainder of this chapter is concerned with a detailed description of the causes, symptoms, prevention and treatment of the more common diseases of sheep.

Bacterial Diseases

Lambing Sickness

Cause: Various types of bacteria picked up from the soil.

Symptoms:
  i) Ewes generally become ill about 2 days after lambing.
 ii) Lambing passage and surrounding tissues become swollen and dark red.
iii) Blood-tinged fluids seep out from tail and thighs.
 iv) Rapid collapse and death.

Prevention:
  i) Use a 'clean' field for lambing. Practise strict hygiene at lambing time.
 ii) Assist lambings only with clean hands. Dress cuts and abrasions with antiseptic.
iii) Vaccinate ewe about 2 weeks before tupping and 2 weeks before lambing. This is one of the diseases guarded against by using the combined vaccine for lamb dysentery, etc. (see p. 233).
 iv) Lambing sickness may lurk in pens or sheds, therefore strict disinfection should be carried out early.

Treatment: Antibiotic injections.

Lamb Dysentery

Cause: Anaerobic bacteria which enter the lamb's body, multiply and produce poisons which are readily absorbed into the bloodstream. On the pasture, the bacteria form resting spores which are very resistant to weather and destruction. Thus land remains infected and capable of infecting for a very long time.

Symptoms:
  i) Many lambs found dead.
 ii) Scouring when 1–10 days old, dying very quickly.

Prevention:
  i) Practise sound hygiene at lambing, by using clean pasture and burying dead lambs.

 ii) Stimulate the ewes to produce immunity and transmit it to the lambs in the colostrum by injection with a combined vaccine 2 weeks before flushing and 2 weeks after flushing. Ewes in their first pregnancy, however, should be injected 8 and 2 weeks before lambing respectively.
iii) If ewes have not been vaccinated, inoculate lambs with lamb dysentery serum within 12 hours of birth.

Treatment: None.

Pulpy Kidney

Cause: Anaerobic bacteria present in the bowels. These are harmless until suitable conditions arise for them to produce poisons. These conditions occur when the diet of the lambs is suddenly changed, i.e., when lambs are moved from a poor pasture to a good pasture or a rape field. The germs can remain on the pastures for a very long time in the form of very resistant resting spores.

Symptoms:
  i) Usually some of the most forward lambs, of 6–16 weeks old, are found dead.
 ii) If seen alive (which is very seldom), the lambs appear dull and unable to stand. Twitching may occur, quickly followed by unconsciousness and death.

Prevention:
  i) Avoid sudden changes from poor to good, lush pastures.
  either
 ii) Inject ewes with the combined vaccine on the same lines as for lamb dysentery. Immunity is transmitted to lambs in the colostrum.
  or
iii) Vaccinate lambs with pulpy kidney vaccine at 10 days old and a month later. This vaccine produces immunity in about 14 days.
  or
 iv) Inoculate lambs with serum when 2–3 weeks old. This provides immunity for about 4 weeks; follow with vaccination. Each outbreak should be treated on its merit and veterinary advice sought.

Treatment: None.

Braxy

Cause: Bacteria picked up from the soil, which causes inflammation of the abomasum (fourth stomach).

Symptoms:
i) Mainly attacks young hill sheep in their first winter.
ii) Sudden deaths after severe autumn and early winter frosts; body becomes ballooned and rapidly decomposes.

Prevention:
i) Inject ewes with a combined vaccine about 14 days before lambing.
ii) Inject lambs with a combined vaccine when they are about 8–12 weeks of age, and in early autumn.

Treatment: None.

Black Disease

Cause: Bacteria picked up from soil which multiply within the liver of sheep damaged by liver fluke.

Symptoms:
i) Sudden death of adult ewes.
ii) Affected sheep linger behind other ewes, they eventually lie down and die.

Prevention:
i) Prevent liver fluke occurring.
ii) Diagnose disease quickly and inject flock with serum.
iii) Use combined vaccine as for braxy. Ewes and lambs are also injected in the following spring, and subsequently before flushing and lambing.

Treatment: Injection of antibiotics in early stages, but since the disease is rapidly fatal the chances of arresting it are few.

Abortion in Sheep

The most important is enzootic abortion, causing increasing losses every year, particularly in Scotland and North East England; it is as yet rare in other parts of Britain. Vaccination is possible but only on veterinary advice, since it may establish an infection in the flock.

Vibrionic Abortion

This occurs fairly frequently and is caused by an organism, *Vibrio foetus*; the incubation period is one week.

There is no cure or vaccination, but if aborted sheep are segregated immediately and the foetuses burnt the outbreak will peter out.

There are other organisms which cause abortion, but they occur infrequently.

Treatment:
i) Avoid stress by careful handling; supply shelter against bad weather.
ii) Vaccines may be of value, if given according to expert 'instruction'.

Pasteurellosis

This disease is becoming more common. It manifests itself in different forms, all caused by *Pasteurella haemolytica*, of which there are at least twelve different types. Enzootic pneumonia of adult ewes is one form; septicaemia, meningitis and joint ill of lambs is another.

Diagnosis is by postmortem examination. The disease in all forms is generally fatal in twelve hours.

Treatment:
i) Enzootic pneumonia responds well to antibiotics. It is advisable to treat the whole flock or group.
ii) Lambs do not respond so well owing to the spread of the disease in the body. Early widespread antibiotic therapy can be very successful.
iii) A vaccine is also available.

Foot-Rot (Fig. 17.1)

Cause: Bacteria which cause inflammation of the soft tissues underneath the horn of the foot.

Symptoms:
i) Lameness; usually beginning in front feet.
ii) Hot and tender feet; pieces of horn are soft and rotten.
iii) Bleeding feet containing foul-smelling matter.

Prevention:
i) Keep flock free of germs by:
   (a) regular examination and paring of feet;
   (b) regular use of foot-bath containing 5% formalin solution.
ii) Keep flock away from any infected land for at least 3 weeks.
iii) Rotate flock as often as possible.
iv) Do not allow sheep with infected feet to enter flock.
v) Vaccinate.

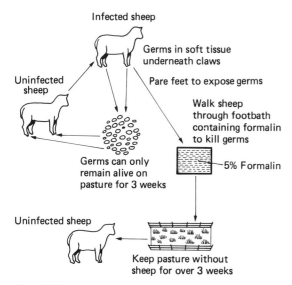

Fig. 17.1 Foot-rot; cycle of infection and control.

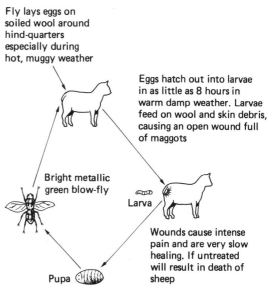

Fig. 17.2 Life cycle of the blow-fly.

Treatment:
i) Pare affected feet well.
ii) Treat with antibiotics or other prescribed dressing such as 5% formalin solution.
iii) If possible allow feet to dry on concrete floor.
iv) Turn out on to field which has not carried sheep for at least 3 weeks and keep separate from healthy flock.
v) Examine feet in about 3 days and repeat treatment if necessary.
vi) Return cured sheep to the flock.
vii) Examine whole flock in 3 weeks' time.
viii) Carry on treatment with sheep still infected and only allow to return to flock after complete cure.
ix) Cull the obstinate cases, thereby eliminating the carriers.

Prevention:
i) Cut away wool from tail region (crutching), because the fly is attracted by damp wool, smelling of dung and urine; use a fly repellent.
ii) Try and avoid excessive scouring due to worm infestation or too laxative a diet.
iii) Dip or spray with a suitable dressing.
iv) Keep a sharp look-out for any signs of strike and treat immediately.

Treatment:
i) If maggots have hatched but not caused wounds, dip sheep.
ii) Remove maggots from open wounds and dress with an antiseptic solution.
iii) Keep a careful watch on sheep, to see if the wounds are healing properly.
iv) Inject with antibiotic.

External Parasitic Diseases

Blow-Fly or Sheep Strike (Fig. 17.2)

Cause: The maggots of several species of blow-fly.

Symptoms:
i) Changed gait and signs of discomfort and pain after maggots have hatched out.
ii) If struck area is in back region, constant twitching of dock.
iii) Sheep tries to gnaw and rub infected part.
iv) Experienced shepherds spot a 'struck' sheep at a distance.

Internal Parasitic Diseases

Liver Fluke or Liver Rot (Fig. 17.3)

Cause: A leaf-like worm or fluke which destroys the liver tissue by burrowing through it.

Symptoms:
i) *Chronic fluke*
    (a) Poor condition and some scouring.
    (b) Accumulation of fluid underneath chin.
    (c) Pendulous abdomen and razor thin back.

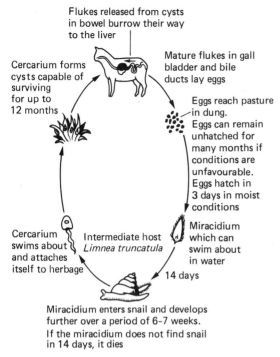

Flukes released from cysts in bowel burrow their way to the liver

Cercarium forms cysts capable of surviving for up to 12 months

Mature flukes in gall bladder and bile ducts lay eggs

Eggs reach pasture in dung. Eggs can remain unhatched for many months if conditions are unfavourable. Eggs hatch in 3 days in moist conditions

Cercarium swims about and attaches itself to herbage

Intermediate host *Limnea truncatula*

Miracidium which can swim about in water

14 days

Miracidium enters snail and develops further over a period of 6–7 weeks. If the miracidium does not find snail in 14 days, it dies

Fig. 17.3 Life cycle of the liver fluke.

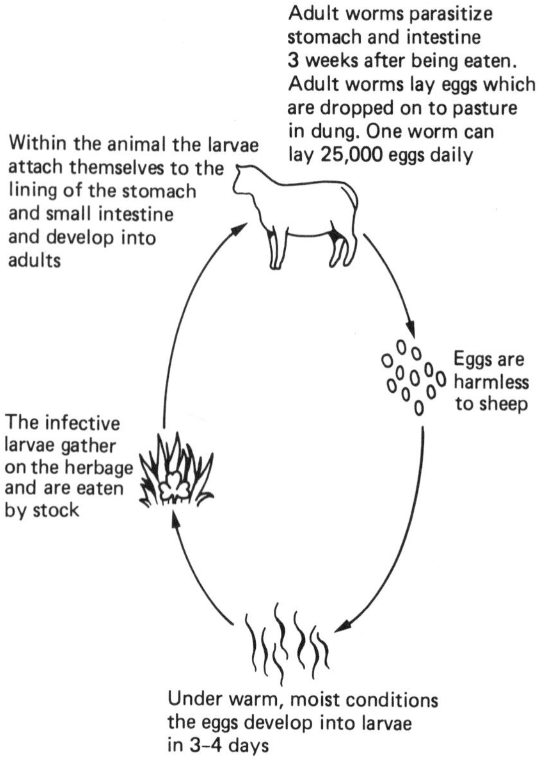

Adult worms parasitize stomach and intestine 3 weeks after being eaten. Adult worms lay eggs which are dropped on to pasture in dung. One worm can lay 25,000 eggs daily

Within the animal the larvae attach themselves to the lining of the stomach and small intestine and develop into adults

Eggs are harmless to sheep

The infective larvae gather on the herbage and are eaten by stock

Under warm, moist conditions the eggs develop into larvae in 3–4 days

Fig. 17.4 Life cycle of a parasitic roundworm found in a sheep.

ii) *Acute fluke*

Sudden death following a short illness.

Prevention:

i) Reduce the number of snails by draining wet places; dress ditches and damp places with a molluscicide. Reduction of the number of snails means that a large number of flukes die because they cannot find their intermediate host.

ii) Keep sheep away from the snail-infested areas; this also prevents the fluke from completing its life-cycle, thus reducing numbers.

iii) Destroy any mature flukes in the sheep by dosing in spring and autumn. In fluke-infested areas, the flock should be dosed monthly from October to April.

iv) Since cattle suffer from fluke, they should be dosed in October or November when brought in and again during the summer. This eliminates a burden of fluke from the cattle and ensures that they will not be carriers.

It is imperative that cattle *and* sheep are treated where fluke is known to exist.

Treatment:

i) Keep sheep in snail-free pastures.

ii) Dosing can be either by injection or oral dosing and even by feeding cake containing a suitable drug.

Care must be taken with some anti-fluke treatments, particularly in the pregnant animal, and veterinary advice should be followed.

Stomach and Intestinal Worms (Parasitic Gastritis) (Fig. 17.4)

Cause: Numerous species of roundworms which lead a parasitic existence in the stomach and intestines.

Symptoms:

i) Many dirty tails and hind-quarters especially in lambs.

ii) Persistent scouring.

iii) Lambs not thriving, even showing a marked loss of condition.

iv) In chronic cases anaemia and swelling of jaw (bottle jaw).

Prevention:

i) Dose sheep about 5 weeks before turning on to clean pastures at lambing time. If pastures have not carried sheep for about 6 months, sheep are clear of worms.

ii) Do not allow young lambs to graze same areas as ewes. This can be done by a system of 'creep grazing' (p. 177).

iii) Move young lambs to a fresh area of grazing every fourth day; this prevents the re-infestation by larvae from hatched eggs.

iv) Dose lambs at 6 weeks of age and subsequently every 3 weeks.

v) Give ewes two doses at monthly intervals in the autumn.

Treatment:

i) If infestation is heavy, dose every 3 weeks and provide uncontaminated grazings.

ii) When infestation is greatly reduced, adopt the above measures described for prevention.

iii) A variety of anthelmintic drugs exist. Examination of faeces for the identity of the worms helps in the choice of treatment.

Nematodirus

Cause: A roundworm which differs from the other roundworms which infect sheep in the following respects:

i) The eggs are able to survive on pastures throughout the winter. These hatch out into infective larvae during late spring and summer;

ii) The adult sheep have a tolerance to these worms and show no symptoms. Lambs are highly susceptible.

Symptoms: The young lambs are very susceptible and become very ill quickly and soon die. Intensive stocking and freedom from other worms allow heavy infestations of these worms during the late spring and summer; the worst time is May and the beginning of June.

Prevention:

i) Graze ewes and lambs on pastures which have been free of sheep for a year. This is usually quite effective.

ii) Dose with appropriate medicine.

Treatment: Dose early with suitable medicine.

Gid

This is the commonest brain disease of young sheep. It also occurs in young cattle.

Cause: Ingestion by the sheep of tapeworm eggs voided by dogs and foxes. These hatch in the sheep's gut and migrate to the brain forming fluid-filled cysts. When the sheep dies, dogs and foxes become re-infested by tapeworms through swallowing the contents of the brain cysts.

Symptoms: Blindness is the earliest sign, followed by staggering and circling. Later the sheep loses condition badly and there is softening of the skull bone due to pressure by the cyst.

Prevention:

i) Dose farm dogs at least three times a year with worm medicine, especially before lambing.

ii) Dispose of sheep carcasses efficiently.

Virus Diseases

Orf, or Contagious Pustular Dermatitis

This is an infectious virus disease of sheep and goats. It can infect other animals and man.

Symptoms: It appears as a thick scab, mainly around the mouth, but can spread to the gums, udder and vulva. It interferes with grazing and sucking and affected animals lose condition; lambs may die from starvation and dehydration due to inability to suck.

Treatment: When the disease first appears segregation of the affected animals may stop further spread in the flock.

Prevention:

i) Examine all new purchases carefully. Do not buy from vaccinated flocks.

ii) Thistles and gorse thorns should be avoided, because of scratching which facilitates the spread of the disease.

iii) Vaccination is by the scratch method usually under the armpit. Limbs only should be vaccinated; ewes are often immune.

iv) Do not vaccinate clean flocks and do not vaccinate lambs when indoors since the disease will build up and become severe.

Metabolic Diseases

Twin Lamb Disease or Pregnancy Toxaemia

This is a metabolic upset generally seen in ewes carrying more than one lamb.

Cause: Because the developing foetus takes up more room within the abdomen of the ewe, this restricts the amount of room in the stomach. It is estimated that the stomach of a heavily pregnant ewe has its capacity reduced to a quarter. Unless she is fed on a concentrated diet she cannot maintain herself in health and her foetus as well.

Symptoms:
i) Ewe appears blind, shows little interest in food, grinds her teeth.
ii) Sometimes a green fluid comes from the nostrils.
iii) Ewe walks with difficulty and finally collapses.
iv) She may abort and recover. Generally however, treatment is not satisfactory and the animal dies.

Prevention:
i) Bulk in the ewe's ration should be reduced and concentrates increased as she becomes more pregnant.
ii) By the time she lambs, the ewe should be receiving concentrates only and no hay or straw.
iii) Availability of adequate mineral supplement is important.

Sway-Back of Lambs

Cause: A break-down of white-matter tissue in the brain and spinal cord; this tissue is vital for conducting nervous impulses to control muscular movement. This break-down is associated with a shortage of copper in the ewe's blood.

Symptoms:
i) Slight unsteadiness.
ii) A marked swaying of hind-quarters, especially when running or turning, may occur.

iii) Lambs severely affected are unable to stand, are blind and quickly die of exposure and starvation.

Prevention: Ensure that the ewes have an adequate supply of copper in their blood:

i) Inject copper during pregnancy.
ii) Drench the ewes with medicines (e.g. worm medicines) containing copper, especially during the last 8 weeks of pregnancy.
iii) Copper therapy should only be used where deficiency occurs; sheep are very sensitive to excess copper.

Treatment: Some forms of the disease respond to treatment by copper following veterinary advice.

Pining

Cause: A deficiency of the mineral element cobalt.

Symptoms:
i) Lambs are unthrifty, their eyes water and wool parts from their backs.
ii) Symptoms of anaemia are shown, increasing weakness and eventual death.
iii) The presence of many 'cull' lambs often indicates cobalt deficiency.

Prevention: Inject with vitamin B_{12}, which contains cobalt.

Treatment: Inject with Vitamin B_{12}, which contains cobalt.

18

Health and Disease in Pigs

Pig losses are not due solely to disease, since many piglets die accidentally, e.g. by being crushed by the sow. The provision of farrowing crates or rails, short litter, creep lamps and well-insulated floors will prevent many of the losses caused by accidents and exposure.

Correct feeding and clean, dry, draught-proof, well-ventilated housing are essential for keeping pigs strong, thriving and resistant to disease. The housing should have a fairly constant temperature and cleanliness is essential. Pig rearing is intensive, whichever system is adopted; this exposes the animal to greater risk of infection. It is essential to clean and disinfect each section rigorously as it is vacated by each lot of pigs to prevent a build-up of disease-causing germs. It is essential that sick pigs are quickly spotted and the disease diagnosed and treated. This may not only save the life of that particular pig, but also prevent further spread of the disease to other pigs. Healthy pigs have a good 'bloom' on their coats, their skins being clear and bright. A dull, harsh coat is a sign of ill health; a rough hair growth indicates that pigs have been kept in cold or damp conditions. A poor appetite is also an indication of poor health.

It is very important to try and maintain a disease-free herd. All sows kept for breeding must be free from active disease, and if possible must not be carriers of disease. Great care must be taken when buying either breeding or fattening stock to ensure that they are free from contagious disease, e.g., swine erysipelas or enteritis. They must also be free from any respiratory troubles, to avoid the risk of introducing virus pneumonia into a clean herd. Once this trouble is encountered, it is very difficult to eradicate.

The remainder of this chapter is divided into two sections. The first section deals with the general preventative measures which may be practised (a) throughout the breeding cycle of the sow and (b) with growing and fattening pigs (Tables 18.1 and 18.2). The second section describes some of the more common pig diseases in greater detail.

DISEASE PREVENTION DURING THE BREEDING CYCLE OF THE SOW

First Service

Infertility is rare in young gilts. It may be due to hormonal imbalance, mineral and vitamin deficiency. An over-fed sow may have difficulty in conceiving; if so, veterinary advice should be sought. The boar can also be at fault.

Pregnancy

Good housing, correct feeding and plenty of exercise are essential. It is advisable not to feed excess quantities of bulky foods. Gilts can be kept fairly free from round-worms and lung-worms, by allowing them to graze only on fields which are ploughed and put through a rotation every 3 years.

Care must be taken to avoid infecting the young piglets with common diseases. The farrowing pen should be thoroughly cleaned and disinfected. This will destroy any roundworm eggs, as well as most bacteria, including those which might cause navel or joint ill. If lice have been troublesome, the whole pen should be thoroughly dusted with a suitable insecticide.

The sow should also be wormed about 2 weeks before farrowing.

Table 18.1. Prevention of disease during the breeding cycle of the sow.

Disease	Disease prevention by:			Disease
	Management		*Feeding*	
Infertility	Good, well ventilated buildings	*Growing period*	Good pastures. Correct feeding to avoid overfatness	Infertility
	Treatment of whitish discharge from vagina	*Heat and service*		
(*Helps to avoid*) general ill health (*Helps to avoid*) milk fever	Good housing. Adequate exercise	*Pregnancy*	Fresh pastures	Roundworms and lungworms
Roundworms	Dosing		Correct feeding	Lack of healthy piglets
Roundworms, navel and joint ill in piglets	Clean, disinfected farrowing pen			Milk fever
Roundworms in piglets	Wash udder and under-parts			
Lice and mange parasites	Parasiticides			
Loss of piglets	Good stockmanship	*Farrowing*		
Post-farrowing fever	Veterinary treatment	*Post Farrowing*	Mineral supplement	Milk fever
Mastitis	Treat swollen, lumpy udders with drugs			
Milk Fever	Treat prostrate sow having full and hard quarters with calcium borogluconate			
	Keep piglets away from sows having post-farrowing fever, mastitis or milk fever for 24 hours			
(*Helps to avoid*) general ill health	Good housing		Correct feeding	Lack of adequate milk which produces strong healthy piglets
Enteritis	Hygiene, vaccination	*Weaning*		

Before the sow is turned into the farrowing pen, her backside and under-parts should be thoroughly washed with soap and water; this removes any roundworm eggs. Lice should also be destroyed with a pesticide application, and mange treated with a sulphur compound.

Farrowing

During farrowing, the sow should not be unnecessarily disturbed, but an eye should be kept open for anything abnormal occurring. If any assistance is necessary, hands should be thoroughly washed and disinfected.

Post Farrowing to Weaning

It is wise to ascertain whether the sow has adequate milk. If there is no milk at all, a gentle massage of the udder may put things right. If this does not stimulate milk flow, then four possible causes of the trouble should be suspected.

1. *Milk fever*
The sow may be prostrate, with full-laid udder. This is extremely rare in the newly farrowed sow. It generally occurs about two weeks after farrowing and is treated by a subcutaneous injection of calcium borogluconate behind the ear.

Calcium deficiency in a newly farrowed sow manifests itself as mania. The animal will attack its attendant and eat its piglets. Again an injection of calcium borogluconate is indicated but care must be taken to restrain her effectively while the injection is being given; the piglets should be taken away for a few hours until she recovers.

2. *Farrowing fever*
This is caused by metritis (inflammation of the

Table 18.2. Prevention of disease in growing and fattening pigs.

Disease	Disease prevention by:			Disease
	Management		Feeding	
	Keep piglets away from sows having post-farrowing fever, mastitis or milk fever for 24 hours	Suckling period	Adequate vitamins and minerals, creep feed	Rickets
Anaemia	Warm, dry quarters. Injection of iron salts at 3 days old			Hairlessness
Septic toes	Administering of antibiotics; as a last resort, amputation of damaged toes			
Baby-pig disease	Isolate pigs refusing to suck and rear artificially			
Roundworms	Dosing	Weaning	Well-balanced rations containing vitamins and minerals	Deficiency diseases
Oedema	Vaccination		Clean feeding troughs and utensils	Bacterial diseases / Roundworms
Erysipelas	Vaccinate		Boil swill	Swine fever / Foot-and-mouth
Virus pneumonia	Warm, dry and well-ventilated houses	Fattening	Clean feeding troughs and utensils	Bacterial diseases
Necrotic enteritis				
Roundworms	Clean and disinfect fattening houses			Roundworms
Lice				
Bacterial diseases	No common dunging channels provided		Well-balanced rations, containing adequate vitamins and minerals	Deficiency diseases
Roundworms				
Necrotic enteritis				
Virus pneumonia	If virus pneumonia or influenza are troublesome, fattening house to be left empty for several weeks after disinfecting		Boil swill	Swine fever / Foot-and-mouth

womb) which might be the result of an epidemic in the house, or due to incomplete expulsion of the afterbirth. It is recognized by the whitish vaginal discharge, high temperature and refusal to eat. Prompt treatment by antibiotics should clear it up in a few hours.

3. *Mastitis*
Irregularly swollen, painful udder; milk may be watery and clotted; high temperature. Again prompt treatment by antibiotics may clear it in time.

4. *Agalactia*
This is a form of post-farrowing shock; such shock should be avoided. The sow is apparently normal but is not secreting milk. An injection of pituitary hormone stimulates normal production of milk.

During the remainder of the suckling period, the sow should be properly fed and housed so as to provide an ample supply of milk to keep the young piglets growing vigorously. This is especially important during the first 3 weeks because the young piglets are totally dependent on their mother's milk supply.

Second Heat

About 2–8 days after weaning the sow comes on heat once more and the breeding cycle is repeated.

DISEASE PREVENTION IN GROWING AND FATTENING PIGS

Pigs from Birth to Weaning

Piglets losing interest in suckling and becoming listless should be examined for evidence of disease. They should be reared artificially away from the sow.

Piglet anaemia is avoided by injecting iron salts at three days old or as prescribed.

Hygienic conditions should avoid navel ill and resultant arthritis in the young pigs. This is shown by lameness, high temperature and disinclination to feed. Treatment by antibiotics can be successful.

Clipping of piglets teeth should be done immediately after birth.

The 'creep' feed of young piglets should contain correct amounts of mineral and vitamin supplements, in addition to the other foodstuffs. Vitamins A, B and D are important and the following minerals should also be included – calcium, phosphorus, manganese, iron, copper, cobalt and iodine. Prolonged deficiency of calcium, phosphorus and vitamins will give rise to rickets. Deficiency of iodine causes hairlessness.

Pigs from Weaning to Fattening

If erysipelas has been troublesome in the past, the young piglets are injected with the appropriate vaccine. Stock kept for breeding should be vaccinated every six months.

A couple of days before the weaners are moved to the fattening houses, they are wormed according to instructions. Care must also be taken to destroy the worms passed out on to the floor.

Changes of feeding and housing at weaning time must be as gradual as possible; this will considerably reduce the risk of oedema.

Throughout this period, the rations must contain adequate vitamins and minerals. Feeding troughs and utensils must also be kept scrupulously clean, to avoid providing ideal places for bacteria to multiply and spread.

If swill is being fed, it has to be boiled first to destroy foot-and-mouth, fowl pest and swine fever viruses; it is illegal not to do so. Swill varies widely in its contents and it can cause poisoning, especially if too much salt is present.

The fattening houses must be thoroughly cleaned and disinfected before the pigs are turned in. These measures will destroy any bacteria, lice and roundworm, etc., present. If virus pneumonia or influenza is troublesome, the house should have been left empty for several weeks. If the houses are kept constantly dry, warm and well-ventilated, trouble from influenza and virus pneumonia and necrotic enteritis will be avoided or reduced. No common dunging channels should be provided in fattening houses since they enable roundworms and necrotic enteritis bacteria together with ringworm spores to spread rapidly.

Lice and mange must be treated promptly.

Young Breeding Stock

Although young and developing breeding stock are not kept with fattening stock, they are susceptible to the same diseases. In addition, young gilts are often allowed to run on pastures and measures must be taken to prevent them from becoming heavily infected with lungworms and roundworms. This can be achieved by worming them regularly and allowing them access to pastures which are ploughed every 3 years and cropped for 2 years before reseeding.

SPECIFIC DISEASES

Virus Diseases

Atrophic Rhinitis

Cause: Not exactly known, but suspected to be a virus; it was introduced to this country by the Landrace. It was a notifiable disease but the Order is no longer in force; the disease is widespread and veterinary advice is essential.

Virus Pneumonia

Cause: A virus. Often transmitted to young piglets by 'carrier' sows which themselves do not show symptoms.

Symptoms:
i) Attacks pigs of all ages, but most common in fattening pigs.
ii) Hard, dry, erratic cough, very noticeable when pigs are disturbed, or at feeding time.
iii) General unthriftiness and failure to grow properly.
iv) On slaughter, lower lobes and edges of lungs

are hard and greyish in colour with reddish rims.

Control:

i) Maintain a clean herd, by very careful purchase of animals. Animals which have any sort of respiratory troubles should not be purchased.

ii) Under intensive housing conditions, leave alternate units vacant for a few weeks after they have become empty. Clean empty houses thoroughly and spray with soda.

iii) Carrier sows should be traced if possible and isolated.

Bacterial Diseases

Enteritis

Cause: Generally *E. coli*, which is a naturally occurring organism in the intestine. Change of diet, chill or dirty conditions can lead to activation of the bacteria with serious outbreaks of the disease.

Symptoms:

i) Diarrhoea affecting pigs of all ages but particularly young ones.

ii) Death may occur suddenly.

Prevention:

i) Ensure clean housing with constant temperature and low humidity.

ii) Avoid contamination of food and water by dung and urine.

iii) Vaccination of in-pig sows can avoid the disease in piglets and in the sows themselves.

iv) Vaccination of piglets at birth.

v) Where pigs are reared intensively, it may be necessary to carry out routine vaccination under veterinary supervision.

Treatment: The bacteria should be identified by taking faecal samples to the laboratory; the correct antibiotics can then be used.

Bowel Oedema

Cause: A bacterial infection, usually *E. coli*, and is associated with sudden changes in diet and management.

Symptoms:

i) Most common in pigs from 8 to 14 weeks old, especially in thriving weaners.

ii) Piglets may throw a fit, have diarrhoea, stagger and become paralysed.

iii) Eyelids are frequently swollen and the skin of the nose is puffy and soft to touch.

iv) In acute cases piglets are found dead.

v) Post mortem shows a jelly-like material in the stomach wall and between coils of large intestine.

Prevention: Improve husbandry; vaccination.

Treatment: Antibiotics injected or given orally may cure the condition.

Swine Erysipelas

Cause: A bacterium *Erysipelothrix*, which is widespread and exists in the soil. Pigs are infected through mouth or open wounds.

Symptoms:

i) High temperature, loss of appetite and general depression, especially during warm, muggy weather.

ii) Raised purple and red patches on skin.

iii) Chronic cases have stiffish joints and heart disease.

iv) Occasionally, onset of the disease is very swift and the first signs are dead pigs.

Prevention: If disease occurs year after year, vaccinate all piglets before weaning and all breeding stock annually; vaccinate sows when not pregnant.

Treatment: Antibiotics and/or serum.

Metabolic Diseases

Piglet Anaemia

Cause: Milk is deficient in iron and this leads to anaemia in the piglets. Deficiency of traces of copper and cobalt may also cause it.

Symptoms:

i) Generally start at about 10 days old.

ii) Piglets become pale and listless.

iii) Greyish diarrhoea followed by death.

Prevention:

i) Keep young piglets warm and dry.

ii) Provide turfs for piglets to nose about in so that they are able to pick up the necessary trace elements.

iii) Inject 3-day-old piglets with an iron salt intramuscularly. Iron salts may also be administered orally by means of capsules, liquids or paste painted on the sow's teats.

Treatment: Administer iron compounds according to veterinary advice.

Baby Pig Disease

Cause: It is caused by *E. coli* infection in the sow.

Symptoms:
i) Piglets lose interest in sucking.
ii) Piglets wander away from sow, hide in straw and shiver.

Prevention:
i) Injection of sow with antibiotics just before farrowing.
ii) Some sows are prone to this trouble and it would be as well not to breed from them subsequently.

Treatment: Give sow antibiotics and re-introduce piglets to mother after 24 hours.

Internal Parasitic Diseases

Lungworms (Fig. 18.1)

Cause: Long, thin, white, thread-like worms in lung tubes. The disease is most likely to occur when pigs are kept in dark, damp pens.

Symptoms:
i) Coughing which may become severe and quickly develops into pneumonia.

ii) Pigs become thin and weak.
iii) Unthriftiness.
iv) Rough coat.

Prevention:
i) Prevent build-up of larvae in the earthworm population by ploughing pig pastures every 3 years and putting them through a short arable rotation before re-seeding.
ii) Rear pigs on clean, concrete floors.
iii) Good housing.

Treatment:
i) Parasiticides can be injected or given in the feed.
ii) If infection occurs, pigs should be moved to concrete floors to prevent further infection.

Roundworms (Fig. 18.2)

Cause: Roundworms (ascarids) in the small intestine.

Symptoms:
i) Death is sudden in severe cases.
ii) Animals are stunted and unthrifty.
iii) Diarrhoea, straining, colic and 'pot bellied'.
iv) Coughing and vomiting, especially at the sight of food.
v) Roundworms may be seen in the vomit and in the faeces.
vi) Infected pigs may fall in fits when food is presented.

1. Mature females lay eggs in lungs
2. Eggs coughed up and swallowed
3. Larva develops inside the egg as it passes through the intestines

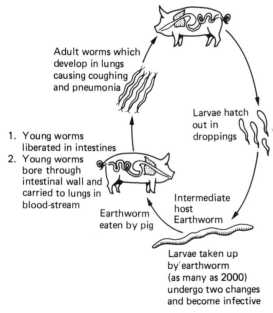

Fig. 18.1 Life of a parasitic lungworm.

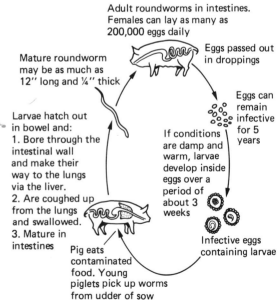

Fig. 18.2 Life cycle of a parasitic roundworm found in pigs.

Prevention: Reduce infection of young piglets to a low level.

i) Clean farrowing pen thoroughly with flame gun or disinfection.

ii) Dose sow 2 weeks before farrowing, and 24 hours later. Wash her thoroughly with hot soapy water (removes any eggs).

iii) Put sow in clean pen, making sure she does not walk over infected ground.

iv) Keep piglets on clean ground until they are 4–5 months old.

v) Prevent pig pastures from becoming heavily infected with eggs (pig-sick), by putting them through a short arable rotation every 3–4 years.

vi) Dose piglets, 9–10 weeks old, with appropriate worm medicines.

Treatment: There are many effective worm medicines.

Many pig-worms, including lungworm, can be transmitted through the bloodstream to the unborn piglet from the mother. Some piglets may consequently be born with a serious burden of worms.

Index

V

vaccines, 212, 233
ventricle, 82
vibrio, 222
vibrionic abortion, 238
villi, 81
virus diseases of cattle, 227
   of pigs, 246
   of sheep, 241
viruses, 213–14
vitamins, 78, 79, 217, 221–2, 224
   deficiency, 230

W

warble fly, 228
water, pigs' requirements, 197
weaning calf, 140
   lamb, 11, 181
   piglets, 14
   weight of lambs, 52
Welsh Black cattle, age of first service, 1
   average weight, 48

beef production, 152
characteristics, 47
performance test result, 49
protein requirements, 107
Welsh Mountain sheep, group breeding scheme, 61–2
   progeny testing, 62
   ram performance testing, 60–1
Welsh pig, 66
Wensleydale sheep, carcass weight, 58
   characteristics, 57
white scour, 230
winter feeding beef cattle, 157
   food supplies, 128–9
   housing sheep, 181
worm infestation, 233, 235

Y

Yorkshire pig, 66

Z

zero grazing, 113